LIVING ON LIVE FOOD

Alissa Cohen

Layout & Design: Enrique Candioti
Cover Concept: Alissa Cohen
Photography: Alissa Cohen
Cover Shot: Robin Roslund

Library of Congress Catalog Card Number: on file
ISBN # 0-9748963-0-6

Cohen Publishing Company
103 Norton Rd
Kittery, Maine 03904
USA

Disclaimer:
Because there is always some risk involved, the author, publisher, and/or distributors of this book are not responsible for any
adverse detoxification effects or consequences resulting from
the use of any suggestions or procedures described here after.
This book is sold for information purposes only; neither the
author or the publisher will be held accountable for the misuse
of the information contained in this book.

THIS BOOK IS DEDICATED TO:

• Bessie, Dave and Harris, my three guardian angels.

• Loretta and Mel, for always believing in and encouraging every-thing I do. You are always willing to jump right in with me.

• Sheila, for always being there and always reaching out when I need you. Your belief in me has allowed me to reach new depths within myself. Your never ending faith in me is deeply felt and always with me. Thank you for helping me create my dreams.

• Stacie, for living the life and bringing me back to the path.

• Dennis, for being the first person to show me I could do anything I wanted to do all those years ago. And now, for "finding me" again and believing in me enough to change your world.

• Lynn, for getting me to the right place at the right time and allow-ing me full experimentation in your kitchen!

• And for Christine, without you this book would not have been possible.

• For all of my friends and clients who have taught me so much, lent me their support and advice, and encouraged me along this path as well as in my life's dreams and pursuits.

Thank you for the invaluable impact you have had on my life.

A special note about the layout of this book:

The large margins on the pages in this book are here for a specific reason. In the first half of the book, the margins allow space for personal notations and thoughts as well as any important facts from this book, the Living on Live Food DVDs or from other sources. In the recipe section, the margins can be used for rewriting and creating your own recipes alongside the original ones. I hope that you will find this a helpful feature of this book.

CONTENTS

RECIPES (PART II)

INTRODUCTION

WHY THIS BOOK? AN INTRODUCTION

I wrote this book for all of the people over the years who have asked me how they can:

- Regain that youthful energy they once had.
- Improve their health after a lifetime of abusing their bodies.
- Heal themselves without surgery or drugs.
- Lose weight.
- Get fit.
- Feel and look younger.
- Stay healthy and in shape without spending hours working out and starving themselves.

I wrote this book because I have never seen anything change peoples lives more, then eating a raw and living food diet!

I have seen people heal themselves of all kinds of diseases, chronic and acute, lose amazing amounts of weight and look and feel younger and healthier, not in years, not in months, but very often, within weeks.

I have witnessed first hand people healing themselves of:

- Diabetes
- Fibromyalgia
- Acne
- Migraines
- Back, neck and joint pain
- Asthma
- High blood pressure
- High cholesterol

THERE ARE NO "INCURABLE" diseases. If you are willing to take responsibility for yourself and your life, you can heal yourself of anything.

— Dr. Richard Schulze

- Hypoglycemia

- Colitis and diverticulitis

- Candida

- Arthritis

- Serious allergies

- Depression, anxiety and mood swings

- Heartburn, gas and bloating

- Skin diseases

- Obesity

- Menopausal symptoms

- Chronic fatigue

- Cancers and other ailments and diseases... just by eating differently.

I wanted to deliver this incredibly good news to as many people as possible. So I wrote this book. I couldn't possibly *not* write it.

IT'S NOT "A DIET."

I refer to this way of eating as a "diet" throughout the book, but I do so reluctantly. The word "diet" implies "sacrifice." It conjures up something rather unpleasant you do for a specified period of time to achieve a specific goal, and then you stop.

This way of eating isn't like that at all. It's not unpleasant · it's wonderful! It's not "sacrificial" · it's highly satisfying! This is not a "diet," it's a gift! A magical, wondrous, empowering, self-honoring, healing gift...the most valuable gift you'll ever receive, if you choose to accept it. If you do, chances are, you'll never want to stop.

DO YOU BELIEVE IN MIRACLES?

If you are sick, or tired, or overweight, then this book can be the answer to your prayers. Does this sound like I'm promising a lot? I *am*! But I'm not exaggerating. You'll believe me almost from the instant you start eating this way. It's a miracle just waiting to happen · to you.

"HOW DO I START EATING RAW?"

In the past, I've responded to these questions by simply saying "eat more fruits and vegetables and stop eating cooked food." Well, that wasn't enough. People wanted more explicit instructions. For a long time, I hesitated. You see, the beauty of eating raw and living food is that it doesn't require a road map. People who regularly eat this way know intuitively what works for them. There's nothing to measure, no calories to count, nothing like any "traditional" diet you may have tried. However, I've discovered that most people really need some clearly expressed directions to get started. And I definitely want you to get started!

In fact, I want you to put this book down when you are through reading it and start eating raw *immediately*. That's the point of this book! It's not about your complete understanding of the buckwheat cell structure, or the acid alkaline balance, or the complete function of enzymes. It's not about understanding every nuance of raw and living food.

It is about changing your life in a direction you may never have thought possible. You're going to discover how to lose weight, heal your body, and achieve optimal health.

So keep reading. You are on your way to creating your own miracle!

Alissa Cohen

TO KNOW WHAT YOU PREFER instead of humbly saying Amen to what the world tells you you ought to prefer, is to have kept your soul alive.

— Robert Louis Stevenson

1

FREEDOM

"FREEDOM" IS NOT a word usually associated with diets. In fact, the last thing anyone on a conventional diet feels is a sense of freedom. This is one of the major differences between the raw and living food diet and every other diet.

Prior to discovering this way of eating, there was never a time in my life when I felt freedom from food - whether I was on a diet or not. I would start a diet believing that I would have control over my food intake, and that I would be able to exercise restraint over my food choices. My constant hope was that I would lose weight and that any food addictions I had would simply vanish. I felt that once I lost the desired weight, I would no longer always be thinking about the food I couldn't have.

I would anticipate the day when I would no longer dream of or have cravings for foods, such as chocolate cake, pizza, or ice cream.

However, these thoughts *didn't* go away. Even when I told myself that I would not diet - that I would let myself eat whatever I wanted, in moderation, to avoid that feeling of deprivation - food was always on my mind. Sometimes more intensely than other times, but it was *always* there. I couldn't bring myself to forget about food. Rare were the times when I wasn't thinking about my next meal.

GOING RAW: A LIBERATION

Once I went raw, I felt, for the first time in my life, completely liberated from food. I just don't *think* about food the way I used to. I don't plan my days around what I eat. I don't agonize over whether or not I'm eating the right foods. I don't have to, because I *know* that whatever I choose to eat, it's a good choice.

If I want to eat fruit, a meal, or a dessert, I just *do* it, and that's it.

I don't have food cravings anymore. And I don't have that fear of wanting to eat and then not being able to stop. Raw and living food gives one's body everything it needs to feel perfectly and nutritionally satisfied.

The raw and living food diet will give you greater health, boundless energy, and increased natural beauty. And it will *free* you from the bondage of food!

"IF YOU WANT YOUR LIFE to be a magnificent story, then begin by realizing that you are the author and every day you have the opportunity to write a new page."

— Mark Houlahan

2

IT'S SO EASY!

THROUGHOUT THE WRITING OF THIS BOOK, the words of a friend and former client kept resounding in my head: "Alissa," Valerie told me, "you've *got* to write a book about how you helped me this week!"

Here's how it happened. Valerie, who had ordered my food preparation videos, called me. She said she wanted to learn more about doing this diet on a daily basis. Although she had spent time at a very prominent facility for raw food healing and education, she could not seem to stay on the diet upon returning home. This frustrated her because while she was on the diet she felt better than she had ever felt before.

Valerie's problem was simply this: She found eating endless salads, avocados, and sprouts boring! Valerie wondered if it was possible for a little more *variety*. She wanted to set up her kitchen · and her life – in a way that would help her maintain a raw and living food diet... *easily*!

A WEEK OF VARIETY AND SIMPLICITY!

Off I went to Palm Dessert, California. As soon as I arrived, Valerie and I got to work. We put away all the groceries I'd bought for the week and then made lunch... which took all of ten minutes.

Then we took a long, leisurely stroll and talked about what she was hoping to gain from my week·long stay. After a long swim in her pool to escape the 112 degree heat, we talked some more, getting to know each other better. Finally we returned to her kitchen to prepare dinner.

In under half an hour we created a feast, including creamy carrot soup, angel hair pasta with marinara sauce, and a raisin·walnut tort for dessert.

At dinner, I met Valerie's family. Her husband joined us and loved the food. Her daughter had not been convinced yet and ordered a pizza.

OKAY, PIZZA IT IS!

After dinner I showed Valerie how to make eggplant pizza with the leftover tomato sauce from the angel hair pasta. The pizza would be put into the dehydrator overnight so that we could enjoy it for either lunch or dinner the next day.

Again, this took maybe fifteen minutes, max!

Valerie and I spent most of our time playing, laughing, shopping, and talking about life. We established a loose routine. When we were hungry we would prepare something simple, after all, I was there for this purpose, but we certainly didn't slave over food. On the contrary, we enjoyed the pool, soaked up the sun, and laughed a lot. Inside, we had fun preparing meals. But often we'd just grab a mango, a piece of watermelon, or some other juicy fruit and dash off to enjoy the blazing sun at poolside.

One night we went out on the town, shopping, dining, and dancing. At the restaurant, I showed Valerie how to order raw food off a menu and how to request small changes to meet her dietary needs.

Valerie lost five pounds that week and felt like she ate more then she had in a long time. My point, there is more to life than what you eat!

I didn't become a raw fooder so I could spend all of my time in the kitchen! Raw food is *not* a lot of work. In fact, it's the *easiest* way to eat. The food preparation is a hundred times faster and easier than cooked food preparation. Once you learn a few simple steps, and get into the groove of doing it, there is no easier diet to follow!

Let's put it into perspective. Say you decided to learn how to cook Greek or French food. You would have to enroll in a cooking class, and/or purchase several cookbooks. You'd have to go out and buy appropriate utensils and appliances. Then you would have to stock up on the necessary spices and other dry ingredients. Finally, you would have to actually try and create some dishes. More than likely, you'd make mistakes before you ever got the hang of it, and you'd spend a lot of time in the kitchen as you learned.

Similarly, there's a certain learning curve involved with raw and living food. You're experiencing some of it right now, just by reading this book. You'll learn new uses for equipment you probably already own along with the benefits of tools you may decide to purchase. Every new venture requires some education, and learning how to master a raw and living food diet is no exception.

That said, the requirements for learning this way of eating are far less exacting! With raw and living food, *you* decide on how much time you want to spend. You can make food preparation as simple or as complex as you choose. Although initially, you'll follow certain recipes included in this book, you'll soon be creating your own.

This is not a rigid, pre-formulated diet. If you enjoy preparing food and spending time in the kitchen, you can easily make beautiful gourmet meals once or twice a day - within minutes! Otherwise you can stick to eating foods in their whole form with no food prep at all! It's up to you.

This diet will fit your lifestyle - *anybody's* lifestyle - regardless of age, gender, family situation, or work environment. Once the decision was made to do it, I have never seen this diet fail for anyone.

ELIMINATE SOMETHING super-fluous from your life. Break a habit. Do something that makes you feel insecure.

— **Piero Ferrucci**

3

MY STORY

ALTHOUGH I BEGAN EATING a sort of quasi-vegetarian diet at age sixteen, there was no dramatic revelation involved. I wasn't thinking about health benefits, animal rights issues, or environmental concerns.

Aside from an occasional hamburger, I simply didn't *like* red meat. I could not stand the smell of fish, and the veins and skin of chicken disgusted me. So, when my parents cooked steak or lobster, I'd opt for a peanut butter and banana sandwich.

If it didn't exactly *resemble* the animal itself, I'd eat it. You know, things like chicken nuggets, meat sauces, sliced turkey sandwiches, or maybe canned tuna fish with lots of mayo.

Around this same time, I also starting working out at a gym and began reading books on health and fitness. Although most of the books were mainstream material, I picked up a few books with a radically different slant. My reading expanded to books like *Fit for Life*, *Diet for a Small Planet*, and others promoting the vegetarian philosophy.

When I read John Robbins' *Diet for a New America*, I became a vegetarian immediately.

While fascinated by Robbins' theories on the physiological impact of eating animals, his exposition on its social, ecological, and economic consequences blew me away! I began reading everything I could find on vegetarianism and whole foods while trying to discover via self-experimentation what this way of eating could do for my body.

I was still eating dairy products and a lot of fat-laden, high-sugar junk food, but because I was young and physically active, I felt good, looked good, and was in terrific shape so I thought!

"I DO FEEL THAT SPIRITUAL progress does demand at some stage that we should cease to kill our fellow creatures for the satisfaction of our bodily wants."

— Mahatma Gandhi

A WAKE-UP CALL I DIDN'T QUITE UNDERSTAND

I figured that since I wasn't eating meat, chicken, fish, or eggs, I must have been healthier than most people I knew, right?

Wrong!

I started experiencing chronic illness, including constant yeast infections, and occasional bladder infections. I tired far too easily. I gained ten pounds and couldn't shed them. Headaches plagued me and my skin kept breaking out.

VICIOUS CIRCLES

Antibiotics were recommended, and I took them. I'd feel better for a week or two, but the infections would return, bringing more recommendations for antibiotics, which I dutifully took. I began to constantly catch colds because my immune system was being weakened by the continuous rounds of drugs I was taking.

During this time, *five* different doctors told me the same thing: "You have a yeast infection. Take antibiotics." This regimen was obviously *not working!* I became frustrated, moody, and began suffering from small bouts of depression.

Incredibly, this went on for *two years* with no end in sight. In fact, things were just getting worse. I was tired, achy and felt lousy - all the time. I remember thinking - at the ripe old age of twenty-two - that it just wasn't any fun "getting old." I remember wistfully recalling my years of health and vibrancy and energy as my "lost youth."

"WHEN IN DOUBT, INVADE THE BODY!"

Finally, a doctor recommended a laparoscopy. Since I didn't know what else to do, I wearily consented. (This involves a fiber optical instrument to be inserted into the abdominal wall through the navel, in order to examine the organs). It was painful and intrusive, and yielded no new information. Amazingly, further exploratory surgery was suggested! *No, thank you!*

My depression grew worse, but something took root inside me...a conviction that the answers I needed weren't going to come to me through the routes I'd been taking. I started look-

"THE OUTER SITUATION is always a reflection of the collective inner situation."

— Peace Pilgrim

ing into other forms of treatment. I began by practicing meditation, and looking into more holistic practices. Most importantly, I decided to be open to any messages I may have
ignored in the past.

AND THEN I WANDERED INTO A LOCAL HEALTH FOOD STORE...

I found this little place about a week after the laparoscopy. It
was filled with supplements, packaged foods, bulk bins, dried
herbs, and other interesting things...and some really interesting
people! A small, L-shaped space overflowing with books beck-
oned me, and on the wall, sitting on the edge of a shelf facing
me was a book titled *The Yeast Connection*.

It might as well have been titled: "Alissa Cohen, READ THIS!"

I plunked myself on the floor, began scanning the pages, and
nearly burst into tears. Then I bought the book, took it home,
and read every word.

The next day I called one of the holistic centers listed in the
back of the book and made an appointment. Within two days,
a seven-page questionnaire from the center arrived in my mail-
box. In filling it out, I realized that nearly all of the questions
were food-related.

A few days later, I found myself in the office of an holistic
health practitioner. He told me that he could run some very
expensive tests on me, but that from what I'd written and what
I'd told him, he thought he already knew what my problem
was...and more importantly, what could be done about it. He
told me I had "Candida."

Well! At last! A diagnosis! Something other than what I had
been hearing for the past two years!

He explained that the condition was an overgrowth of yeast-
like parasitic fungi. Unlike a simple yeast infection, the condition actually worsens with antibiotics because antibiotics kill
not only the bad bacteria but also the good intestinal bacteria
needed to help fight off the fungi. Treating it with antibiotics
was creating a vicious cycle of infection and drugs.

IN A DARK TIME, the eye

begins to see.

— Theodore Roethke

A LIFE-CHANGING MOMENT

The practitioner then told me something astounding...that I could easily rid myself of this condition by changing my *diet*. At that moment my life changed completely.

Even though I had been "into" health and nutrition, and although I was a vegetarian, I had never really thought that I could *cure* myself with *food*! I knew that diet was connected with feeling better, losing weight, etc... but I never realized what a key role food could play in healing disease!

I wondered why all those doctors I'd seen never mentioned this to me. As I left with a bag full of vitamins and minerals to strengthen my broken-down immune system, and another bag of herbs to cleanse and rebuild my body, I admit I was feeling a little skeptical. After two years of pain, and hearing five different doctors' counsel continued surgery, I wondered if simply eating differently could work.

At the same time, though, I was getting excited about the idea that food could heal me; no more medication and no more surgery, just a change in diet?

Once home, I attacked my kitchen, tossing out everything with sugar in it. Out went all the junk food, mayo, peanut butter, ice cream. Out too, went anything that was processed or contained yeast: bread, pasta, cereals, frozen pizza. I was ready to start my new diet.

I began eating more vegetables, whole grains, beans and tofu. Within four days I started to feel a difference. Friends saw an immediate change in my disposition and I was feeling better each day. My energy increased and my headaches disappeared along with most of my extra weight. I almost couldn't believe it! I had suffered for years and within a few weeks I was healed! I had no more recurring yeast infections.

I was both angry and sad with the doctors for totally avoiding the whole concept of nutrition. It upset me knowing that other people would go through years of unnecessary pain and anguish. I wanted to learn more about healing the body through food, herbs, meditation and alternative medicine, thus I began reading everything I could get my hands on about holistic medicine and healing. I started to learn how the body, mind, and spirit work together. The more I read, the more I wanted to know.

I quit my job, feeling that I should be doing something more along the lines of what I believed in.

Since I had practically turned the health food store into my second home, I applied for a job there and was quickly made a manager. The owner was very knowledgeable about vitamins, minerals, herbs and healing foods. She was willing to teach me anything I wanted to know. Meanwhile, I took courses in health and nutrition. I studied psychology and physiology. I became a personal trainer, holistic health counselor and a mind-body therapist. I explored many avenues of personal growth, not just for myself, but with an eye toward teaching and sharing with others. It was a very exciting time for me. I began to see, from my own experience and through many of the people that I worked with, that food could be a very strong, if not *the* strongest component in maintaining and improving good health... and in helping to *heal* all kinds of sickness and disease.

THE AWAKENING

It soon became evident that different foods produced different effects on my body and mind. When I ate lots of fruit, salads, or fresh juices, I felt wonderful. When I ate so called "good" vegetarian food like tofu, tempeh, wheat pasta, and cooked grains, I felt lethargic. Since the effect was subtle, I tried not to put too much credence in it. What was I supposed to do? Live on fruits, vegetables, sprouted nuts and seeds? Who could do *that*?

It was at this time that I met a woman who would become my soul sister. Christine worked at the health food store I man-

DO NOT WEEP, DO NOT WAX

indignant, understand.

— **Baruch Spinoza**

aged. My first day on the job we felt an instant connection. We would talk and laugh for hours. The days would fly by and we quickly became best friends. I learned a great deal from her about spirituality and metaphysics. Not only was she fun to be with, she was willing to try any and all of the crazy diets I'd come up with. We experimented with traditional, ayervedic, macrobiotic and high protein diets. Then we began experimenting with the raw food diet.

Although there was very little information about raw and living food at that time, we did have Ann Wigmore's book · *Recipes for a Longer Life* · that acted as our guide. A pioneer in the raw foods movement, Ann Wigmore started a healing retreat in Boston in the 1970s. She would use raw and living food, juice fasting, and wheat grass to heal people who came to her facility. They came from all over the world, suffering from all kinds of diseases including obesity, cancer, diabetes and more.

Her book is not a complex one; mostly recipes, but something in it spoke deeply to me. It made sense in such a simple, yet powerful way: "Live foods produce live bodies; dead foods produce dead bodies." This is what I had been feeling intuitively!

BABY STEPS

And so we began, Christine and I on our initial journey into the world of raw foods. There was one problem, we really didn't know what we were doing.

We started by eating salads for lunch and lots of fruit. Then we would experiment by eating all figs one day, all almonds the next. By the third or fourth day we'd be starving, and heading out for pizza!

Despite a rather rocky beginning, the seed had definitely been planted. For the next two years, I continued to experiment with the raw food diet. It was a solitary effort.

Available information was practically nonexistent. I knew of no one else who was eating this way so there was nobody to talk to about it.

Eventually, I opened my own health food store, pretty much forgetting about raw food, and focusing on whole foods, natural herbs, and supplements.

A few years later I sold the store and created my "Holistic Fitness" consulting business. I'd visit clients in their homes, put them on diets, teach them how to exercise and basically act as a life coach.

MY MIRACLE

There are those moments in life that, although we may not realize it at the time, turn out to be crucial turning points. Little did I know that a family reunion in Florida in 1995 would prove to be one of those.

My sister and I have always had an interesting connection. Whenever we spoke on the phone we'd invariably discover that we were reading the same book or taking the same class. I'd send our mother a birthday card and she'd send her an identical one. We always found this very amusing. But during that family weekend in Florida we realized just how deep our connection really was.

It happened aptly enough, in the kitchen. While my sister prepared food, I studied her in sheer wonder. Although we had spoken frequently over the phone, I hadn't actually seen her in years. I knew that, in the past, numerous ailments left her feeling hopeless about ever feeling completely well again.

But now, after years of intense pain and suffering, she seemed completely pain free! The change in her appearance amazed me - she looked fantastic. She appeared at least fifteen years younger than when I had last seen her. Her face was relaxed and unlined. Her hair was beautiful, shiny and healthy looking. Her skin was smooth and bore none of the blotches I remembered. She'd lost about twenty pounds and radiated vibrant health. It didn't stop with her looks. My sister's energy seemed boundless, she seemed positive, happy, and calm.

While I studied her my sister chattered away. She talked about a "new" diet she and her boyfriend had discovered. It was called the "Raw and Living Food Diet," and she could hardly contain her enthusiasm about it. She swore it was the best thing she'd ever done.

I couldn't believe it! Raw food had found me again; this time in the person of my absolutely gorgeous sister!

We ate only raw food all that weekend, and talked and talked and talked about the diet. Once home, I dug out all my old raw food recipes and continued to eat only raw and living foods. I was amazed at how fantastic I felt within just a few *days* of eating this way. I lost five stubborn pounds in the very first week! My body buzzing with energy, I felt like I was on a natural high. I had never felt this good in my life. I only needed a few hours of sleep each night and my energy soared.

I began making all sorts of different meals, desserts, and other concoctions. I called friends, letting them know what I was doing and told them about the amazing results I was experiencing. I felt rejuvenated, vibrant, and totally alive!

AND OF COURSE, I CALLED CHRISTINE.

Christine had gained a lot of weight and was now up to 233 pounds. She had been trying every diet imaginable...with no results.

When I told her I was back on the raw food diet and loving it, she thought I was crazy...understandably so, remembering the old "almond and fig" days. She couldn't believe I was "at it" again.

I pleaded with her: "Let me prepare all of your food for two weeks. I promise you, you'll lose weight and feel great!"

Shamelessly tempting her into giving me a chance, I told her she could eat living pizza, raw ravioli, carob fudge and other whole foods - without limitation and *without* counting calories or fat grams.

Finally, she gave in.

In the beginning, Christine would call me at least three times a day. "You're making too much food for me," she'd protest. She couldn't imagine *losing* weight by eating three meals, plus two desserts (like banana cream pie or black forest cake) a day. "Eat *everything*," I told her. "And don't weigh yourself until the end of the two weeks you promised me!"

At the end of *one* week, Christine, who was chronically late for work since she overslept regularly, was up at six in the morning, working out and meditating.

At the end of two weeks, Christine had lost 14 pounds. And over the next four months she would lose 80 more.

Christine knew - and *I* knew - that I was at a turning point. It was time for me to switch my focus with my clients. I put them all on the raw and living food diet. Within a week, each one of them began to see amazing results.

As for me, I felt better than I had since my teenage years. My energy shot through the roof, and I began to look younger and younger.

I had found the fountain of youth. It wasn't a magic pill, it wasn't some fad diet, it wasn't some mysterious potion I had to drink, it was much simpler than that.

The fountain of youth was found in the most delicious, natural foods this planet has to offer...the fountain of youth *is* raw and living foods.

TO REMAIN YOUNG, one must change.

— Alexander Chasea

Here I am in my mid-twenties on cooked food! (Above and below).
Even though I was a vegetarian at the time, I was severely lacking in
energy and vitality. I was always fluctuating with a 10-15 pound weight
gain and had many aches and pains.

Here I am RAW! (This page)

Here I am at 36 years old. Look at the difference! I'm at my ideal weight and I am free of aches and pains. I have more energy now than I ever had in my life! I'm healthier than I've EVER been!

4

THE NATURAL WAY TO BEAUTY

"BUT I'M NOT SICK OR OVERWEIGHT. IN FACT, I FEEL JUST FINE!"

Maybe you're reading this, thinking that you don't have any medical problems, you don't need to lose weight, and you're feeling fine. Why would you want to change to a raw and living food diet?

Everyone wants to look good. Most of us spend an inordinate amount of time trying to make ourselves look the best we can. Think of how much time you spend fixing your hair, cutting it, coloring it, styling it. How much time do you spend putting on your make-up in the morning? And how often are you touching it up throughout the day? Maybe you spend a half hour every other day in a tanning salon or covering yourself with tanning lotion to achieve a sun-kissed glow. How many hours do you spend at the gym, trying to change what you don't like or trying to hold on to what you have achieved? Do you have acne or uneven skin tone? Have you noticed lines appearing in your face? When you look at old photographs, do you see yourself looking progressively older as the years go by? Maybe your hair is turning gray or falling out, maybe you have more wrinkles, puffiness under your eyes, sallow skin, age spots, teeth problems, bleeding gums, deep creases in your neck. Or maybe you simply notice that the old sparkle in your eyes and that natural healthy glow are no longer there.

What if I told you that by eating a raw and living food diet you will begin to turn back the hands of time? What if I told you that by eating a raw and living food diet, you will start to look younger and more beautiful or handsome? That you could turn your hair back to its natural color and stop hair loss, that you could erase wrinkles and deep creases and age spots, that your circles, bags, and eye puffiness would disappear, that your acne and blemishes would be gone, and that you would look better without make-up and that you would have a natural sunny blush? That your teeth would be tighter and your gums would stop bleeding? And that your skin would glow and your eyes would sparkle?

HEALTH IS NOT SIMPLY the absence of sickness.

— Hannah Green

TAKE CARE OF YOUR BODY with steadfast fidelity. The soul must see through these eyes alone, and if they are dim, the whole world is clouded.

— Johann Wolfgang Von Goethe

IT IS NOT LENGTH of life, but

depth of life.

— Ralph Waldo Emerson

What if, by cleansing your body from all of its excess fat, you could see quicker results from workouts and have a faster recovery time... all of this by just changing your diet? You can!

"WHY THIS HAPPENS?"

A major reason why a raw and living diet helps reverse or slow down the aging process is the high levels of certain vitamins, trace minerals and anti-oxidants found in this type of food. Many of the world's leading age researchers believe that these substances are extremely beneficial in helping to arrest and in many cases actually *reverse* aging at the cellular level.

In his book *Conscious Eating*, Gabriel Cousens, M.D. writes about cooked food and the role it plays in skin health:

"Ammonia, which is a breakdown product of a high flesh food diet, is directly toxic to the system. It has been found to create free radical damage, cross-linking (a process associated with skin wrinkles and aging), as well as depleting the body's energy."

About biogenic foods, which are raw and sprouted nuts, seeds, grains, and grasses, Cousens adds:

"They help to reverse entropy and the aging process. These are high-enzyme, raw foods that have the capacity to revitalize and regenerate the human organism."

In their book *The New Raw Energy*, Susanna and Leslie Kenton examine a powerful enzyme abundantly present in uncooked fruits, vegetables, and sprouted nuts, seeds, and grains. They write:

"We know, for example, that there is a special enzyme called superoxide dismutase (SOD for short) which discourages the formation of 'rogue' molecules called superoxides and free radicals which do serious oxidative damage to every part of the body."

In other words, superoxides and free radicals can cause premature aging. Raw and living food gives our bodies the powerful enzymes to keep them at bay.

Enzymes are what keep us alive! They also keep us healthy, young and beautiful and they're never so abundant as they are in raw and living food!

We need the antioxidants that are rich in raw and living food to keep our skin, hair, nails, and eyes glowing and healthy. We need them for inner health *and* for outer beauty!

RAW FOODERS ARE EASY TO SPOT

They're the ones who glow with radiance! The ones with the most energy, the creamiest skin, the firmest bodies, the shiniest hair and the most sparkly eyes...and they *always* look years younger than their age. No diet I've ever seen · *including* vegetarian or vegan diets · even comes close to producing the healthy, all-over beauty, raw and living food accomplishes.

Raw and living food people feel good about themselves and happy to be alive!

It's a wonderful feeling to know that you look the best you possibly can. Looking better makes you feel better and feeling better is imperative for good health.

WHAT YOU DO SPEAKS so loudly that I cannot hear what you say. — **Anonymous**

5

WHAT IS RAW AND LIVING FOOD?

BY NOW, YOU'RE PROBABLY starting to wonder what exactly raw and living food *is* and what you can and cannot eat on this diet, right?

Ok, let's examine some of the basic details!

Raw and living food consists of uncooked fruits, vegetables, nuts, seeds, and *sprouted* grains.

These foods are not processed, heated, cooked or altered in any way. They are nothing more than whole foods in their natural state.

You can eat *any* raw fruits, vegetables, nuts, or seeds.

If you sprout grains and beans, you can eat those, too.

For even more variety (do you realize how many different kinds of fruits, vegetables, and seeds there are?) I've also listed some other foods that you can enjoy: raw carob powder, olive oil, and nut butters, for example.

FRESH FRUIT AND FRUIT JUICES Partial list includes: apples, apricots, avocados, bananas, blackberries, blueberries, cantaloupe, cherimoyas, cherries, coconuts, cucumbers, dates, durian, figs, grapefruit, grapes, kiwis, lemons, limes, mangoes, melons, nectarines, oranges, papaya, peaches, pears, persimmon, pineapples, plums, sapotes, strawberries, tomatoes, tropical fruits, zucchini. These are all fresh, ripe, raw and hopefully organic! No fruits that come in a can or jar: they are *not raw.*

FRESH VEGETABLES AND VEGETABLE JUICES Partial list includes: beets, bok choy, broccoli, cabbage, carrots, cauliflower, celery root, celery, chives, collards, corn, dandelion, eggplant, endive, escarole, fennel, garlic, kale, kohlrabi, leeks, lettuces, mushrooms, mustard greens, okra, olives, onions, parsley, parsnips, peas, peppers, radishes, sorrel, spinach, sprouts, squash, Swiss chard, turnips, watercress.

These must also be fresh, ripe, raw, and hopefully organic! Do not eat any vegetables that come in a can or a jar: they are *not raw.*

NUTS AND SEEDS: RAW AND UNSALTED ONLY! Partial list includes: almonds, brazil nuts, cashews, filberts, flaxseeds, hazelnuts, macadamia nuts, pecans, pine nuts, pistachios, pumpkin seeds, sesame seeds, sunflower seeds, walnuts.

BEANS, LEGUMES, GRAINS: SOAKED AND SPROUTED ONLY!*
Partial list includes: barley, buckwheat, chickpeas, lentils, mung, quinoa, rye, wheat.

DRIED FRUITS: NO SUGAR OR SULFATES ADDED! Partial list includes: apples, apricots, bananas, dates, figs, pears, prunes, raisins

SEAWEEDS: RAW AND NOT TOASTED! Partial list includes: dulse, hijiki, kelp, nori, wakame.

*All grains, beans, legumes, nuts and seeds should be *soaked* and *sprouted*. Even though nuts and seeds are raw, they contain enzyme inhibitors. This means that their enzymes are lying dormant. When you eat them, your body will have to use its own enzymes to break them up. That's not good. But the good news is, if you soak and sprout them, you'll activate their enzymes! Sprouting is easy. Read about it on page 275.

ADDITIONAL FOODS TO ENJOY!

OLIVE OIL Always buy organic, first cold pressed, extra virgin olive oil in *dark* bottles, so it's protected from the sun and other light.

APPLE CIDER VINEGAR Used for years to improve health and create a balanced metabolism, apple cider vinegar is a powerful antioxidant. It contains amino acids, along with essential vitamins, minerals, and enzymes. It's been known to help break down cholesterol formations in the blood vessels and to reduce high blood pressure.

RAW HONEY There are tons of honey brands on the market, most are heated and processed. Make sure the label clearly indicates *raw* honey!

RAW CAROB POWDER A terrific chocolate substitute, this powder is made out of ground pods from the Mediterranean evergreen tree. Health food stores tend to sell it roasted. You don't want that. Get it *raw* from reputable stores or through mail order sources.

BRAGGS LIQUID AMINOS (OR NAMA SHOYU) An unheated, non-pasteurized soy product, it tastes like tamari and is used in its place for a salty or soy sauce-like flavor.

SEA SALT Why not just regular table salt you ask? The best explanation I've found is in Rhio's *Hooked on Raw*. I quote:

"White table salt is the by-product of the processing of earth salt after the valuable minerals have been extracted for sale to industry. The salt is subjected to a complicated process of refining which includes heating the salt to over 2,000 degrees. The minerals are precipitated out of the salt, *going through numerous processes*, and then the salt is re-crystallized. To make the salt free flowing, an anti-caking agent is added, which has the unfortunate side effect of turning the salt purple. Since no one is going to purchase purple salt, it is bleached, and then glucose, talcum, aluminum silicate and...a few other things are added. The end product is 97.5% sodium chloride with no trace elements. *This salt is poison to the body.*"

On Celtic sea salt, Rhio writes: "This salt is harvested from the ocean in a 9,000-acre, pristine area of Brittany, in north-western France. The area has been protected by the French government as an historic site, so that ancient traditions can be preserved for the future generations.

To produce the salt, ocean water is channeled into a series of shallow ponds. The sun and wind evaporate the water, leaving a mineral-rich brine. The salt farmers (known as paludiers) then hand rake the brine with wooden tools, and within hours, crystals form and are gathered by hand. The method used for the whole process is a 2,000-year-old tradition in Brittany. This salt is unheated and unrefined. The `Grain and Salt Society' offers three different kinds of salt. The light gray and the flower of the ocean are sun-dried and unheated. The fine ground has been heated to 200 degrees."

SPICES AND HERBS You can use dried spices in recipes to liven them up, but try sticking to fresh herbs and spices as often as possible to get their most beneficial effects. Kelp powder is a good substitute for salt, and it's great for imparting a "fish-like" taste to foods. And it's *loaded* with minerals. Herbamare is a sea salt/herbal combination · great in dips!

RAW TAHINI, ALMOND BUTTER, AND OTHER NUT BUTTERS
Make your own using a juicer or buy them at a health food store. Make sure they're labeled "raw" or they're *not*!

Now remember: these are all just *partial* lists to give you an idea of what raw food is. Others, perhaps not as common, exist...your choice is almost endless!

6

WHAT RAW AND LIVING FOOD ISN'T

RAW AND LIVING FOOD is NOT cooked, heated, or processed. Nor, with a few · just a few · exceptions, is it bottled or in jars. And it's never in cans!

FOODS TO WAVE FAREWELL TO...

Here's a partial list of foods I hope you'll say good-bye to... There aren't many, as you'll see, but they're important to note, because they're NOT part of the raw and living food diet.

HALF OF GETTING what you want is knowing what you have to give up to get it.

— Bill Phillips

MEAT AND POULTRY: Any kind

SEAFOOD: No, you can't have sushi!

DAIRY: Cheese, yogurt, butter, margarine...anything from a cow or a goat!

EGGS

PACKAGED, CANNED, OR PROCESSED FROZEN FOODS: Cookies, cakes, chips, pretzels, soups, cereal... *anything* pre-packaged on conventional grocery store shelves

COOKED GRAINS OR BEANS: Rice, pasta, breads, muffins, crackers, bagels, tofu, tempeh, seitan, tvp, imitation soy products, wheat substitutes... *anything* cooked

"STORE-BOUGHT" JUICES: THESE ARE PASTEURIZED!: Even if it comes from a health food store, if it comes in a bottle, a can, or a carton, sugarless and without additives, they're not raw. Fortunately, with inexpensive juicers available, you can easily make your own!

OTHER NON-CONSUMABLES INCLUDE: Coffee, soda, caffeine tea, sugar, alcohol, vinegar (except apple cider), tobacco, drugs, artificial sweeteners, condiments, chemicals, preservatives.

7

WHY RAW AND LIVING FOODS ARE BETTER

SWITCHING TO A RAW and living food diet has helped so many people feel well and healthy for the first time in their lives.

A raw and living food diet feeds your body and your cells with vitamins, minerals, enzymes, and other life-giving substances that cooking destroys.

While there are many factors connecting raw and living food to improved health, the two most important are probably *enzymes* and *acid alkaline balance*.

ENZYMES

Cooking food to a temperature of 112 degrees Fahrenheit (this temperature feels warm to the touch) destroys all its enzymes. This is a problem because life itself depends on enzymes. We need enzymes for every bodily function: walking, talking, breathing.

As we age, our bodies' natural source of enzymes becomes depleted. We need to replenish this source through the foods we eat. If we do not do this · if we continue to cook away the enzymes in our food · then we eventually begin to use our own natural enzyme reserves. Meanwhile, the cooking process makes it more difficult for our bodies to break up and digest the food we eat. The food begins to become stored in our bodies as toxins, leading to all sorts of disease.

In his book, *Intuitive Eating*, Doctor Humbart Santillo, N.D., writes:

"A human being is not maintained by food intake alone, but rather by what is digested. Every food must be broken down by enzymes to simpler building blocks. Enzymes may be divided into two groups: exogenous (found in raw food) and endogenous (produced within our bodies). The more one gets of the exogenous enzymes, the less will have to be borrowed from other metabolic processes and supplied by the pancreas. The enzymes contained in raw food actually aid in the digestion of that same food when it is chewed. One can live many years on

IT IS NOT THE FOOD in your life, it's the life in your food.

— Anonymous

a cooked food diet, but eventually this will cause cellular enzyme exhaustion which lays the foundation for a weak immune system and ultimately disease."

When we are born we are given a limited amount of enzyme energy that has to last us a lifetime. Think of this as your "enzyme bank account". If we do not make regular deposits to this account from eating exogenous enzymes that are found in raw foods, and we continue to eat cooked foods that use up our enzyme supply, we become more susceptible to aging, disease, and premature death.

Enzyme destruction via cooking food is detrimental in so many ways. Not only does it affect our immune system, but also our brain function and energy levels.

Doctor Edward Howell in his book, *Enzyme Nutrition*, writes: "Humans eating an enzymeless diet use up a tremendous amount of their enzyme potential in lavish secretions of the pancreas and other digestive organs. The result is a shortened life span (65 years or less as compared with 100 or more), illness, and lower resistance to stress of all types, psychological and environmental. By eating foods with their enzymes intact and by supplementing cooked foods with enzyme capsules we can stop abnormal and pathological aging processes."

THE ENERGY-ENZYME CONNECTION

Have you ever become sleepy after a meal? Here's why:

Your body's energy is sapped by trying to digest all of the cooked food.

Some people try to increase what energy they have by drinking coffee and/or taking artificial stimulants. Doctor Santillo states that as "metabolism increases, enzymes are used up, a false energy output is experienced, and the individual feels a sense of well-being. The end result will be lower energy, a more rapid burnout of enzymes, and premature aging."

I've noticed that coffee is one of the hardest things to give up for people new to the raw and living food diet. Often people will experience severe headaches for a few days.

But very soon, you will be feeling far more *real* energy than you could ever get from a cup of coffee!

All of the live food entering your body will rejuvenate and feed your cells with the high quality nutrients and enzymes it needs. And with the absence of cooked, nutritionally inferior, lifeless, heavy foods, your body will feel light and energized. It is very common for people who eat raw and living food to feel a type of "buzz" - a natural, very pleasant high. Most also notice needing far less sleep.

ENZYMES AND YOUR STATE OF MIND

People - myself included - have experienced a markedly improved state of mind and clarity when eating raw and living foods. Within days of beginning this diet, people notice mood improvements. The mental "haze" lifts. They feel more energized, but also more at peace; more able to focus and concentrate.

In his book *There are No Incurable Diseases*, Doctor Richard Schulze explains this phenomenon:

"Your brain is just like any other organ in your body. It can only work well when it is supplied with sufficient blood and that blood must be rich in nutrients. Your brain also creates waste as it works - thinking, problem-solving, meditating, or stimulating millions of nerve cells, or manufacturing numerous metabolic chemicals that tell your body to do everything from balancing your hormones to recovering from jet lag. Often while viewing an autopsy that opens the skull and dissects the brain, or when reading a post mortem pathology report, some part of the brain tissue is usually anemic and physically covered with yellow mucus and waste. This proves the lack of blood and the retention of waste. When viewing the brain of someone with a brain disease, the brain usually looks even worse. Medical doctors and scientists would like to make this more complicated.

It isn't. From slight memory loss to Alzheimer's disease, from bad hair days to chronic depression, even insanity, ALL brain and emotional dysfunction has its roots in bad circulation, nutritional depletion, and waste build-up."

Feeling emotionally clearer is often the first thing people who go raw notice, followed by increased energy and the healing of physical problems.

So, why continue eating cooked foods that deplete our enzyme reserve, leading to poor physical and mental health, when we can eat delicious raw foods, filled with enzymes and life-sustaining energy, improving our health and quality of life?

LIVE FOOD, LIVE BODIES.

Dead food, dead bodies.

— Ann Wigmore

ACID-ALKALINE BALANCE

While there is *much* to say on this subject, I'm giving you a very brief overview, so you can begin thinking about the effect the food you eat has on the acid-alkaline balance in your body.

An overly acidic body is found in most people with acute or chronic diseases. A few of the many common symptoms of overly acidic bodies include: arthritis, depression, headaches, lethargy, gastritis, dulled mentality, canker sores, fatigue, muscle stiffness, stomach aches, chest pain, constipation, irritability, sinus problems, acid reflux, and sleep problems.

But an overly acidic body can lead to far more serious problems. For example, cancer cells live better in an acid environment.

Doctor Ted Morter in *Dynamic Health* states:

" When your body is too acid for too long, it plays the game of life with a lineup of backup systems. These backups are either substitute minerals, or ammonia. When your body is too acid - when your normal pH is too low - the systems and organs of your body work overtime just to stay even. But systems and organs aren't designed to function flat-out in red-alert mode all the time. They need rest just as you do. If the red-alert goes on for months or even years, systems and organs become exhausted. An exhausted body can't compete with disease. Eventually, disease wins the game."

Just as enzymes effect brain function, so do acid levels effect your mental state. As Gabriel Cousens in *Conscious Eating* writes: "The major consequence of systematic acidosis is a depression of the central nervous system. An acidic person often experiences dulled mentality, slower thinking processes, headaches, and depression. Fatigue and muscle stiffness are other major symptoms. Pain in the lower back and generalized muscle stiffness is secondary to a low calcium state. The calcium loss of other alkalizing minerals are used up in buffering the acidity. The more acidic a person becomes, the more irritable he or she becomes as the calcium, magnesium, potassium, and sodium are lost from the muscle and nerve cells. Tension in the neck and shoulders, arthritis, and osteoporosis are also typical problems. Muscle spasms and twitching also occur from the low calcium. There is a general sense of fatigue and weakness from a toxemia that develops because the kidneys are working so hard to excrete the acids that they do not function as well in eliminating other types of systemic toxins that continue to build up in the course of everyday life."

Cousens adds that, when the body becomes abnormally acidic, "it is at this point that the acidity begins to negatively affect the function of the body's enzyme system."

HOW DO OUR BODIES BECOME TOO ACIDIC?

Diet is *the* major factor.

A diet too high in acid-forming food will cause the body to become too acidic. And what are acid-forming foods? Sadly, the typical American diet - high flesh foods, high sugar, high fat, low complex carbohydrates - is acid-forming. Meat, fish, poultry, eggs, dairy, white sugars, flour products, pasta, breads, most cooked grains, most beans, most nuts, candy, soda, coffee, tobacco, alcohol, chemical additives, preservatives, drugs, and synthetic vitamins are all acid-forming.

Edgar Cayce - along with most scientists and nutritionists - believes that our diets should be made up of 80% alkaline foods and 20% acid foods.

So how do we get our bodies to the proper pH balance while creating an internal environment that is slightly alkaline? We eliminate acid-producing foods, and enjoy a diet high in raw fruits and vegetables. *Raw* - because when you cook food, you make it more acidic.

When your diet is made up of raw fruits, vegetables, sprouted nuts, seeds and grains, you will shift from an acid state to a more alkaline state.

Almost all fruits and vegetables are alkaline-forming. Certain types - oranges, grapefruit, lemons, and limes come immediately to mind - are acid *externally* but alkaline *internally*.

However, most grains, beans, nuts, and seeds are acid-forming. That's why it's so important to *sprout* them: sprouting changes these acid-forming foods to alkaline forming foods!

Be sure to eat only RIPE fruit, not just because it tastes better but because most unripe fruit is acid-forming!

To sum it up: eating a raw and living food diet is the best way to ensure your body's optimal pH balance.

8

SHOPPING FOR RAW AND LIVING FOODS...

...WILL BE EASIER THAN YOU THINK!

When people tell me that there are no places to shop for raw and living food in their immediate area, I invariably discover that they just don't know where to look. Remember, people throughout the world eat only raw and living food, and this diet is increasing in popularity. You shouldn't have any trouble at all.

The best places to shop are health food stores, farmers' markets and co-ops.

If there's a large health food store in your area - one that carries a large variety of fresh produce, nuts, seeds, and whole grains, it's probably easier for you to shop there and get just about everything you need in one spot.

In certain areas of the U.S., farmers' markets are abundant. They tend to carry lots of organic produce, and some also carry nuts, seeds, and many varieties of sprouts. Depending on the size of the market, you may be able to purchase most of what you need there.

Co-ops are also wonderful places to shop. They are generally stocked with all the standards, plus many of the harder-to-find items - fresh raw nut and seed butters and raw olives, for examples. The co-op I shop at carries items in bulk which is handy, and the people are more than happy to place special orders for items not in stock.

Happily, many supermarkets now carry organic produce and a sufficient variety of other whole foods to support a raw and living food diet.

Check out your phone book. Talk to people at health clubs and at supermarkets carrying some organic produce. I'll bet you'll find you're loaded with resources.

On the off chance that you're not, there's still no real problem. Delivery companies exist that will bring fresh produce right to your doorstep. There are also mail order companies - check out the resource section at the end of this book - selling special order dried fruits, nuts, seeds, grains, nut butters, and more.

AS I SEE IT EVERY DAY you do one of two things: build health or produce disease in yourself.

— Adelle Davis

9

YOUR RAW AND LIVING FOOD KITCHEN

DO NOT LET A LACK OF *any* of these items stop you! When I first started eating raw, all I had was a food processor and a blender. Don't put off the diet until you've assembled all the gadgets or you'll never get started!

Most kitchens already contain the basic necessities for a raw and living diet · knives, vegetable peelers, bowls, pie plates, strainers, a food processor, blender, etc. But the items listed here will make an easy diet even easier.

FOOD PROCESSOR

It's almost essential, because it makes the difference between taking ten minutes to prepare a meal or two hours. You'll need one for all the grinding, chopping, blending, mixing, and shredding of nuts and veggies required for making the recipes I've included in this book. Of the many different brands, I'm happiest with one of the less expensive models that sells for under $40. You needn't spend a lot of money on a food processor. Just make sure it has a large enough cup size.

BLENDER

Also important. Any kind will be sufficient for making smoothies and dressings and some of the other recipes in this book.

JUICER

There are many different brands on the market, ranging in price from about $30.00 to $600.00. I've found that even the less expensive models work well. They may not last forever, but they're certainly adequate, so please don't let the fact that you don't have a few hundred dollars to spend on a juicer stop you! A juicer isn't an essential appliance to start your diet, but a drink of collards, kale, spinach, Swiss chard, cucumber, celery, and an apple is a great way to get your greens.

With a *Green Life* juicer, *Samson* or *Omega* juicer, you can make fruit and vegetable juices and also juice wheatgrass and chop and mince. A *Champion* juicer (less than $200.00) also

"IF YOU CAN organize your kitchen, you can organize your life."

— **Louis Parrish**

makes fruit and vegetable juices. All of these models also let you homogenize which means you can make your own nut butters, fruit ice creams, and the like.

There are also a variety of other juicers · such as the *Juice Man, Jr.* and *Breville Juicer* · which work well in juicing fruits and vegetables.

VITA-MIX

Many of my clients love this. It's an expensive, heavy-duty blender. It's sold as a juicer that uses the pulp and whole fruit or vegetable. It's great for making smoothies, dips, and soups: they'll come out very smooth and creamy. You can also grind nuts and seeds in it which you cannot do in the food processor. This is a very fast and powerful machine that whips recipes together very quickly and gives foods a texture not easily accomplished with other appliances.

DEHYDRATOR

Your dehydrator will be your "raw food oven." I use mine often to make all kinds of delicious meals. You can use your dehydrator to give foods a thicker, firmer consistency like nut loaves, lasagna, pizza, cookies, breads and burgers or, when left in your dehydrator longer, foods can take on a crispy, dry texture, like real crackers. Though certainly not a necessity, a dehydrator will allow you to prepare a much wider variety of items that will have the "taste" of having been cooked. This can be important, especially when you're first starting out.

Important: Make sure your dehydrator features a temperature control to enable you to maintain temperatures below 112 degrees, thereby preserving the enzymes. Most models without temperature controls have thermostats starting at 140 degrees or higher. These will destroy all the life-giving properties you are trying to maintain. Check the resource section in the back of this book for a temperature controlled dehydrator.

SALADACCO

This little hand-held appliance is essential for making angel hair pasta from zucchini and squash. There are two settings. One lets you make very fine angel hair type strands, which can be used for beets, yams, zucchini, and other vegetables. The other setting is for paper thin slices. I love mine for making potato chips and ravioli shells. You can also make beautiful salads with it and it's inexpensive: about $25.00.

COFFEE GRINDER

Great for grinding small seeds like flax and sunflower that can't be ground with your food processor. Not a necessity, but it's nice to have and usually costs less than $10.00.

10

HOW TO START RAW...TODAY!

ARE YOU READY TO STOP FEELING SICK and tired? Are you ready to be healthier and look better than ever?

Then after you read the following paragraph, I want you to put this book down, go into your kitchen, and start cleaning house.

Throw out everything that isn't raw. Get rid of all the favorite foods stuffed into your refrigerator and freezer. Toss all the boxes, bags, and cans of food in your cabinets. Don't save *anything*, "just in case." If you're serious about getting healthy, you don't need any "just in cases." "Just in case I can't do this," "just in case I crave something," "just in case people stop by and I need to feed them." There are millions of "just in cases." And they are all impediments to your good health. So get up, go to your kitchen, and get rid of everything you now know simply isn't good for you. (You might want to give this food to friends, family, or a food pantry. In that case, do it *now*. Don't come back to this book until the foods you don't need are out of your house. I'll wait.)

"YOU MISS 100% of the shots you never take."

— Wayne Gretsky

* * *

CONGRATULATIONS AND WELCOME BACK!

I usually don't require my clients to follow strict rules or guidelines. Everyone has different needs, and this diet works best when an individual finds his or her own way.

If you're already familiar with raw and living food, and would like to substitute, say, a different kind of fruit or vegetable for one that I suggest, go right ahead. If you want to use a different recipe in place of the one I tell you to make in any given week, that's fine. Do what feels right for you.

Again, this diet is mostly about freedom! You don't have to eat certain things at certain times. You don't have to weigh anything, or count calories or mysterious "points" every day.

If you want to, you can eat only bananas for days, or pineapple in the morning, a salad for lunch, and more veggies for dinner. Since this diet adapts beautifully to each individual, I encourage you to experiment.

However, if this diet is completely new to you, then I *strongly* suggest that you follow my recommendations for the first few weeks until you feel comfortable and find your own rhythm of eating.

In reviewing the "diet" books on the shelves, I've found that there is either a vast array of confusing menu choices, or there are strict guidelines regarding what and how much and when to eat. My approach is different and far more effective. It's the same system I use when I work with clients on a one-on-one basis.

EAT MORE!

The biggest mistake people make when they first go raw is, they don't eat enough!

Now, I know that many raw food teachers tell their students to eat minimally, and that overeating anything, including raw food, creates problems. And while they're technically correct, it's simply not practical to expect people who have been eating a standard American diet to suddenly switch to a mono diet of minimal amounts of fruits and vegetables. I've seen people fail on this diet · needlessly, in my opinion · when they do not give themselves time to adjust.

So, eat when you're hungry, and give your body time to adjust to this less-filling food. Eventually, you will require progressively less raw and living food because your body will be getting all the nutrients it needs from a smaller volume of food.

Remember: when you eat cooked, dead food, you need to consume a great deal of it to get the nutrients you need. Additionally, according to Gabriel Cousens in *Conscious Eating*, "Cooked food [also] seems to stimulate the craving for cooked food because the organs are not getting the nutrients they would normally get in uncooked food. The body naturally

WE ARE INDEED MUCH MORE

than what we eat, but what

we eat can nevertheless help

us to be much more

than what we are.

— Adelle Davis

craves more nutrients, which would translate into an uncontrol-lable appetite and lack of willpower."

Many overweight people are literally starving to death from malnutrition.

THIS MORNING I ATE 6 BANANAS FOR BREAKFAST.

Does this shock you? It shocks a lot of people.

But, somehow the notion of someone sitting down to eggs, toast, bacon, and hash browns; or a bagel smeared with cream cheese or topped with lox; or a heavy, fat-laden pastry, all washed down with coffee seems "normal."

Here's my point: breakfasts like the above have little or no nutritional value...but they're *filling*!

So don't eat just one banana for breakfast and then wonder why you're still hungry! I'm not telling you to stuff yourself, but I *am* telling you to eat enough so that you're satisfied. This way you won't be hungry an hour later and begin to doubt this diet.

IMPORTANT: LEARN HOW TO MAKE RAW FOOD DISHES!

Even if you eat very simply · mostly fruits and salads · the day will come when you wake up really hungry, or you'll have a sud-den desire for something more at night, or you'll simply want something different to eat.

At that point · if you haven't learned how to make a few raw dishes · you may begin to think that you can't continue on the diet; that there isn't enough variety in it for you.

Therefore, I strongly urge you to learn how to make a few dif-ferent meals. Consider it an "insurance policy" toward the pro-tection of your new healthy diet.

BE PREPARED!

While it's true that the easier you make this diet, the better, it's also important to educate yourself on the fun and filling dishes you can prepare.

Too many people · people who have heard about this diet from other sources · have told me they thought it was "boring," and "unsatisfying."

None of *my* clients ever say that! Not after they work with me and learn how to prepare food and balance out their diets. I want you to have the same successful experience they've had.

On some days, you won't be hungry. On other days, you'll need more food. Listen to your body! Be prepared to give it what it needs. Stock your refrigerator with healthful foods and have the ingredients available to whip up a dessert or something filling if needed, to satisfy a craving.

You'll notice the many testimonials in this book. Most of them describe their daily diets, but every one is different. Note that not one of these people give an exact calorie count or an exact amount of food they eat on any given day.

You won't find a "daily exercise guide" in this book, nor will you find "rules" about specified meal time periods. You don't need such things! If you follow the guidelines in this chapter, and read the entire book, you'll know exactly what your own, unique body needs.

And you'll see results!

IF YOU'RE HUNGRY, EAT. IF YOU'RE NOT, DON'T!

Sounds logical, doesn't it? But people constantly eat for reasons other than nourishment. These reasons are largely emotional.

Find an alternative to eating. Write in a journal, exercise, do something creative, have fun! Don't use food as a distraction · or an escape · from life issues. Use it to make your life better than it's ever been before!

Ready? Then let's go shopping!

11

YOUR FOUR WEEK RAW AND LIVING FOOD SHOPPING AND FOOD PREPARATION GUIDE

THIS GUIDE HAS WORKED WONDERFULLY with my clients and requires shopping only once a week. Best of all, besides whipping up a smoothie, salad or recipe of that nature, this guide only requires that you prepare food twice a week. Make sure your kitchen is stocked with the items I've called "The Essentials." You might want to copy the "Essentials" list and take it, along with the "Week 1" list with you to the supermarket, co-op, or farmer's market. If you need a food processor, blender, or juicer, give yourself time to stop at the department store.

You may want to order a *Saladacco* today...you'll be able to make angel hair pasta, pad Thai, and other delicious dishes in minutes! You might also consider ordering a food dehydrator now: it may take some time to arrive.

If you prefer not to buy a dehydrator at this time, use recipes in this book that don't require one for Week 4, and make up your own plan.

THE ESSENTIALS

With these basic ingredients on hand, you'll always be able to whip up something tasty if you get a craving. Buy extra amounts of nuts, dried fruits, and other condiments, since they're not as perishable as fresh produce.

Vegetables: lettuce and salad greens, avocados, carrots, cucumbers, celery, mushrooms, etc.

Fruits: oranges, bananas, grapefruit, pineapples, apples, mangos, grapes, pears, lemons, melons, etc.

Frozen Fruit For Smoothies and Desserts: (DON'T buy packaged frozen fruit · freeze your fresh fruit yourself · unless you can get organic frozen fruit with no sugar added) strawberries, blueberries, bananas (always peel bananas before freezing), etc.

A Variety Of Dried Fruits: dates, apricots, raisins, etc.

A Variety Of Raw Nuts and Seeds: macadamia nuts, cashews,

PEOPLE BECOME really quite remarkable when they start thinking that they can do things. When they believe in themselves they have the first secret of success.

— Norman Vincent Peale

almonds, walnuts, pine nuts, flax seeds, pumpkin seeds, sunflower seeds, etc.

Honey (make sure it says "raw" or it's not!)

Olive Oil

Apple Cider Vinegar

Bragg Liquid Aminos or Nama Shoyu

Raw Almond Butter

Disclaimer: I Know That This Is A Lot Of Food!

I'm very much aware of the fact that I am asking you to prepare a great deal of food. In fact, that's almost always the first thing my clients tell me when I start them on this diet!

But please prepare it all, especially in the first couple of weeks. There are two main reasons for this. One, as I've said before, it's important to know how to prepare delicious raw and living food meals. Secondly, these simple recipes will give you a great deal of variety as you introduce yourself to this new way of eating.

On the other hand, I'm certainly not asking you to eat huge quantities of food throughout the day!

Many of my beginning clients find themselves sharing the food they prepare with family and friends. I think that's great...and there's certainly enough to do that!

Later on, you can halve some of the recipes, or make smaller portions than what the recipes call for.

In any case, while I hate the idea of wasting food, I do want to prepare you: you'll definitely have food left over during this first four weeks.

If you feel as if you're eating too much, then stop eating! Omit a meal on the plan. By all means, listen to your body!

WEEK 1: INGREDIENTS' SHOPPING LIST AND FOOD PREPARATION

Take a look at the meals you'll prepare this week, and take note of the ingredients required.

Fettuccini Alfredo (Page 381-382)

Mock Salmon Pâté (Page 380)

Date Nut Torte (Page 483)

Alissa's Dressing (Page 475)

Pad Thai (Page 396)

Collard Rolls (Page 437)

Banana Ice Cream (Page 516)

Creamy Italian Herb Dressing (Page 474)

WEEK 1: INGREDIENTS' LIST (DON'T FORGET TO TAKE ALONG THE "ESSENTIAL'S" LIST, TOO!)

This list contains everything you'll need for this week's recipes. You will obviously buy spices, oils and other condiments in larger quantities then what are listed here, and you'll buy produce and nuts in larger quantities, too (it's pretty hard to buy garlic in cloves, for example, and ginger is generally sold by the root.) Of course, feel free to buy more fruit, veggies, and greens! I've listed the exact amounts, with an eye toward the dishes you'll prepare this week. You may see some duplication because of your "Essentials" list. Don't worry about it. It's better to have too much than not enough.

PRODUCE

Avocado (1)

Basil (1 cup)

Bananas (6) (Remove peel and freeze as soon as ripe)

Carrots (1)

Celery (2 stalks)

Collard leaves (2 very large, or 3-4 small)

Garlic (4 cloves)

Ginger, fresh (2 Tablespoons)

Lemons (3)

Lettuce (2 cups)

Mung bean sprouts (4 cups)

Onions (2 large)

Oranges (2)

Parsley (1/4 cup)

Pepper, red (1)

Portobella mushrooms (1 cup)

Raisins (2 cups)

Tomato (1)

Scallions (3)

Squash, summer (3)

Zucchini (3)

NUTS/SEEDS/DRIED FRUIT

Cashews (1 cup)

Macadamia nuts (1 cup)

Pine nuts (1 cup)

Walnuts (4 cups)

Dates (1 cup)

SPICES/CONDIMENTS

Almond butter (1 cup)

Apple cider vinegar (3/4 cup)

Bragg Liquid Aminos

Cilantro (optional)

Honey (6 tablespoons)

Italian seasoning (2 tablespoons)

Olive oil (2 1/2 cups)

Sea salt

FOOD PREPARATION: WEEK 1

Day 1:

Fettuccini Alfredo (Page 381-382)

Mock Salmon Pâté (Page 380)

Date Nut Torte (Page 483)

Alissa's Dressing (Page 475)

Day 3 or 4:

Pad Thai (Page 396)

Collard Rolls (Page 437)

Banana Ice Cream (Page 516)

Creamy Italian Herb Dressing (Page 474)

WEEK 2: INGREDIENTS' SHOPPING LIST AND FOOD PREPARATION

Take a look at the meals you'll prepare this week, and take note of
the ingredients required.

Angel Hair Pasta with Marinara Sauce (Page 395)

Almost Tuna (Page 383)

French Dressing (Page 474)

Sunny Pâté (Page 384)

Sweet Nori Rolls (Page 405)

Stuffed Portobella Mushroom Caps (Page 389)

Blueberry Pie (Page 484)

Caesar Dressing (Page 475)

WEEK 2: INGREDIENTS' LIST

This list contains everything you'll need for this week's recipes
in the exact amounts. It's likely that you already have some of
what you'll need from last week's shopping trip. Again, feel
free to buy more fruit, veggies, and greens!

PRODUCE

Alfalfa sprouts (3 cups)

Apple (1)

Avocados (2 whole)

Bananas (2)

Blueberries (5 cups)

Celery (2 stalks)

Garlic (9 cloves)

Ginger, fresh (1 Tablespoon)

Lemons (8)

Lentils, sprouted (1/4 cup) *or* 1/2 cup mung

Lettuce (2 cups)

Mung bean sprouts (1/4 cup) *or* 1/2 cup mung if lentils aren't being used

Nori sheets (4)

Onion (1)

Onion, red (1)

Parsley, fresh (bunch)

Portobella mushroom (1 large)

Scallions (1 bunch)

Tomatoes (4)

Tomatoes, sundried (12)

Zucchini (4 large)

NUTS/SEEDS/DRIED FRUIT

Almonds, sprouted (2 cups)

Pine nuts (1 cup)

Sunflower seeds (3 1/2 cups)

Dates (1 1/2 cups)

SPICES/CONDIMENTS

Almond butter (3 Tablespoons)

Black pepper (1/4 teaspoon)

Bragg Liquid Aminos (3/4 cup)

Cayenne pepper (1 teaspoon)

Cumin (1 teaspoon) optional

Ground yellow mustard seed (1/2 teaspoon)

Flax oil (1/2 cup)

Honey (1 cup)

Kelp (1 Tablespoon)

Miso, white (1/2 Tablespoon)

Olive oil (1/2 cup)

Paprika (1/4 teaspoon)

Tahini (1/2 cup)

Vinegar (2 Tablespoons)

Sea salt

FOOD PREPARATION: WEEK 2

Day 1:

Angel Hair Pasta with Marinara Sauce (Page 382)

Note: prepare sauce and noodles, but toss before serving if you don't want it a bit watery.

Almost Tuna (Page 383)

Blueberry Pie (Page 484)

French Dressing (Page 474)

Day 3 or 4:

Sunny Pâté (Page 384)

Sweet Nori Rolls (Page 405)

Stuffed Portobella Mushroom Caps (Page 389)

Caesar Dressing (Page 475)

WEEK 3: INGREDIENTS' SHOPPING LIST AND FOOD PREPARATION

Take a look at the meals you'll prepare this week, and take note of the ingredients required.

Pesto Lasagna (Page 423)

Pineapple Sundae (Page 520)

Potato S alad (Page 447)

Broccoli Soup (Page 355)

Kale Salad (Page 456)

WEEK 3: INGREDIENTS' LIST

This list contains everything you'll need for this week's recipes in the exact amounts. It's likely that you already have some of what you'll need from previous shopping trips. Again, feel free to buy more fruit, veggies, and greens!

PRODUCE

Apple (8 cups)

Avocados (3)

Basil, fresh (1 1/2 cups)

Broccoli (2 cups)

Celery (2 sticks)

Cilantro, fresh (3/4 cup)

Corn (2 ears)

Dill, fresh (2 cups)

Garlic (10 cloves)

Ginger, fresh (1 Tablespoon)

Jicama (2 pounds)

Kale (1 head)

Lemons (5)

Mushrooms, portobella (3-4)

Onions (2)

Pepper, red bell (2)

Pepper, yellow bell (1)

Pepper, green bell (1)

Pineapple (3 cups)

Tahini (1/2 cup)

Tomatoes, ripe (5)

Squash, summer (4)

Strawberries (6) optional

Zucchini (4 large)

NUTS/SEEDS

Almonds (1 cup)

Cashews (3 cups)

Pecans (1/2 cup) optional

Pine nuts (1/2 cup)

SPICES/CONDIMENTS

Black pepper (1/8 teaspoon)

Bragg Liquid Aminos (1/2 cup)

Cayenne pepper (1/2 teaspoon)

Chili powder (1/2 teaspoon)

Cumin (1 1/2 teaspoon)

Honey (1 teaspoon)

Olive oil (1 1/2 cups)

Tahini (3/4 cup)

Herbamare

Sea salt

FOOD PREPARATION: WEEK 3

Day 1:

Pesto Lasagna (Page 423)

Pineapple sundae (page 520)

Day 3 or 4:

Potato Salad (Page 447)

Broccoli Soup (Page 355)

Kale Salad (Page 456)

WEEK 4: INGREDIENTS' LIST AND FOOD PREPARATION

Take a look at the meals you'll prepare this week, and take note of the ingredients required. At this point, you should be really into the "groove" of making and enjoying delicious, raw and living food meals and snacks! Since this week's recipes are rather sparse when compared to those prepared in the previous three weeks, feel free to prepare more! Whip up a batch of Spinach Dip, for example. Create some wonderful salads. Blend yourself some terrific smoothies! Let your body guide you!

Remember: this week's plan calls for a dehydrator. If you don't have one, repeat some of the meals from a previous week, pick new recipes from the book...or, better yet, make up your own!

Vegetable Flax Crackers (Page 346)

Pecan Carrot Burgers with Curry Sauce (Page 385)

Crêpes with Strawberry Topping (Page 379)

Berry Bars (Page 489)

WEEK 4: INGREDIENTS' LIST

This list contains everything you'll need for this week's recipes in the exact amounts. It's likely that you already have some of what you'll need from previous shopping trips. Again, feel free to buy more fruit, veggies and greens!

PRODUCE

Bananas, RIPE (7)

Blueberries (2 cups)

Broccoli (2 cups)

Carrots (5 medium)

Celery (6 stalks)

Cilantro (3 1/2 cups)

Coriander (1/2 teaspoon)

Dates (1 cup)

Fennel (1 teaspoon)

Lemon (1)

Mushrooms, button (1 cup)

Onion (1 cup)

Pepper, orange (1)

Spinach (2 cups)

Strawberries (2 1/2 cups)

Sundried tomatoes (1 cup)

NUTS/SEEDS

Brazil nuts (1 cup)

Cashews (1 cup)

Flax seeds (2 cups)

Macadamia nuts (1/2 cup)

Pecans (1 cup)

Walnuts (1 cup)

SPICES/CONDIMENTS

Black pepper (pinch)

Bragg Liquid Aminos (2 teaspoons)

Curry (1/2 teaspoon)

Honey (1/2 cup)

Olive oil (2 Tablespoons)

Vanilla (1 teaspoon)

Sea salt

FOOD PREPARATION: WEEK 4

Day 1:

Vegetable Flax Crackers (Page 346)

Crêpes with Strawberry Topping (Page 379)

Day 3 or 4:

Pecan Carrot Burgers with Curry Sauce (Page 385)

Berry Bars (Page 489)

SOME GENERAL GUIDELINES:

- In the morning, try to eat only fruit, smoothies or juices (vegetable or fruit).
- After noon time, eat any of these dishes you've prepared at any time throughout the day.
- Include in your daily diet fresh salads, fruits and vegetables.
- Try to have a large, green salad at least once a day. If you need more variety, choose from the many other delicious salad dressing recipes in this book.
- After following the above Four Week Shopping and Food Preparation Guide, you should be proficient at raw food preparation.
- It is important · especially during the first week · to eat whatever and as much raw and living food as you want!

REMEMBER: THIS DIET IS FLEXIBLE!

If you want to use other recipes instead of those I've listed in this guide, that's fine. You don't have to worry about substituting one meal for another in terms of calorie count or fat grams. Again, if you don't have the dehydrator required for the meals recommended in Week 4, don't worry about it. You should have plenty of ingredients in your cupboards and refrigerator to prepare some healthful and delicious substitutes.

And if, for instance, you'd rather have the macadamia cream sauce over fruit, rather than the portobella mushroom caps, go right ahead!

Although you will surely lose weight, no matter what you eat at the onset of this diet (as long as it's raw and living food), this first week or two is the time to practice honing your raw food preparation skills. If you follow my guide you will be pleasantly surprised at what you have learned in only a few days...and how easy it is! You'll have all the knowledge needed to continue this way of eating, and you'll be able to prepare delicious raw food meals in minutes!

ADDED TIPS

When I first went raw I'd get cravings for sweets. If this happens to you, just mix up a couple of tablespoons of raw almond butter and honey, and throw in a few raisins. Eat a date, grab a piece of fruit, have some tahini on celery.

You'll notice that the more time-consuming recipes are not recommended in this guide. Instead, I'm recommending some of the easiest dishes: those that take only minutes to whip up.

Eat whatever it takes to keep you satisfied for the first week. Have salads, make smoothies, make the Banana Papaya Pudding, whip up some Guacamole, a soup, make more dressings...or make more of the meals you've already had!

Don't think you *must* have "three square meals" a day! Have a large bowl of fruit for lunch or dinner, a dessert for lunch or dinner, or a smoothie. This way of eating is about getting in tune with what your body wants and needs...not what you've been told to eat!

Most importantly: Keep your refrigerator and cupboards stocked full of enough raw and living food! I can't emphasize this enough! If you're hungry, and you have no food in the house, and nothing to take with you when you go out, you'll find it difficult to refrain from eating things your body doesn't need - or want.

"YOU ARE IN CHARGE of your feelings, beliefs, and actions. And you teach others how to behave toward you. While you cannot change other people, you can influence them through your own behaviors and actions. By being a living role model of what you want to receive from others, you create more of what you want in your life."

— Eric Allenbaugh

12

TAKING IT OFF

IN MY BODY-BUILDING DAYS, I'd usually eat six or seven meals a day. But on some days · because I didn't have the time, or the right food with me · I'd eat only twice a day. And oddly enough, or so it seemed to me, on those days I wasn't able to lose weight.

I had assumed that by eating less frequently I would lose more weight then when I ate more food more frequently. I found out that this is not always the case. Here's why:

When you cut your calories, your metabolism starts to slow down. When you eat smaller meals more frequently throughout the day, you fuel the fire, causing your metabolism to run at a higher velocity. This, in turn, causes more calories to be burned...even in a resting state!

Therefore, when trying to lose weight, eat smaller meals more frequently, rather than one or two large meals each day.

Once you've been eating raw and living food for the period of time needed for your digestive system to work properly, you won't need as much food. A few small meals a day will be sufficient.

But, if you find that you are not losing the weight you would like to lose, if you've reached a plateau or you're eating a light diet but still are not losing weight, try this:

Add a few extra meals to your diet. By meals, I don't necessarily mean a huge serving of a prepared raw food entrée. It could be just a piece of fruit or a vegetable or a serving of a lighter meal prepared with mostly fruits and vegetables and LESS nuts and oils.

MAJOR TIP: START EXERCISING!

You really didn't need me to tell you this. You've heard it a million times before, but it bears repeating: exercise increases your metabolism, and increased metabolism results in increased weight loss!

MY TYPICAL DIET AND EXERCISE ROUTINE...

...doesn't really exist. Most of the time I eat fruit in the morning or a green drink, a salad for lunch, and more fruit or veg-gies for dinner.

I'm always changing my diet around so my metabolism does-n't get accustomed to the same old pattern.

I hesitate to even print my "eating pattern" here, because it varies so much. On the other hand, so many people have asked for my "typical" diet that I decided to simply jot down what I ate for a given fourteen-day time period.

FOURTEEN DAYS OF EATING

Again, please just look at my recorded food intake as an exam-ple. Please note, too: I work out every morning · before eating anything · for one to two hours. My exercise includes weight lifting, running, or walking. Later in the day I frequently exer-cise some more, doing activities such as walking, roller blading or yoga. That explains why I tend to have my first meal in the later morning hours.

Day 1
10:00 AM: 4 oranges
2:00 PM: large salad*
5:00 PM: a few olives
7:00 PM: 2 raw cookies

Day 2
9:00 AM: Banana Shake
1:00 PM: large salad*
6:00 PM: 1/2 melon

Day 3
11:00: AM: 2 mangos
5:00 PM: large salad*

Day 4
10:00 AM: 1/2 pineapple
12:00 noon: small salad*

3:00 PM: Sweet Potato Chips with Guacamole

7:00 PM piece of Torte

Day 5

9:00 AM: banana, pineapple, and coconut smoothie

1:00 PM: small salad*

4:00 PM: 1 avocado with Bragg Liquid Aminos

8:00 PM: piece of Torte

Day 6

10:00 AM: green drink

1:00 PM: Collard Roll

4:00 pm: apple

6:00 PM: piece of Torte

Day 7

10:00 AM: green drink

1:00 PM: coconuts (milk and meat)

5:00 PM: 2 pears

Day 8

11:00 AM: bowl of blueberries

2:00 PM: an avocado, tomatoes, a few Flax Seed Crackers

4:00 PM: 1 pear

6:00 PM: 4 Fudge Balls

8:00 PM: Orange Banana Smoothie

Day 9

11:00 AM: orange and grapefruit juice

3:00 PM: large salad*

7:00 PM: Stuffed Portobella with Guacamole

Day 10

11:00 AM: wheat grass shot

4:00 PM: large salad*

7:00 PM: piece of Blueberry Pie

Day 11

12:00 noon: bowl of blueberries

4:00 PM: Mock Salmon Pâté on a bed of lettuce

8:00 PM: cup of Broccoli Soup

Day 12

9:00 AM: 5 oranges

12:00 noon: a scoop of Mock Tuna

2:00 PM: handful of grapes

4:00 PM: Sweet Nori Rolls

8:00 PM: spoonful of almond butter

Day 13

12:00 noon: persimmons

4:00 PM: persimmons

7:00 PM: persimmons

Day 14

12:00 noon: tomato and mushroom salad

2:00 PM: large salad*

5:00 PM: 1/2 durian

*ABOUT THOSE SALADS

Although they mainly consist of a big bowl of greens, I might "plump up" my salads by adding tomatoes, cucumbers, avocados, cilantro, onions, and/or sprouts. My dressings are always different. They're usually simple, but I sometimes add an avocado, or other veggies and herbs just for variety.

Caution: Watch the oil! Many people think that olive oil is good for you...and while it's not inherently bad, a half-cup of it is definitely not good. Enjoy a little bit, but be aware of how much you're using!

AGAIN: MY DIET VARIES!

In the summer, when the weather is warm, I tend to eat more like days 2, 3, and 7. Days like 8 and 12 are typical "grazing days." Very often I'll find that I'm eating light - like days 2, 3, and 7 - for a week or maybe even two weeks. And then I'll have days like 8 and 12 for a few days in a row.

Or, sometimes I'll find myself alternating: one day light, the next day more food, and so on.

This whole diet is about listening to what your body needs!

It's not about trying to squeeze yourself into a pattern you think you need to follow rigidly...nor, again, is it about counting calories, points, fat grams or those white-knuckled trips to the scale.

SPEAKING OF SCALES...THROW YOURS AWAY!

You want to lose weight? Lose your scale.

I've always hated scales. What good are they really? What are they weighing, muscle or fat?

If you're working out, the scale can be your real enemy. When you first start exercising, it's actually normal to gain at least a few pounds. You'll feel like you're losing inches, and your clothes will fit better, but your scale won't tell you that.

I've seen people lose inches, look terrific, and then become discouraged when they consult the "Almighty Scale". Ridiculous! And so unnecessary!

Measure your progress by how you feel, how you look, and how your clothes fit, not by a number on a scale. You're not a number!

Like I have been saying all along, this way of eating is about freedom!

Feed your body the proper foods, allow your body the time it needs to adjust, and you'll become slim, beautiful, and healthy. It's that simple!

"YOU ARE HERE for a purpose. There is not a duplicate of you in the whole wide world; there never has been, there never will be. You were brought here now to fill a certain need. Take time to think that over."

— Lou Austin

13

FOOD COMBINING

CORRECTLY COMBINING YOUR FOOD is a very important aspect of healthy eating!

In the beginning, though, except in certain cases, I suggest you don't get too caught up in food combining. The chart in this chapter is a wonderful guide, but nothing will beat your own intuition and feelings once you begin to cleanse your body with the raw and living food diet.

If you have diverticulitis, colitis, or other intestinal problems, pay more attention to the food combining principles. Or, if you're not losing weight as quickly as you'd like to, you might check how you're combining your food.

WHY IS PROPER FOOD COMBINING IMPORTANT?

Different foods are digested at different rates. When we eat them together, the digestion of foods that normally pass more rapidly through the digestive track can be delayed by more slowly digested food. This can often result in gas, bloating, heartburn, or other digestive problems. Often, our own taste buds alert us to this potential problem. For example, you may notice that a piece of watermelon eaten with a handful of nuts just doesn't taste good. Or some other combination may not seem very appealing. In many cases that's your own body telling you what the chart in this chapter will tell you!

SOME BASIC TIPS:

- Fruit digests in the quickest amount of time; within an hour or two. Acid, sub-acid, and sweet fruits all have different digestion rates, so it's best to eat only from one fruit group at a time.

- Because of its fast digestive rate, fruit doesn't combine well with any other foods, and it's best to eat it alone on an empty stomach. If you *do* eat fruit with other foods, always eat the fruit first, and allow as much time as possible for it to digest.

- Melons should *always* be eaten alone. They have the shortest digestion time.

- Drink fresh vegetable or fruit juices on an empty stomach at least thirty minutes before any other food. Fluids digest quickly. This is also important because they dilute the digestive enzymes.

- Most fruits and vegetables *do not* go well together.

- All greens, sprouts, and vegetables combine well together.

- Avocados are the exception to the rule: they combine well with most fruits and vegetables.

THE HIGH ENERGY DIET NUTRITION GUIDE

SYNERGISTIC FOOD COMBINATIONS

Legend: EXCELLENT | FAIR | AVOID

Food Groups (vertical axis): Lettuce & Celery · Vegetables · Legumes · Starches & Grains · Fats & Oils · Proteins · Acid Fruits · Sub Acid Fruits · Melons · Sweet Fruits

FOOD GROUPS

Lettuce & Celery	Vegetable	Legumes	Starches / Grains	Fats / Oils	Proteins	Acid Fruits	Sub Acid Fruits	Melons	Sweet Fruits
Lettuce	Artichoke	Dried Beans	Barley	Avocado	Almonds	Acerola	Apple	Ambrosia	Abayut
Bibb	Asparagus	Broad Beans	Buckwheat	Butter*	Brazil Nuts	Blackberries	Apricot	Banana Mel.	Atemoya
Boston	Broccoli	Kidney Beans	Carrots	Coconut	Cashews	Carambola	Blueberries	Canary	Bananas
Butter	Brussels Sprts	Lentils	Chestnuts	Cream*	Eggs*	Currants	Cherries	Cantaloupe	Canistel
Cos	Cabbage	Lima Beans	Corn (Dried)	Dairy*	Filberts	Gooseberries	Grapes	Casaba	Carob
Endive	Cauliflower	Mung Beans	Malanga	Lard*	Fish*	Grapefruit	Guava	Christmas	Cherimoya
Iceberg	Cucumber	Navy Beans	Millet	Margarine*	Fowl*	Kiwis	Loquat	Crenshaw	Dates
Little Gem	Eggplant	Pinto Beans	Oats	Olives / Oil	Meat*	Kumquat	Mango	Emperor	Dried Fruits
Loose Leaf	Fresh Beans	Soybeans	Pasta / Bread	Canola Oil	Pignolia Nuts	Lemon/Lime	Mulberries	Gala	Figs
Lollo Rosso	Fresh Peas	White Beans	Potatoes	Corn Oil	Pine Nuts	Oranges	Nectarine	Honeydew	Longan
Red Romaine	Okra	Chick Peas	Quinoa	Macadamias	Pistachios	Passion Fruit	Papaya	Lychee	Mammea
Romaine	Spinach	Corn Peas	Rice	Palm Oil	Pumpkin Sds.	Pineapple	Paw Paw	Muskmelon	Mayan
Round	Sprouts	Dried Peas	Rye	Peanut Oil	Sesame Seeds	Pommelo	Peach	Orange Bloss.	Mutingea
Celery	Summer Sqsh	Edible Pod	Wheat	Pecans	Squash Seeds	Strawberries	Pear	Orange Flesh	Persimmon
Celeriac	Sweet Peppers	Garden Peas	Winter Sqsh	Safflower Oil	Sunflower Sds	Tamarind	Plum	Persian	Plantain
Celery Root	Swiss Chard	Peanuts	Yams	Sesame Oil	Walnuts	Tangerines	Raspberries	Santa Claus	Sapodilla
Fennel	Zucchini	Pigeon Peas	Yucca	Sunflower Oil		Tomato		Watermelon	Sapote
				Vegetable Oil					Sugar Apple

1) Locate two food items on the list of foods to determine their food groups.
2) Locate the food group of one food item on the horizontal listing and the other food item on the vertical listing.
3) Find the intersection of the two food groups to determine the compatibility of the combination. Choose white. Avoid black. Use caution with gray.
4) Repeat with each combination to ensure that all foods in the meal are completely compatible.

Disclaimer: This chart is intended as a basic introduction to food combining. There are many exceptions, subtleties and nuances of food combining that are not covered within the scope of this chart. (See "Food Combining Made Easy" by Dr. Herbert Shelton for complete details.) Individual preferences and digestive abilities must always be considered.

* Not recommended but included for clarity.

© 1996 Dr. Douglas N. Graham

14

THE THREE FOOD GROUPS

PROBABLY FOR AS LONG AS YOU CAN REMEMBER, you've been told that there are, depending on the decade, any number of "basic food groups" which defined the so-called "healthy" Standard American Diet. Lately we've been told that the ideal diet can be found in a "pyramid."

THE RAW AND LIVING FOOD DIET HAS ITS OWN FOOD GROUPS:

Leafy greens and vegetables

Sweet fruits

Non-sweet fruits

Fats (avocados, nuts, olives, coconuts)

Regardless of how it's presented · in a circle, a triangle, a square, or any other shape, the important thing to remember is this:

Selecting foods from all the principal groups · fats, greens, and fruits · will insure a properly balanced diet. If you do not eat from all three sources your body will eventually become nutritionally out of balance. It's that simple.

BUT AGAIN, THERE'S NOTHING RIGID ABOUT THIS DIET!

It is *not* necessary to include all three of these food groups in each meal you eat! Even if you're eating a very spartan diet · fruit in the morning, fruit for lunch, a salad with avocado and dressing for dinner · you've achieved a balanced diet!

You'll probably notice very early on that you're not eating enough of something. Your body will let you know.

Soon after I went raw, I would crave orange juice minutes after over indulging in nuts, or nut butter. I'd crave fruit after eating a lot of greens. After eating a lot of fruit, I'd crave nuts and greens. You can see a pattern emerging, right?

Now, these effects are far more intense, and therefore more

Opening a durian on the set of the *Living on Live Food* DVD

noticeable, if you go 100% raw. If you are eating any cooked food, they're pretty subtle...you might not even notice them. If you go raw 100%, your natural cravings will kick in, leading you almost unerringly into a balanced diet.

VARY YOUR DIET TO MEET YOUR GOALS

What are you trying to accomplish?

If you want to lose weight, eat more fruits and vegetables and minimize the fats. Reduce the amount of nuts and extra oils eaten, and get your fat from avocado and other fatty fruits such as olives.

To optimize athletic performance it's important to eat from all three sources. Sweet fruits will keep your blood sugar up, leafy greens give you needed minerals, and you'll get more endurance from the fats.

For healing purposes, greens are essential! If you have diabetes, candida, or any other disease sensitive to sugars, eat more vegetables and fats. Non-sweet fruits - like tomatoes, zucchini, bell peppers, and cucumbers - will keep you balanced. As your body begins to heal - and it will! - you can slowly add fruit back into your diet.

YOUR BODY: THE ULTIMATE INDICATOR

The longer you eat raw and living food the more intuitive you will become when it comes to choosing the proper foods at any given time. It may seem difficult at first to "hear" what your body is asking for, but once you've cleansed it of its cooked, dead food residue, you'll be able to hear it loud and clear!

15

GREAT EXPECTATIONS

YOU'RE UNIQUE.

I'd love to be able to map out exactly how you will react from this new way of eating: physically, emotionally, and even spiritually. But because you are different from every other person in the universe, I can't do that. But I *can* give you a general heads up on what you may expect in the beginning of the raw and living food diet.

WEEK 1

You'll more than likely lose at least a few pounds this week. If you have a lot of weight to lose, you could lose 5 to 10 pounds. Since your fiber intake is increasing, you might experience some bloating or gas. The cleansing and other changes to your system is beginning, so some aches and pains are perfectly normal. If your previous diet was rich in cooked and highly processed foods, it will take a while to cleanse your system; the process may result in a tired and/or weak feeling. (On the other hand, I've seen people feeling more energetic in their very first week.)

WEEK 2

You may notice that you are sleeping less, and have more energy. Now that the newness of this diet has worn off a bit, you may also start to crave certain cooked foods. Past conditioning issues may crop up this week: it's important to remind yourself why you're doing this. You may notice some heightened awareness and feel that a "mental fog" is lifting. Many of your usual aches and pains may disappear. Your face may look different: less puffy, with smoothed out lines. All in all, you'll probably start feeling better emotionally and physically, during this week.

WEEK 3

You ought to be getting into a good flow this week, able to sense what your body needs and wants. You'll know if you're eating too much of one food group, and not enough of another.

TELL ME WHAT YOU EAT, and I'll tell you who you are.

— Jean Anthelme Brillat-Savarin

You will continue to feel healthier. Your skin will glow, your eyes will shine, and you (and others!) will notice a major difference in your disposition. Your mood will lighten. Your mind will be even clearer than last week. You'll be startlingly aware of the difference in your overall health as a result of eating raw and living food, as compared to the low energy, sluggish, and unhealthful effect that eating cooked, processed food had on you. It's quite possible that you have lost a significant amount of weight by the end of this week.

WEEK 4

You will begin to realize how this way of eating can revitalize and rebuild your body from the increased energy and improved state of being you will now be experiencing. You will come to realize an important truth: that fruits, vegetables, nuts, and seeds are *real food*...food that not only helps your body to survive, but to thrive! You may experience a more heightened state of well-being, along with an increased zest and appreciation for life. You may feel better than you have felt in a very long time. You'll be spending less time preparing meals, and more time enjoying the ease of this diet. Again, you may have lost a significant amount of weight by now. Long-standing aches and pains, along with chronic health problems may be waning or gone entirely.

DIFFERENT STROKES

We're not all carved out of a single cookie-cutter. I've worked with people who've lost over 10 pounds within the first week, felt more energetic than ever before, and found aches and pains in joints, muscles, intestines, and other places disappear.

I have also worked with people who have not noticed any drastic changes at first other than some weight loss. Though rare, it has happened. In most cases, these people had been very ill or extremely overweight.

If you happen to fall into the latter group, rest assured: you will surely lose weight and begin to heal your body. Other indi-cations of optimal health may be delayed by - or hiding behind - the extra weight or the illness that has taken over your body, but they will materialize!

I've worked with people who hadn't even begun to detox until they'd lost fifty pounds because the toxins had been stored in all those extra fat cells. Their bodies were simply unable to effectively eject those toxins until a great deal of the excess fat storing them had been eliminated.

Once you begin to lose weight and heal yourself, you *will* experience the other wonderful effects of this diet.

100% FOR 30 DAYS

Again, you're not like everybody else, and so you may very well experience different changes in your body at times different from other people. This is why I ask you: please make a 30-day commitment to follow this diet 100%. By the end of 30 days, you will have experienced significant - if not life-changing! - results.

MY EXPERIENCE

When I first went raw, I almost immediately noticed increased energy and a reduced need for sleep. Within weeks, the aches and pains in my joints began to vanish. Then the most amaz-ing thing happened, my back pain disappeared!

For fifteen years, I suffered from back pain. Often intense, sometimes mild, but always there. I could hardly believe that it was finally and forever, gone!

A few years prior to committing to a 100% raw food diet, I was diagnosed with fibromyalgia.

Fibromyalgia symptoms can be numerous. Its pain can be described as deep muscular aching, throbbing, shooting, and stabbing. Quite often, the pain and stiffness are even worse in the morning. Jaw pain (TMJ), sleep disorders, fatigue, sensitivi-ties to odors, noise, bright light, medication, various foods,

TAKE YOUR LIFE into your own hands and what happens? A terrible thing; no one to blame.

— Erika Jong

restless leg syndrome, nausea, mood swings.

After changing my diet to include mostly raw foods but still continuing to include cooked foods into my diet at times, I felt a lot better. But I was never completely pain-free. There was always some sort of pain in my joints, or back. I suffered from headaches and low energy.

Since going 100% raw, I have had exactly *zero* symptoms of fibromyalgia. None.

And, amazingly enough, I no longer need to wear glasses in order to read!

And you know those little lows, or bouts of mild depression we all experience at times? Mine disappeared after a couple of weeks on a 100% raw food diet. No longer did I feel an underlying boredom, or inexplicable sad moments. Early on, whenever I'd go off this diet, it would only take a week for those moods to creep back. This astounded me.

I've always been a generally upbeat, happy person. But on raw food, I feel even clearer in my mind, more at peace with myself, more grateful for the gift of life. I don't get upset as easily as I once did. Problem-solving is a snap.

I truly feel as if a veil has been lifted from my eyes, allowing me to discover a beautiful new existence.

And that's why I maintain that this is so much, much more than just a "diet." I hesitate to call it a "way of life," because that implies that an entire life change is necessary. It's not! All you have to do is eat raw and living food. Everything else will take care of itself.

16

SEEING THE RESULTS

ONE OF MY GOOD FRIENDS, after losing sixty pounds, and after healing many of her physical ailments, always insists that the weight loss and healings are "secondary" benefits to this diet. Here's what she says:

"Inner harmony, peace, and the sanity I've gained from eating raw and living food... that's what I'm most grateful for. That is what has truly changed my life."

I have never seen anyone go on this diet and fail to lose weight. I've never seen anyone start to eat this way without gaining more energy or without feeling better emotionally as well as physically.

Just you wait (and you won't have to wait long)! Wait until you see - very quickly - how your skin glows, and how your face takes on a whole new beautiful shape after going raw for awhile. Menstrual problems will regulate themselves. Your body will reshape and repair itself.

There are so many benefits to this diet! I am constantly amazed at the changes I witness in my clients and in friends. I have seen people look like they've shed twenty years off their lives. I have seen previously sick people glow with superb health, all within a few months. I would like to see this happen to you. It will happen to you. This diet *will* affect you positively on every level: physically, mentally, emotionally, and spiritually.

A JOURNAL: TRACKING YOUR PROGRESS

Keeping a journal - at least for the first month - is an excellent idea. It will help you realize more fully all the wonderful changes you will experience. So often we are able to see changes in others but have a difficult time seeing them in ourselves.

Take for example the "Garden Road Group." It all started when a group of nine people approached me having heard me speak at a seminar in their community. Each wanted to try this diet. They asked me if I would meet with them once a week and lead a support group.

The nine people - all who knew each other - started the diet

"SUCCESS MEANS fulfilling your own dreams, singing your own song, dancing your own dance, creating from your heart and enjoying the journey, trusting that whatever happens, it will be okay."

— Elana Lindquist

at the same time. I met with them, as we agreed, once a week for six months. (Support groups can be enormously helpful! You might want to consider forming one for this diet with friends and family members.)

Here is the "Six Month Progress Report for the Garden Road Group.'"

Lauren: 39. Stay-at-home mother of three. Lost 58 pounds. Off allergy medication. No longer victim to excruciating migraine headaches that she had suffered with for over fifteen years. No longer catching colds every two months. Has more energy. Needs less sleep. Is less irritable. Feels happier and more loving toward children and husband.

Susan: 29. Dental assistant. Lost 23 pounds. Healed painful PMS symptoms. Completely cured severe case of acne. Skin is healthy and smooth. No more mood swings. Has more energy.

Peter: 55. Attorney. Lost 52 pounds. Desire for alcohol gone. Quit smoking. High blood pressure under control; off medication. Hemorrhoids gone. Insomnia gone. Needs less sleep, has more energy.

Janice: 58. Lost 85 pounds. All symptoms of multiple sclerosis are gone. Heartburn, gas, bloating after every meal gone. No more constipation. No more joint pain and cramps. No more body odor. Has more energy.

Tracy: 37. Teacher. Lost 79 pounds. All symptoms of diverticulitis gone. Off pain medication. No more lower back pain. No more dry, irritated, itchy scalp. No more hypoglycemia. Has more energy.

Judith: 47. Nurse. Lost 62 pounds. Off diabetes medication after 12 years. Blood sugar stabilized at 70. Memory greatly improved. Has more energy.

Sasha: 38. Graphic designer. Lost 18 pounds. Chronic Fatigue Syndrome symptoms gone. Depression gone. Needs less sleep, has more energy.

Nancy: 50. Business owner. Lost 29 pounds. Sinusitis gone. Arthritis in shoulder and hands gone. Facial lines smoothed out. Sluggish feeling gone. Has more energy.

Sandra: 48. Restaurant owner. Lost 43 pounds. Healed bad case of eczema that has been causing pain on her legs, arms, and face for 5 years. Hip pain gone. Thinking better and more clearly. Needs less sleep, has more energy.

Keep in mind: these are just *some* of the symptoms these people got rid of. Most of them had other aches, pains, and minor irritations that aren't even mentioned here.

MEMORIES CAN BE HELPFUL!

By the end of the fourth month, most of the "Garden Road" members had forgotten how sick they used to be! On occasion, someone would bring a guest to the group. When this happened, each member had an opportunity to speak, telling his or her story. Invariably, I'd notice that almost all of them would forget about certain ailments they had healed. They would talk about their weight loss, but their main focus was on how well they felt at the moment. I found myself having to remind them of the diseases each had overcome.

The thing is, they felt so fantastic that they simply couldn't imagine living life any other way... or that they *had* at one time lived their lives in another way. Each became so far removed from the person he or she used to be just a few months earlier.

In so many ways this is the best, healthiest attitude. But in another way, it can be dangerous. Sometimes, when we start to feel really good, it's easy to stray into our old habits, forgetting how bad those old habits used to make us feel.

This is why I strongly suggest keeping a journal. When - or if - you feel like eating some cooked food, or indulging in some other unhealthful habits, all you need to do is page backwards through your journal. You'll not only see how far you've come... you'll be reminded why you have chosen the path you are on right now.

"I'VE MISSED more than 9,000 shots in my career. I've lost almost 300 games. 26 times, I've been trusted to take the game winning shot and missed. I've failed over and over and over again in my life. And that is why I succeed."

— Michael Jordan

17

DETOXING

(LET'S GET IT OVER WITH!)

DETOXIFICATION IS, quite simply, getting rid of the poisons (or toxins) in your body. For most people it's not a very severe process, but it is a reality, so we'd better talk about it.

The process begins when we begin to clear the body of all the accumulated waste that has built up from years of bad food, drugs, and alcohol.

Have you, or someone you know, ever started a diet or health regime, only to initially feel bad? When this happens, some people will think: "this diet is making me sick." Or "this health food is not for me."

As the body begins to detox, the poisons and toxins are thrown into the blood stream as the body tries to rid itself of them. That results in unpleasant sensations, that is why you may feel worse before you feel better when you begin eating raw and living food. Detox symptoms may include headaches, nausea, skin rashes and breakouts, colds, fever, fatigue, irritability, and the temporary increase of existing aches and pains.

In his book *Living Foods for Optimal Health*, Brian Clement gives the perfect analogy for this process:

"This internal cleansing," he writes, "is a lot like house cleaning. Have you ever walked into a house that had been tightly closed up and left untouched for a few years? Things often look relatively clean and in order · until you take out the broom and suddenly stir up a dust storm. If you then get out a pail of water and a scrub brush and create scattered puddles of muddy water, you might well find yourself sitting in the middle of the room, wondering if your efforts are worth the mess you've created."

"So it goes with the body. There's no doubt it's worth the effort, but you may experience symptoms that can be discouraging unless you really understand what is actually going on. The toxins being discarded are saving you from more serious disease that would result if you keep them in your body too much longer · possibly hepatitis, kidney disorders, blood dis-

IN THE MIDDLE of difficulty lies opportunity.

— Albert Einstein

ease, heart disease, arthritis, nerve degeneration, or even cancer."

Depending on the way you've been eating and living, detox symptoms may come and go for several weeks. Once this process is done, you will begin to feel better than you ever have, and your body will be able to get to work, healing itself on a deep, cellular level.

PATIENCE... A WORTHWHILE VIRTUE

Please be patient and give your body the time and support it needs.

I've seen clients become very impatient with this process. They don't like *any* discomfort (who does?) and want to feel well immediately (who doesn't?).

The reality is, if you've been abusing your body for ten, twenty, thirty, forty, fifty or more years, eating cooked, dead food and not taking care of yourself, then please don't insist that your body heal itself in two days! That's simply not fair!

After eating cooked food most of our lives, we need to have some patience in the cleansing process. Try and see it as I do: a miracle. It is nothing short of miraculous that an abused body, once shown some kindness, will work like crazy to become healthy and whole again!

ABOVE ALL, DON'T STOP THE PROCESS!

As I said, for most people, detoxing won't be all that severe. You may experience some minor irritations in the first few days of your new diet. You may have a headache, you may feel a bit tired and/or cranky. Most of my clients have experienced only a few mild days of gas, bloating, and a vaguely uneasy feeling. That's usually about the worst of it. Hang in there! If you stop the detox process by eating cooked food, or by taking medicine, you'll just have to go through it again.

In *Conscious Eating*, Gabriel Cousens writes: "Many people think that the phrase 'toxins in the body' is just some jargon of food faddists. Research over the last 100 years shows that these bowel toxins actually exist. Not only do they exist, but they also have a tremendous negative impact on mental and physical well-being. Toxins usually come from a process called 'intestinal toxemia,' an overgrowth of putrefactive intestinal bacteria in the small and large intestines. These toxins are then released into the blood stream and from there affect both our mental and physical functioning. Intestinal toxemia is predominantly caused by a high-protein and low complex carbohydrate diet."

Cousens continues: "Intestinal toxemia not only has been associated with severe mental symptoms, such as psychosis, but with a variety of mental imbalances. As early as 1917, Drs. Satterlee and Eldridge presented 518 cases at an *American Medical Association* conference that had mental symptoms which were cured by removing the intestinal toxemia. The reported symptoms of intestinal toxemia which are familiar to many people: mental sluggishness, dullness, and stupidity; loss of concentration and/or memory; mental incoordination, irritability, lack of confidence, and excessive and useless worry; exaggerated introspection, hypochondrias, and phobias; depression and melancholy; obsessions and delusions; and hallucinations, suicidal tendencies, delirium, and stupor. Senility symptoms are also common with intestinal toxemia."

WHY YOU SHOULDN'T STOP THE PROCESS

A client came to me, suffering from diabetes, skin disorders, intestinal problems, obesity, and asthma. Her asthma symptoms - primarily, shortness of breath - would kick in whenever she got sick. When this happened, she would check herself into the hospital where she would be given antibiotics.

After six months on the raw and living food diet, my client lost seventy pounds and healed many of her disorders. She remained, however, subject to colds which would last from a few weeks to a month or more.

Accustomed as she was to viewing antibiotics as "cure-alls," she tried to treat her colds with them. I tried · unsuccessfully at first · to convince her not to take these drugs because they would suppress the expulsion of her remaining toxins. But, in her understandable panic, and no doubt remembering the asthma attacks of her past, she took them despite my advice.

I kept on trying. I explained how the body simply cannot heal itself when antibiotics suppress the immune system and other organs and systems. I told her she was putting her body through a vicious cycle; that when she got sick, it was her body's way of trying to get rid of something. I told her that if she continued to suppress her system with drugs, she would stuff back down whatever her body was trying to free her from. In time, her wise body would once again attempt to rid itself of these toxins, prompting her to once again suppress the process with drugs.

If this type of cycle continues, it will result in the suppression of much toxic waste and just plain garbage. This can lead to all sorts of serious diseases.

Thankfully, my client finally decided to allow her cold to run its course. She didn't take any medication. I warned her that the first time she did this, things might get very intense. All the covered up sickness, I told her, will be coming up, getting ready to clear out. In her case, years of suppressed illnesses were going to have to resurface.

So, when she got sick, she rested. She listened to what her body was telling her. She took short walks in the fresh air, and when her body wanted sleep, she slept. She stopped fighting her body.

She read, took naps, and stopped eating solid food. She only drank fresh juices and water.

For the first few days, she was scared, couldn't breathe well, and her cold seemed out of control. She got sicker, and, without the drugs, felt worse than she'd ever felt. Her temperature climbed to 101 degrees.

LIFE SHRINKS or expands in proportion to one's courage.

— Anais Nin

And then, her fever broke. Her body removed what it needed to remove and her *true* healing process finally began. After a week she was recovering nicely. Once her cold disappeared, she realized she'd felt better than she ever had before. Her body had released a ton of the old junk... junk that was *always* there, only hidden. Junk that kept her below optimal health, even when she thought she was well.

This story is an unusual one. I'm not relating this story to frighten you. On the contrary, I use it to illustrate just how important it is to let the detox process run its course.

Detoxification isn't necessarily fun but it *is* necessary.

Listen to the warning signs your body is sending you! Be grateful that your body in its divine wisdom is giving you that headache, cold, ache, or pain. Don't try to suppress them. That makes about as much sense as turning the annoying fire alarm off while ignoring the fire itself!

18
STAYING RAW

Picking out lunch in Italy

IF YOU DON'T THINK cooked food has a negative impact on your body, go raw for a few weeks. Then eat a meal with dairy or meat or just a lot of additives and preservatives in it - like pizza, pasta, nachos, or cheese sticks. Go to the movies and get a big bucket of buttered popcorn. Bring home some ice cream, go out for Mexican, Chinese, or fast food. Snack on cookies, chips, chocolate, and soft drinks, and see how you feel the next day... it won't be pleasant, I assure you. (And I really don't recommend you try this experiment!)

I have tried to prove myself wrong many times. Believe me, I

IT IS NOT BECAUSE things are

difficult that we do not dare; it

is because we do not dare that

they are difficult.

— Seneca

tried desperately! When I first went raw, I would eat raw food all week and revert to my old ways on the weekends. Not only did I feel badly on Monday; it was very difficult to want to start all over again.

I would eat raw for as long as I could, a month or so, without having a craving. But then I would let myself eat a little bit of cooked or processed food. This only increased my cravings for cooked food until I found myself eating more and more cooked food every day... and going right back to feeling lazy, run down, and tired.

I was trying to find a "balance" with raw food, because I didn't want to be "extreme" (or "radical" or "intense") about it. I figured my body would tell me what it wanted.

My body seemed to "want" pizza and bean burritos quite a bit and eventually it dawned on me: maybe this isn't really what my *body* wanted so much as my mind did. I finally made the decision to go 100% raw, and *that's* when things started to drastically change. That's when my body started to cleanse and heal and detox to the point where I really *could* rely on it to tell me what I needed. And believe me, it wasn't pizza and burritos. It was fresh fruit, vegetables, fats like avocados and olives, and nuts and seeds.

In his book *Intuitive Eating*, Humbart Santillo writes about allowing the body's natural instinct to take over. "Before you become intuitive about your body's nutritional needs," he writes, "you must first clear the playing field · clean out the body; detoxify it to a certain stage so that it starts giving you dependable feedback. You rarely get this on the traditional American diet because that diet is always overstimulating the glands. Stimulating foods, spices, drugs, and chemicals build up toxins in the tissues and circulate through the bloodstream. Consequently, you are stimulated to eat more food, and soon even the wrong food feels natural because you are so far away from natural living."

GOING ALL THE WAY

People often ask me if they can start out slowly · at, say, 50% raw food · and then gradually increase the percentage. I tell them that the more raw fruits and vegetables they add to their diet, the better, of course. But if they · and you · are looking for relief from sickness, disease, obesity, or just plain ill health, then the difference between eating 95% raw and 100% is like night and day.

By keeping even the smallest bit of cooked food in your body · be it 50%, 5%, or even 1% · you keep the cooked food cravings alive.

I've met too many people who eat 95% raw for awhile, but who eventually are drawn back to cooked food. Why? Because they keep that doorway open! When you go 100% raw, you may initially go through some difficult moments · there are, after all, not only cravings but also emotional issues associated with food · but you will overcome these moments, usually within a few months. On the other hand, if you continue to eat 99% raw and leave even that 1% crack open, you will be struggling constantly with your addiction to, and craving for, cooked food.

Now, I *have* met people who have successfully transitioned from a cooked food diet to an all raw diet by gradually increasing the amount of raw food they eat · from 40% to 50% and gradually all the way up to 100% · slowly, and over a period of months, to a year. They are rare.

I find this method very difficult for the vast majority. It's like trying to eat one chocolate chip cookie and then putting the bag away. That never worked for me. It was either the whole bag, or none. I chose none. In the end, that was the easiest · and best · choice.

ADDICTIONS ARE ADDICTIONS

Imagine an alcoholic telling himself: "I'll just have one shot in the morning and that'll be it." He may be able to do that for a

"YOUR PRESENT CIRCUM-STANCES don't determine where you can go; they merely determine where you start."

— Nido Qubein

short period of time. But eventually he'll want more. He'll be thinking about when to have his next drink, planning on where and how to get it, and the addiction will win out.

Smokers who want to quit generally end up going "cold turkey." Otherwise, by continuing to smoke "just one or two a day," they continue to keep the cravings alive.

The same holds true for cooked food! We don't like to think of ourselves as addicted to cooked food. Yet I believe it is an addiction, and what's more, I believe it's the hardest to overcome. It's been ingrained in us since birth. And after a lifetime of eating cooked food, giving it up can be very challenging. The very notion of giving up cooked food - completely and forever - is new to most people...and can be very unsettling.

IT'S SO IMPORTANT TO STAY RAW.

In my seminars and classes, people get really excited about going raw. They love the food, finding it hard to believe that it tastes so good and it is not cooked. When I tell them why we should all eat raw and living food, how to prepare it, and how to begin, it all sounds sensible and easy. Every person ends up announcing: "I'm going raw! This is incredible!"

I know they mean it. And most of them actually do it, at least for a period of time. But eventually, most of them succumb to old habits and patterns. They begin to eat a little bit of the cooked food they make for their families every night. They go out to dinner with friends and decide to splurge "this one time," or they go to a party and think it won't hurt to have a little cooked food on this "special occasion."

Again, by allowing the very substance we are trying to avoid to be ingested into our bodies, we allow it to slowly creep back into our lives, and we will continue to keep the cravings alive. Also, indulging in even the smallest of certain, seemingly harmless substances - like coffee, mints, or a bit of alcohol - can be very detrimental. I've found that if these little crutches are kept in the diet, they will keep a person connected to the old ways of eating and eventually pull that person back into his or her old eating patterns.

When you make the decision to start this diet, do it 100%!

TURNING UP THE INTENSITY

There are people who believe it's better to move into a raw food diet slowly, to transition the body over a period of time in order to avoid rapid detox. I have found the opposite to be far more effective. When I introduce people to the raw and living food diet I start them at 100%. If they begin to detox quickly, great! Let's get it all out!

One problem with going too slowly is most people never get there. When they start feeling detox symptoms they panic and stop the process by eating more cooked food. Another problem: it takes longer to see results. And when people don't see results, they often tend to abandon the diet altogether. If you want to see results, are serious about healing your body, losing weight, or just being the healthiest you can be, then make a serious commitment to doing this 100%.

I love what Dr. Richard Schulze, in his book *There are No Incurable Diseases*, writes about this:

"99% of the time my student doctors were doing all the right things, just not enough of them and not often enough. I always tell them: 'TURN UP THE DARN INTENSITY.' The main problem is that most natural doctors are afraid of hurting someone. They don't want to break the patient - to push them too far."

Dr. Schulze talks about how most of these patients are drinking pints of harmful beverages, smoking cigarettes, and are on a steady diet of animal foods and bad attitudes... and how they would put anything - drugs, coffee, sugar, booze, and fast foods - into their bodies without a second thought. He writes:

"They never questioned that maybe one bag of greasy potato chips or junk snacks was a dosage when they ripped open the next bag, munched it down and changed the TV channel. They didn't call the manufacturer to see if maybe they were overdoing it. They just partied hearty. BUT NOW, in healing ourselves, we are concerned about taking an overdose of herbs. We are worried that one too many cups of ginger tea will be too rough. GIVE ME A BREAK!

"If people used half as much determination, energy, and intensity healing themselves as they used partying, tearing themselves down and trying to kill themselves, they could have healing miracles, almost immediately."

Amen!

TREATING THE ADDICTION

I've spent years seeking out the most successful method of teaching people how to go raw, and how to stay raw. After working with many, many people, I've found that the most effective way to stay on this diet is to treat cooked food like any other addiction. I've concluded this after seeing how people struggle with cooked food. At first I was hesitant to write this. After all, most people eat cooked food and hardly any one would consider himself or herself an addict because of it, but this is what I have concluded based on my experience. Of course there are always exceptions, but I've counseled hundreds of people, and advising them to go 100% raw · to give up *all* cooked food · has made the difference between struggling through this path with difficulty or shifting into this diet effortlessly and successfully.

Finally, going 100% raw, right from the onset, will prove to be valuable "life insurance" for your new way of eating. The amazing benefits you'll experience will be an incredible inspiration to you to return to this diet should you happen to go off of it.

"I READ AND WALKED

for miles at night along the

beach, writing bad blank verse

and searching endlessly for

someone wonderful who would

step out of the darkness and

change my life. It never

crossed my mind that that

person could be me."

— Anna Quindlen

19

SIMPLE VS. RADICAL
(OR: SANITY VS. INSANITY!)

THIS DIET WORKS! I know hundreds of people who have healed themselves of all kinds of diseases, simply by eating this way. Diseases that doctors had deemed incurable. Diseases that were supposed to keep them on medication for years. Diseases that had them feeling helpless, and hopeless about ever regaining their health.

Diabetes, arthritis, obesity, chronic fatigue, cancers, high blood pressure, diverticulitis... I've seen people heal themselves from these diseases and many, many more.

Many doctors have forgotten this vital truth: *the human body is self-healing*.

I'm glad doctors exist, of course. If I cut my hand off preparing one of my delicious raw food recipes, please, take me to the hospital!

But if you have a chronic or acute disease, there are alternatives to having pieces of your body removed, or living on drugs that create other problems, and wear the body out so it cannot repair itself. Countless numbers of people have found this alternative in the healing power of raw and living foods.

"ISN'T THIS A RADICAL WAY TO EAT?"

People ask me this all the time. Radical???

Eating fruits and vegetables is radical? But eating the inside of a cow or chewing the flesh off of the bones of chickens *isn't* radical???

This diet is *not* radical. It may be different from what you know now, different from what you have been brought up on, and different from what all of the commercials selling millions of dollars worth of high fat, high sugar, over-processed foods · and all the people who make money off of them · want you to believe. And it's different from the messages the meat and dairy industry have spent billions of dollars on.

"ISN'T THIS INTENSE?"

That question always amazes me, but never so much as when it

DESTINY, OR KARMA, depends on what the soul has done about what it becomes aware of.

— **Edgar Cayce**

comes from people preparing to go on medication, or to have surgery. When I tell people they can heal themselves on this diet, and they say: "well, that seems a little intense; I don't think I can do that", I am simply blown away.

Medicating yourself and being cut open *isn't* intense? They can go through *that* but they can't start eating better? I've had people look at me in utter shock, when I tell them about this diet and what it can do for them. They say: "You want me to cut out cooked food and eat raw food? That seems a little intense."

What's intense is the way people are living their lives now! "Enjoying" a regular diet of animal products, sugar, coffee, alcohol, fast food, recreational and prescription drugs, artificial additives, cigarettes, household toxins, and little or no exercise... that's pretty intense to me!

I see people abusing their bodies without giving it a second thought... until something happens.

I see people searching for that magic weight loss pill or that perfect diet.

I see people starving themselves and working out for hours a day to achieve that perfect body.

And I see people going to the extremes of invasive surgery and drugs to get rid of disease.

Yet, when I tell people to eat whole foods, they think *that's* "intense."

YES, IT'S DIFFERENT

It's not that this diet is "radical," or "intense." It's just different. Different from what we have been brainwashed to believe, and different from what most people do.

Many times we don't change what we know isn't working for us, or isn't good for us, because we get stuck in our habits. It's not that we don't know when something is hurting us, or when we could be doing something better... it's that it takes effort

IF YOU DO what you've always done, you will get what you've always gotten.

— Anonymous

and courage to change · especially if you're about to do some-thing that is different and not mainstream.

In his book *The Raw Life*, Paul Nison states:

"People tend to avoid the truth about health because once they realize and accept the truth, great effort must then be expended to change habits. Most people are too lazy to want to get involved. If you feel lazy, you already have a symptom of toxemia, as laziness is a symptom of disease. The truth will always be the truth, no matter how many people deny it or run from it.

Here is a great saying from Mark Twain: 'whenever you find that you are on the side of majority, it's time to pause and reflect.' Even back then Mark Twain knew that just because you are different doesn't mean you are wrong."

20
SIMPLIFYING

LET'S LOOK INTO THE FUTURE...

You've been eating raw food, preparing meals, and doing great... but you're getting tired of preparing a lot of meals, and always having to be armed with raw foods whenever you go out.

Or, you notice lately that you don't have the Mock Turkey prepared for lunch, the burgers aren't ready for dinner, the crackers haven't finished dehydrating. You wonder if it might be just as easy to grab some fast food, or eat something you may have cooked for your family.

In other words, your healthy new way of eating is beginning to feel like a chore.

If you find yourself in this situation, there is an ideal solution:

KEEP IT SIMPLE!

This may sound like a contradiction, but it isn't. I truly believe · and my experience with clients has confirmed this · that you need to learn some basics when first starting on this diet. These basics include learning how to prepare the food, and getting used to having food with you wherever you go... especially for the first few months.

However, you can't keep this up forever. Eventually, you'll want to simplify things. Don't make it hard for yourself!

When I first started eating this way, I prepared tons of food, took food with me whenever I set foot out of my house, and always had an over-abundance of food at home.

THAT WAS THEN, THIS IS NOW.

Today, I eat much more simply. For example, I eat fruit in the morning, and have more fruit, a green drink or a salad for lunch, and maybe an avocado or guacamole for dinner. I vary this menu, of course, but I don't think too much about it.

Sometimes · especially if I've had a huge salad with avocado for lunch · I'll skip dinner completely. Other times I'll stuff a cabbage leaf with veggies, eat some almond butter on celery, or have some bananas. At times I'll crave dessert and eat a raw one for dinner.

It's funny, when people ask me what I eat I have to pause... because I'm just not conscious about it anymore.

IT MAKES LIFE A LOT EASIER.

A client of mine · a woman in her late fifties · went 100% raw on the day we started working together. She stayed raw through a series of pretty traumatic events: the death of her mother, a reunion with siblings she hadn't seen in over thirty-five years, her only son moving out of her house, and a three-week trip to Africa!

When I asked her if she had found it difficult to stay raw during all of this, her answer was an emphatic "no."

"As a matter of fact," she told me, "eating this way made it far easier for me to deal with all of these events. Physically, I felt very well, and I certainly didn't have to worry about preparing food on top of everything else!"

So, when people tell me they've got "too much on their plates" to try this diet, I know that they're just not ready to make the commitment. This diet is *anything* but difficult.

AGAIN...MAKING LIFE EASIER

With this diet, your body will be much healthier, and far more able to fortify you during difficult times. And the longer you eat this way, the more you will be convinced that life will be easier if you keep it simple.

"BUT ALISSA, YOU'RE CONTRADICTING YOURSELF!"

I know it seems that way, but I'm really not.

When you begin this diet, yes, it's *vital* that you make a lot of dishes, buy a lot of food, and take food with you wherever you go.

But living this way simply won't work for you three to six months down the road. At some point you'll need to make this diet as simple and as easy as possible: the way it was meant to be!

Don't worry... in most cases, this will happen naturally. Eventually you will intuitively seek out simple, easy approaches to this diet. The client I described a few paragraphs ago, for example, is well into her second year of eating raw and living food, which consists basically of fruit, nuts, flax crackers, and amazing salads. Once in a while, she may make a more elaborate meal, but basically, this is her diet. It works for her and it will work for you!

21

DON'T INDULGE THE THOUGHT!

IT'S HAPPENED TO ME, and it'll happen to you.

You smell or see cooked food · at a restaurant, at someone's home, or in your own home · and your mind will be off and running. Cooked food looks good, smells good, and, you'll begin to think about how good it might *taste*. You might think: "well, maybe just this once." If you don't give in, you might, like I have in the past, *think* about the cooked food for hours.

In these situations, my advice is simple: *don't indulge the thought.*

The instant you realize you're being drawn into it, get rid of the thought. Drown it out by thinking about how good you feel eating raw food and how great you'll feel about yourself for not indulging yourself in cooked food. Remember your goals. Think about why you're eating a raw and living food diet.

At first, you will have to do this consciously, but eventually, it will become second nature. As soon as these thoughts appear, you'll be able to shut them out, tap into that future you truly desire, and have the courage to pursue your dreams by saying "no" to what isn't in your best interest.

KNOW HOW YOUR SUBCONSCIOUS WORKS!

Your subconscious mind works in *images*, not in words. It "sees" the images that your mind creates with words; it doesn't "read" the words themselves. This is why you simply must *not* indulge the thought, not even for an instant! Quash it immediately, and get rid of it definitively! Don't let that image live!

For example: let's say you see a piece of chocolate cake. Here are *wrong ways* to mentally handle the temptation:

"I am not going to eat that piece of chocolate cake."

Or,

"I don't want that piece of chocolate cake."

Or even,

"Chocolate cake tastes terrible! I hate chocolate cake!"

EVERYTHING WE SAY

and do has an effect

on the world around us.

— Madonna

These thoughts simply won't work. Why? Because you're still *indulging the thought* of chocolate cake! Your subconscious won't "read" the words "I don't want," or even "I hate." However, your subconscious will clearly "see" the image of · you guessed it · chocolate cake. So, for all your efforts, chocolate cake will still be on your mind.

Don't indulge the thought of unhealthful food. Don't allow it *any* space in your mind.

Practice, until it becomes second nature to you, thoughts like these instead:

"I choose to eat healthful foods that nourish my body."

And,

"Fruits and vegetables are more delicious than anything else I could possibly eat."

And,

"Raw and living food makes me healthy, happy, and beautiful!"

I AM HAPPY and content

because I think I am.

— Alain–Rene Lesage

22

ENJOY LIFE NOW!
BEYOND FOOD

BELIEVE IT OR NOT, FOOD ISN'T THE MOST IMPORTANT THING
IN MY LIFE! HERE ARE SOME OTHER VITAL ELEMENTS I'VE
FOUND ESSENTIAL IN BECOMING THE BEST I CAN BE.

THE TIME TO START ENJOYING your life is right now!

Don't wait until you reach your physical goals - losing weight, healing diseases, or feeling better - to start doing what you love to do!

What do you want to do? Whatever it is, do it now! Go to the beach, ride a bike, take a walk, exercise! Read a book, take a class, make new friends. Dance, meditate, play a round of golf, skydive, scuba dive, paint, sing, dance!

Whatever it is that you've been putting off doing until you reach your goal weight, or heal your ailments, do it NOW!

You can't wait to live your life until "the time is right." *Now* is the right time! This is it! This is your life! Start living it fully and watch for miracles to happen.

WHAT YOU FOCUS ON EXPANDS

If you sit around waiting for your life to change, waiting to do all the things you've always wanted to do while focusing on your current weight, physical condition, or bad health, you'll only continue recreating your unhealthy life.

If on the other hand, you start doing the things you want to do, those things will become a part of your reality.

Everything you do, say, and think contributes to your self-image. And your self-image creates your reality. By doing those things you want to do, and by acting like the person you want to become, you're creating your future: right now!

WHY ACCENTUATE THE NEGATIVE?

A client asked me to help her lose 150 pounds, heal her diabetes, high blood pressure, allergies, and many other disorders. She started out great: by staying 100% raw for three months, she lost 55 pounds. After the first two months, her doctor took her off of her diabetes and high blood pressure medication.

Whenever my client and I were with other people, we'd tell them about these amazing results. Correction: *I'd* tell them.

JUST BEING ALIVE doesn't mean you're fully living.

— Izzy

EXPECT your every need to be met, expect the answer to every problem, expect abundance on every level, expect to grow spiritually.

— Eileen Caddy

YOU MUST BE the change you

want to see in the world.

— Gandhi

Often, she would actually *downplay* the wonderful results she had accomplished.

When I questioned her about this privately, her response was: "Well, I'm still on other medication and the diabetes and high blood pressure *could* return, and I *could* gain that weight back."

Her response confused me completely. Why would she · why would *anybody* · choose to look at these negatives when the positives were so wonderful? Finally, it dawned on me.

CHANGE CAN BE SCARY

This woman had become accustomed to living her life as a sick, overweight person. There were, in some strange ways, payoffs in it for her.

She had become used to having other people do things for her, because she couldn't (or wouldn't) do them for herself. She got to lie on the sofa, eating, watching television, and feeling sorry for herself. She had been, quite literally, "enjoying" poor health.

The notion of taking complete responsibility for herself frightened her. If she wasn't sick and tired anymore, what would that mean? What else could she talk about? She clung to her role of the overweight, ill woman because she knew how to do it. She was comfortable being uncomfortable.

Inevitably, she began to stray from the diet. I didn't want her to sabotage what she'd accomplished so I kept working with her... but on a different level.

ADDRESSING ISSUES BEYOND FOOD

We frankly discussed the "payoffs" her ill health afforded her, and why they were holding her back. After this, she began to lose more weight and heal some of her other ailments: sore feet, stiff joints, frequent colds, and many allergies. Yet again, after two more months of obvious success she began to yo-yo on the diet.

So we looked again · and more closely · at her goals, and

what she really wanted her life to be like. Yes, she said, she had certainly wanted to lose the weight and the ailments. But, she added, she really couldn't "imagine" herself thin and healthy because she hadn't been that way for such a long time. The problem identified, we continued to work on her self-image.

DEFINE YOURSELF NOW

You must have a clearly defined image of what you want to look like, feel like, and be. If you don't know what you're trying to create, how can you create it?

You wouldn't hire, for example, a builder without telling him what you wanted him to build, would you? He'd either be at a complete loss, or he'd build you a parking garage when what you really wanted was a summer home!

You need to know what you're working toward in order to achieve it. You need a self-image.

This image can adapt as your life changes, but it still has to exist.

Knowing how to eat a raw and living food diet isn't enough. If you don't know *why* you're doing it - if you don't have a dream - you will fail.

My dear friend Lazaris says: "It is important to have an image that can hold all of the realities that you have. Reality follows image. If your image cannot support the reality you will not create the reality. In other words, if your image cannot hold that success, you will not have that success."

It has been shown that when overweight people go on diets and lose weight, it can take them up to 18 months to "see" themselves as thin. This is why people so often regain lost weight. I've seen this phenomenon myself. After losing a great deal of weight, one client kept right on buying clothes in her old size: far too large for her new body. Her image was not matching her reality.

Lazaris continues: "Your thoughts and feelings are what make

THE SECRET OF INNER PEACE is accepting truth, in all circumstances, as your guide.

— Anonymous

up your image. When you have an image that is filled with love, that is always happy, that is always successful, then that image will attract realities to support it. It will consume success to keep itself alive. Not only is the negative image limiting, but the positive image is expanding."

In her book *Think Yourself Thin*, Debbie Johnson writes: "Even if everything outside of you tells you that you look a certain way, you *always* have the option to disagree. You have the power and the right to imagine yourself the way you want to be. In doing so, Soul creates change. Your divine gift is imagination, and you have the free will to use it as you choose. What do you choose?"

DESIRE, ask, believe, receive.

— Stella Terrill Mann

23

A MOVING EXPERIENCE

YOU KNOW THAT OLD adage: "use it or lose it?" It's more than a saying. It's the truth! You need to start moving your body.

Obviously I don't know what your current condition is, so begin at a level comfortable for you.

If you're extremely overweight, or very sick, don't start training for a marathon... but *do* start moving your body! This is so important.

The benefits you'll reap are outstanding. Your lymphatic system, your muscles, your bones, and your joints all depend on exercise to function properly, so do your heart, other organs, veins, and arteries.

Your entire body simply works better, and more efficiently when you exercise. I strongly believe that a fit, healthy body results in a stronger and healthier mind. Depression, anxiety, and fatigue can be reduced dramatically through exercise. Get those endorphins · those feel-good chemicals that are released with physical exertion · working on your behalf. Exercise!

Whenever I go a few days without exercise, I notice a distinct difference in my personality. I get cranky, tired, and moody. My body feels heavier and stiffer. But after a workout I think more clearly, have more energy, and feel more balanced and at peace.

WHY CHEAT YOURSELF?

If you're creating a body that is fat, sick, and tired, you're cheating yourself out of so many terrific, enriching life experiences. Create a healthy, fit body, free from sickness and disease, and open yourself to a world of endless possibilities.

Don't impose needless limitations on yourself. If you're blessed in other areas of your life · a great family, a job you love, good friends, love, joy, and material wealth · that's wonderful. But without optimum health, you will not be able to enjoy these gifts to their fullest extent. In fact, when you feel bad from having a sick, unhealthy, out-of-shape body, these gifts

NEVER BE BULLIED into silence. Never allow yourself to be made a victim. Accept no one's definition of your life. Define yourself.

— Harry Feinstein

tend to lose meaning. It's hard to feel gratitude for, and joy from those gifts you have when you're not feeling well.

EXERCISE LIKE YOU MEAN IT!

Any type of exercise is better than none at all. A leisurely afternoon walk is lovely. Taking the dog down to the beach is good for the body and soul. But to really get all of the benefits from exercise that you can, start moving your body, sweating, feeling the blood flow and your heart pump! Push yourself beyond what you normally do!

I once had a client who would stop exercising as soon as she began to sweat. I'm *not* kidding! I had to actually convince her that sweating was *supposed* to happen! She was afraid "she was pushing her body too far."

When she would eat a pint of ice cream, an entire large pizza, or a half dozen donuts while lying around all day, she never worried about "pushing her body too far." But a little bit of sweat terrified her! I found that amazing.

If you've lost weight but have reached a plateau; or if you want to speed up the weight loss, then start exercising!

WHY WAIT?

I met John just after he started his own business. At 25, he exuded competence, confidence, and self-assured power. He had an incredible vision, along with the ability to inspire and motivate people within minutes. His captivating blue eyes sparkled with excitement and passion, and I knew within moments after meeting him that he would become very successful.

We talked a lot about raw and living foods, health, and fitness. And while the topics interested him greatly, he was, as he said, "too busy for all of that" at the time. He said he had to be "out of balance" for awhile, and that his sole focus had to be on making his business a success.

Within a year or so, John developed physical problems. Along

THE HIGHER YOUR ENERGY level, the more efficient your body. The more efficient your body, the better you feel and the more you will use your talent to produce outstanding results.

— Anthony Robbins

with being extremely stressed out, he started experiencing indigestion and heartburn whenever he ate. His back and neck ached when he sat for too long a time. He started getting headaches and caught colds frequently. His energy ebbed. He certainly didn't look healthy: his skin was broken out, his face puffy, and those beautiful blue eyes that used to snap with excitement were now bloodshot and dull.

His health, inevitably, began to adversely affect his business. When he wasn't feeling well, he'd avoid the office. That exuberance and infectious enthusiasm, once so inspiring and motivating, had almost disappeared. He wasn't making decisions or coming up with brilliant ideas as readily and as easily as he did just a short while ago.

John asked me to accompany him as he checked out some business ventures. The trip would take three days. I agreed, provided that he would eat raw food with me and work out while we were away.

Within three days of eating fruits and vegetables, walking, and being outside in the fresh air, John literally began changing before my eyes. The old John was making a comeback, and a quick one! Since he was doing both things together · eating raw foods *and* exercising · the change was virtually immediate.

He realized at the end of those three days that it was time to rethink his decision to put health and fitness on the "back burner" until he'd "gotten successful." Following our three-day trip, John continued to eat raw food and work out every day.

Within weeks, he was feeling younger and healthier and each day it kept getting better. He was developing new ideas, making more connections, and making better deals. His business took on a whole new life, and he told me he felt like he'd been reborn.

John and I talked about his experience. We talked about what success really is, and how it isn't limited to monetary gain, rather, it encompasses every area of our lives.

If you're "out of balance" in one area, then *all* areas of your life will eventually suffer. If you're not successful physically, it's extraordinarily difficult to create other successes.

IF YOU THINK YOU DON'T HAVE TIME TO EXERCISE…

… please think again. Remember John! His life is so much more manageable now, and so much more fulfilling, now that he's exercising. (Remember: when I first met him, he didn't think he had the "time" to exercise!)

Here's the truth:

If you're *not* exercising, you're actually *wasting* your time! Why? Because your mind and body are not functioning at top efficiency.

Once you start exercising, you'll have more energy, and you'll find more time in the day to do it. Maybe you'll need less sleep, and therefore gain an extra hour in the morning. Maybe you'll switch off the television at night and exercise instead.

Maybe you'll work out, rather than take an hour lunch break. Or maybe you'll not go shopping, not go out for a drink, not sit at your computer, not talk on the phone, not _____ (you fill in the blank), and instead, take this half hour or more and devote it to making yourself healthier almost instantly!

THE BENEFITS OF FITNESS

Don't box the concept of "being fit" into nothing more than drudgery at the gym. It's so much more than that!

Fitness is:

Feeling good about slipping into clothes that express who you are (and tossing those stretch pants, bulky sweats, and big shirts).

Waking up each morning feeling good about yourself, and who you are.

Looking forward to going places, doing new things, experiencing new adventures.

And so much more!

When was the last time you rowed out into the middle of the lake, reveling in the peace and calm water as you watched the sunset?

Or the last time you gardened all day, playing in the grass, flowers, and sunlight, without an ache or pain to show for it?

Or the last time you worked out or played hard at your favorite sport, and weren't exhausted afterward?

Or danced all night and had energy to spare?

Have you ever stood at the top of a mountain you just climbed, drinking in a breathtaking view, while enjoying the satisfaction of knowing your own two feet got you there?

Start moving! A wonderful, adventure-packed life is waiting just for you!

'ON WITH THE DANCE, let the joy be unconfined!' is my motto, whether there's any dance to dance or any joy to unconfine. **— Mark Twain -**

24

LET THE SUNSHINE IN!

SUNLIGHT CONVERTS CHOLESTEROL into much needed Vitamin D. Despite the bad press the sun gets because of skin cancer, we need sunlight to be healthy!

In his book *A Handbook for Vibrant Living: Eight Keys to Vibrant Health*, Loren Lockman offers a good explanation of what actually happens to the average person who basks in the sun for too long:

> "Sunlight on the skin causes the body to speed up the elimination of toxins through the skin. Because the average person eats a SAD [standard American diet], drinks alcohol, etc., etc., they tend to be overburdened with toxins. As sunlight draws these toxins out of the body, they are consistently in contact with the skin. Over a long enough period of time, this constant contact leads to skin cancer just as surely as retaining toxic particulates (cigarette smoke, asbestos, or coal dust) in the lungs, toxic SAD-based waste in the colon, or alcohol in the liver leads to cancer of that part of the body. In every case, when the body is forced to retain toxins for an extended time, that part of the body tends to develop cancer."

Lockman adds:

> "With a clean system, there is no more risk of skin cancer than there is of lung cancer, colon cancer, or liver cancer."

The sun's rays can help heal many disorders: skin problems, hormonal imbalances, depression, obesity, and infections, just to name a few. Try to expose as much of your body to the sun as possible, as its beneficial ultra-violet rays will not penetrate sunglasses or clothing. (It's important to allow the sun's rays to enter our eyes!)

Doctor John Ott, the foremost light expert in the world, suggests that we get between 30 and 60 minutes of sunshine each day.

25

LET'S CLEAR THE AIR

CLEAN AIR is crucial to our overall health, but often we take the oxygen we breath in for granted.

Indoor air pollution can often be controlled more easily than outdoor pollution. So start being aware of your indoor air environment. Chief indoor culprits include household cleaning products, fumes from furnaces and other appliances, and gasses from upholstered furniture and carpeting.

Two very simple solutions:

Sleep with your windows open to allow for fresh air circulation.

Fill your living space with houseplants. Plants will act as a filter and help to cleanse your air.

And speaking of air, start treating yourself to more! Deep breathing exercise is an excellent practice to increase oxygen flow into our systems, and it helps dispel toxins.

26

GIVE IT A REST!

(YOUR BODY THAT IS)

SLEEP is one of your body's best sources of energy.

While you sleep, you give your body an opportunity to rebuild and heal itself.

Sleep deprivation affects us physically and emotionally. Without adequate sleep we cannot function at our full capacity. With healthy sleep, we can accomplish wonders!

It's been shown, for example, that people who get the proper amount of sleep and rest achieve far more noticeable results in weight loss and health improvement efforts than those who do not.

How much sleep is enough for you?

This varies greatly, but here's a hint.

If you depend on an alarm clock to wake you up, feel tired upon rising, and/or need coffee or other stimulants to feel awake, you're probably not getting enough sleep.

27

ARE YOU READY?

WHEN YOU ARE EATING a raw and living food diet your world will look different to you. Your senses will sharpen. You will see, smell, feel, taste and hear things at a much deeper level. Your intuition will amplify and you will gain a far more positive outlook on life. I believe this happens because of the high vibration inherent in raw and living foods.

IT'S ALL ABOUT ENERGY

Everything in this world is made up of energy. From the chairs we sit on, to the cars we drive; from the people we are, to the foods we eat... it's all about energy.

Living food is made up mostly of water, unlike heavy, dense, cooked food in which all that good water has been dried out.

When we feed our bodies living food — alive with water, living enzymes, vitamins and minerals — we're feeding ourselves a much different vibration than those heavy, dense, cooked foods can offer. This vibrancy translates into a lighter, less "bogged down" feeling. If you're not used to it, it can be initially alarming. It might feel very different from what you are used to and therefore feel comfortable with.

Many people use food as a way to suppress themselves; to stifle emotions they don't want to feel. Cooked food can numb us to those aspects of our life we may not want to look at... much like alcohol or other drugs do.

SEEING CLEARLY CAN BE UNSETTLING

Living food heightens your vibration — your energy. When this happens, you tend to feel really well. But this same heightened energy also highlights those parts of life that are not so good, or those parts not working for you: job, relationships, living environment, health, and so on. Since they're highlighted, they become difficult to ignore. Decisions may have to be made, certain issues faced and addressed. This can be difficult or scary. If you feel as if you are not ready to go about changing those aspects of your life that are not working for you, then you may want to escape from the heightened awareness that highlights them.

I HAVE ALWAYS been delighted at the prospect of a new day, a fresh try, one more start, with perhaps a bit of magic waiting somewhere behind the morning." — **J.B. Priestly**

Eating cooked, dense, dead foods is a sure way to do just that. They will lower your energy, your vibration. They will help you feel relatively safe, comfortably numb.

I believe a main reason that some people decide to go off of a raw food diet or get slowly lured back into a cooked food diet and begin eating what is so popularly (and so ironically) known as "comfort food," is to dull those sharply defined edges of what a heightened sense of awareness can feel like. Standing "naked "in your life, seeing things for what they really are, can be a very scary feeling without hiding behind extra weight or the anesthetizing feeling that cooked food will provide.

Because of this, it is so important to begin to examine what is holding you back and keeping you stuck in a bad situation, ill health or weight problems.

MAKE WAY FOR THE NEW YOU!

When you begin to examine the reasons for your current state, some painful issues will rise to your consciousness. This is *not* a bad thing, even though it may not feel good initially.

Don't stuff them back down! Let them up and then let them out, either on your own or with the help of a professional thera-pist. Like ridding your body of physical toxins, it's important to rid your mind of mental and emotional poisons.

It's not about will-power or determination. It's about sifting through the garbage in your mind, and all of the mistaken beliefs you've been fed. It's about finding the truth, and having the courage to change the rules to make yourself healthy, happy, and free!

When it comes to creating an unwanted acidic condition in your body, bad food isn't the only culprit. Stress, worry, and anxiety can do their damage, too. To be healthy and disease free, recognize that your emotional state has a major role to play. Release those old negative thoughts...and begin creating the life you truly desire!

28
MEDITATION

PARTS THAT FORM THE WHOLE

When I wasn't taking care of myself by eating well, I didn't want to meditate or to exercise. After, say, consuming an entire pizza, I certainly didn't feel like jumping on the treadmill... and I felt more like sitting in front of the TV, rather than sitting in quiet solitude. It's like a domino effect: whatever we do in one area of our lives affects the other areas.

But this can work in a positive way, too! Instead of letting one domino knock down the other areas in your life, meditation can help reverse that process. I've found that by shutting out the physical world for a few minutes every day, I've been able to find that inner peace that helps me to bring clarity to every aspect of my life.

Nourishing the soul is equally as important as nourishing the body!

LIKE AN ABILITY or a muscle, hearing your inner wisdom is strengthened by doing it.

— Robbie Gass

29

LEARNING HOW TO HAVE FUN

TO ME, THE SINGLE MOST important lesson we can learn in life is how to have fun.

Learning how to have fun means finding out what gives you pleasure and excitement, and what makes you feel happy and brings you joy: *today.*

A five-year-old's definition of fun will differ from what it is at age 15, and, again at, say, 20, and it will continue to change at age 30, 40, 50, and so on.

Often, people simply don't know what makes them happy or how to have fun. They continue to do the same things they've been doing for years, not taking into consideration that they may have changed. If · and this usually happens · those activities start becoming stale, they somehow figure "that's life." But that's *not* life!

HOW I LEARNED TO HAVE FUN

It took me a long time. For years I would try to do the things my friends loved to do. I'd go out to clubs, to movies, out for drinks. Then I became bored with it all. I tried to figure out the source of that boredom, tried to figure out what it was that I needed to do to make this "fun" stuff work for me. That was my mistake.

I was trying to do the things everyone else I knew did.

I wasn't being creative. I wasn't listening to my inner voice.

My inner voice was telling me that I liked to be outside in the sunshine and that I liked to play in the water at the beach, that I liked to create forms and shapes with clay, to eat freshly cut watermelon outdoors, instead of being stifled in a dimly lit restaurant; that I liked to write, to work out, to dance, to hang out with friends, talking about the meaning of life or laughing all night, instead of being parked in front of the TV or trapped inside a movie theater.

WE WILL DISCOVER the nature of our particular genius when we stop trying to conform to our own or to other people's models, learn to be ourselves, and allow our natural channel to open.

— Shakti Gawain

When I *did* start listening to what really felt right to me and began to act on it, something wonderful happened: people with the same interests began to appear in my life. I found more and more things that were fun to do, and lots of people to do them with.

When I finally learned how to have fun my life became a fascinating, ever-changing adventure!

When you allow yourself to have fun, it raises your resonance, it puts you in a good mood. You begin to feel grateful for everything in your life, for life itself!

You attract happy, joyful people to you, and you become a virtual magnet for good things overflowing in your life.

Learn to enjoy every moment!

Learn how to have fun moving your body in exercise. Let yourself feel the life it pumps into you.

Learn how to have fun with the food you eat, and how to have fun making it.

Savor the knowledge that you're healing your mind, body, and spirit, while having fun doing it.

Find pleasure in everything you do: working, playing, eating, sleeping, everything!

Learn to have fun... because that's what life is all about.

A daily ritual - relaxing in my jacuzzi with a coconut!

30

SIX STEPS TO SUCCESS

THE KEY TO SUCCESSFULLY achieving all of the magnificent gifts the raw and living food life offers can be summarized in six simple steps.

I. EDUCATE YOURSELF

Learn how to prepare both the simple and the more complicated raw and living food recipes contained in this book. Familiarize yourself with proper food combining. Master the techniques of sprouting and dehydrating. Investigate the best places to shop for organic raw and living foods.

Find a support group, start a potluck, and read more!

II. KEEP A JOURNAL

Buy a small notebook you can take with you; record every bite and every sip you take.

Many people overlook this step thinking that it's not important. It is. In fact, it's crucial.

Why? Because most of us are not always conscious of what we put in our mouths. You feed the kids, for example, and think you just had a bite of the crust of the grilled cheese sandwich, or the leftover bite on the peanut butter and jelly sandwich. You think the only fat you ate on a given day was the olive oil in your salad dressing.

In reality, it could well be that the "one bite" you took was half the sandwich, or that the salad you ate also had nuts in it, or that you also ate a Nut Pâté, a dessert after lunch, more nuts later in the evening, along with a huge helping of almond butter!

Write it all down. If you do, you won't be able to lie to yourself, or forget. Be honest with your list; it's for your eyes only.

A good example of a journal is included in the "Testimonials" section of this book. See Rachel's story.

III. VISUALIZE

In his "Body for Life" video, Bill Phillips interviews a man determined to lose weight and get into shape. The man tells Phillips that every night, before going to sleep, he would visualize the body of professional bodybuilder Frank Zane, known for his incredible symmetry and beautiful physique. Each night, this man would picture his head on Frank Zane's body. So much did he internalize this vision that, as he said, he would be shocked in the mornings as he passed his bedroom mirror because he didn't look like what he had pictured the night before! The man continued to visualize his head on that magnificent body, continued to work out and diet, and within three months, the result was astonishing. The video shows the man standing side by side with Frank Zane: they look almost identical!

Visualize what you want right now: your fit body, your boundless energy, your robust health. Visualize the life you desire, and then take the steps necessary to get there.

Close your eyes for a few minutes right before you go to sleep and immediately upon awakening. With your eyes closed, picture what you want. See yourself as exactly how you want to be. Feel all of the emotions that go along with that scene. If you can imagine smells and sounds, all the better. The more real you can make it, the more real it will be. Don't worry if you don't feel or see a lot the first few times you try this. Just keep doing it. It will get easier. And it will work.

IV. HAVE FUN

Every week, write down five things you can do to have fun... anything that brings you joy and is fun for *you*! Catching a movie, going to the beach, visiting a museum, watching a sunset, taking a stroll in the park, browsing through a book store, going out dancing, drawing, painting... whatever you truly enjoy.

Make a new list every week, and make sure you do all of these things every week! People make "to do" lists all the time to make sure they get their chores done. Why not make a "to do" list to make sure you get some fun in your life?

Having fun changes your outlook, puts you in a good mood, and allows your creativity to flow. You will be inspired to have a good day, be happy, treat yourself well, and take care of yourself.

V. SET GOALS

Setting goals helps you become more focused, giving you a guideline for the daily steps you need to take, in order to

"YOU ARE ALREADY what you are becoming. If you ever wonder what your life will be like, look at yourself right now. It will be the same, except with a few more gray hairs, unless you change...now!" — **Lazaris**

achieve what you want to accomplish. Goal setting is similar to creating an outline for a book. The outline is the hard part: figuring what you want to say and why. After that you just fill in the chapters.

Once you know · specifically · what your desires are, then you just start living your life in such a way that you'll reach them.

On a blank piece of paper, write down at least three goals you want to reach within the next month: how you want to look and feel, the weight you want to lose, illnesses you want to heal. Be as specific as possible. Study them every morning when you wake up.

As you begin to reach your goals, you will notice something happening. You will notice that you are changing and becoming different from what you were. You will notice that, in achieving what you truly desire and by changing your state of health, you are taking control of your life. Other aspects of your life will begin to change also. When one part of your life improves so do other parts. When you succeed in one area a ripple effect occurs affecting other areas of your life. Don't hold yourself back from the change. Don't hold yourself back from what you want to achieve in your life because it may be different from what you know, or different from what other people think it should be.

Too many people in this world are not living their dreams, not living the life they want to be living because they are afraid of being different. Please don't be one of them.

Those who live joyous, happy, healthy, successful lives today weren't afraid to be different. Don't you be afraid, either. Instead, allow yourself to be unique! You must be, in order to become who you really are.

VI. MAKE A 30-DAY COMMITMENT

You already know from experience that a month isn't such a long time at all. How often do we ask ourselves: "Where did the month go?" And when you consider the fact that we're talking about changing · for the better · the rest of your life, one month seems like an awfully short amount of time to invest.

Invest one month in yourself. The returns you'll receive will be astonishing.

THE MOST WASTED of all days is one without laughter.

— E. Cummings

31

FREQUENTLY ASKED QUESTIONS

Q. WHAT ABOUT PROTEIN (AND CALCIUM)?

A. This is by far the question I'm asked most frequently.

Protein does not create protein in your body. Amino acids create protein in your body. And the best source of amino acids are leafy green vegetables.

When you eat meat, fish, or chicken, you're not getting as much protein as you think you are. Take chicken, for example. Say there are 20 grams of protein in a chicken breast. Once you cook it, you destroy half the protein. Now your body has to digest and assimilate this heavy, dense source of 10 grams of protein, that will take up to 100 hours. How much do you think is getting stuck in your body as toxic waste by the time it reaches your colon? How much protein from a cooked chicken breast will you actually get? Maybe a few grams, if you're lucky.

When I speak to bodybuilders and athletes about this, they often insist that animal protein is the best protein available. If it's such a good source, why do they need so *much* of it? Some of my bodybuilding friends feel it necessary to eat large portions of meat with each of their *six* daily meals!

Many green vegetables are excellent sources of high quality protein. A bowl of uncooked greens or sprouts may only contain a few grams of protein, but you can digest and assimilate all of it because they still have all of their vitamins, minerals, and enzymes intact. This makes this protein far more useful to your body.

YOU COME OUT AHEAD IN TWO WAYS:

First, you're getting high quality protein *without* the other harsh and dangerous substances, like hormones, antibiotics, chemicals, drugs, and other unknown substances forced upon farm animals to make them as fat as possible in the cheapest possible way. Second, you're getting a lot more protein while eating a lot less food.

In *Conscious Eating*, Gabriel Cousens writes: "According to the

American Dietetic Association, pure vegetarian diets in America usually contain twice the required protein for one's daily need. Harvard researchers have found that it is difficult to have a vegetarian diet that will produce a protein deficiency unless there is an excess of vegetarian junk foods and sweets. In fact, if vegetarian protein is consumed in its live state, even less protein is needed because research shows that one half of the assimilable protein is destroyed by cooking."

John Robbins, in *Diet for a New America* reports: "If we ate nothing but wheat (which is 17% protein) or oatmeal (15% protein) or pumpkin (15% protein), we would easily have more than enough protein. If we ate nothing but cabbage (22% protein) we'd have over double the maximum we might need. In fact, if we ate nothing but the lowly potato (11% protein) we would still be getting enough protein. This fact does not mean potatoes are a particularly high protein source. They are not. Almost all plant foods provide more. What it does show, however, is just how low our protein needs really are. There have been occasions in which people have been forced to satisfy their entire nutritional needs with potatoes and water alone. I wouldn't recommend the idea to anyone, but under deprived circumstances it has been done. Individuals who have lived for lengthy periods of time under those conditions showed no signs whatsoever of protein deficiency, though other vitamin and mineral deficiencies have occurred."

No lack of protein or muscle growth!

CONSIDER THE SOURCES OF THE "INFORMATION" YOU'RE GETTING!

Robbins also notes that the National Dairy Council has spent tens of millions of dollars to make us believe that osteoporosis can be prevented by drinking more milk and eating more dairy products. Yet throughout the world, he reports, the incidence of osteoporosis correlates directly with *protein* intake. Recent research has shown that with a greater intake of meat and dairy products, there is a *higher* rate of osteoporosis... not the other way around! In fact, the world health statistics show that osteoporosis is more common in precisely those countries where dairy products are consumed in large quantities: the United States, Finland, Sweden, and the United Kingdom.

Most of the research that has been done on protein has been funded by the meat and dairy industries. We have all been taught, in school, from television, from our parents, to drink our milk so we will grow up with healthy bodies and strong bones. In his book, *Living Foods for Optimal Health*, Brian Clement agrees: "Unfortunately the meat and dairy industries speak louder than medical journals. Their multimillion-dollar advertising campaigns ignore what even the most conservative medical investigators no longer deny - excess protein robs our bodies of strength. With their high protein content, milk and meat actually contribute to the accelerating development of osteoporosis. Certainly most people do not know that one teaspoon of sea kelp mixed in a glass of water gives approximately a thousand times more calcium (without animal protein) than an eight ounce glass of milk. You can bet you won't hear that information pop up in a catchy jingle. This false fan fare is not new. Remember when the manufacturers of Wonder Bread convinced your family in the 1960's that white bread could build strong bones in twelve ways? Wonder has since had to recant. But we were 'duped'."

The more protein in our diets, the more calcium we lose. Eating a high protein diet rich in dairy products is *not* a good way to get your calcium. Your best sources are green, leafy vegetables such as collards, kale, cabbage, lettuce, along with apricots, figs, sesame seeds, sunflower seeds, almonds, and other raw foods.

Intuitive Eating author Humbart Santillo writes: "On a low protein diet, less calcium is needed since the body doesn't need additional calcium to neutralize the by-products of heavy protein consumption. Moreover, the high phosphorus content of protein foods causes a lowering of calcium in the blood, and this leads to calcium loss in the bones. When one starts lowering the protein content and increasing the amounts of vegetables and fruit in the diet, blood calcium normalizes, and calcium loss from bones is diminished."

Numerous studies directly oppose the National Dairy Council's recommendation of 1200 milligrams of calcium per day. For example, the *Medical Tribune* reported, in a major study in 1984, that "vegetarians were found to have significantly stronger bones."

Take a look at these statistics from researchers at Michigan State and other major universities. They found that, in the United States, by age 65:

- Male vegetarians had an average bone loss of 3%
- Male meat-eaters had an average bone loss of 7%
- Female vegetarians had an average bone loss of 18%
- Female meat-eaters had an average bone loss of 35%

Another study published in the *New England Journal of Medicine* shows that calcium supplementation has no effect on the rate osteoporosis occurs as compared to women who took no supplementation.

Nathan Pritikin also points out an interesting fact about osteoporosis:

"African Bantu women take in only 350 milligrams of calcium per day. They bear nine children during their lifetime and breastfeed them for two years. They never have calcium deficiency, seldom break a bone, rarely lose a tooth. Their children grow up nice and strong. How can they do that on 350 milligrams of calcium a day when the National Dairy Council's recommendation is 1200 milligrams? It's very simple. They're on a low protein diet that doesn't kick the calcium out of the body... In our country, those who can afford it are eating 20% of their total calories in protein, which guarantees negative mineral balance, not only of calcium but of magnesium, zinc and iron. It's all directly related to the amount of protein you eat."

WHEN PEOPLE SAY "I'M CRAVING PROTEIN"...

David Wolfe points out in *Sunfood Diet Success System*, "When someone says 'I need protein,' what they really need and want is fat. Most people and nutritionists cannot distinguish between the desire for fat and the desire for protein. People can give up steak much easier than cheese, because steak is mostly protein whereas cheese is mostly fat."

High animal and dairy protein consumers tend to experience higher rates of breast cancer, 40% more coronary disease, more hypertension, 2.3 times more colon cancer, 3.6 times more prostate cancer, and 10 times more lung cancer than non meat-eaters.

As far back as 1961, *The Journal of the American Medical Association* estimated that 97% of heart disease could be prevented by a vegetarian diet!

Kidney stones are also a serious problem resulting from too much protein. Excessive protein puts an enormous amount of stress on the kidneys. It doesn't just disappear from the body. Kidneys have to work very hard to get rid of it, and it can begin to degenerate the kidneys and to cause hypertrophy and inflammation.

Recent research is debunking many other previously held "truths." Take iron, for example. Vegetarians suffer less from anemia than meat-eaters, yet most people do not believe this. Why? Because we've been told by the meat industry that the best source of iron is · you guessed it · meat!

Gabriel Cousens, author of *Conscious Eating* has this to say about anemia:

"Why do vegetarians have less anemia? The answer, I believe, lies in the leafy greens, which often have a higher concentration of iron than flesh foods. For example, according to the USDA Handbook No. 456, gram for gram, kale has fourteen times more iron than red meat. Spinach, Popeye's comic strip power food, has approximately eleven times the iron as ground beef. Strawberries, cabbage, bell peppers, and even cucumbers have more iron per weight than ground beef or sirloin steak. Researchers have also found that Vitamin C, which is high in fruits and vegetables, significantly enhances the body's ability to assimilate iron."

More important than *what* we eat is what we can digest and assimilate.

Q. WHAT DO I DO WHEN I GO OUT TO EAT OR I'M ON THE ROAD?

A. Most restaurants serve wonderful salads these days. After a while you will know where the best places in your area are. And you will also become very skilled at menu reading.

I always look at everything on the menu. I have found that just asking for an "all raw salad," doesn't always work. Most people don't understand what "raw" means. I used to order salads, asking for all the raw veggies the restaurant had. Invariably I'd be presented with a salad containing something like *roasted* red peppers and *grilled* eggplant. Not good.

Read the *entire* menu. At an Italian restaurant, for example, see if penne pasta with zucchini and tomatoes is offered. Maybe there's a portobella chicken dish, or an angel hair dish covered with pine nuts. Look at all the ingredients in the entrées offered, as well as the salads and see what you can put together.

Ask questions! I always order an entrée sized salad (so I don't end up with a tiny side version) and then I ask what kinds of raw vegetables the restaurant has on hand. For instance: "Do you have portobella mushrooms that are *not* marinated or cooked?" "How about zucchini and summer squash, are they cooked?" "What about the pine nuts, are they roasted or raw?"

My mother started doing this when she went out to eat with friends. They wondered why she asked the server so many questions and even laughed at her, telling her she was being ridiculous. She ignored them and continued on with the conversation as if she were doing nothing out of the ordinary. Two months after starting this diet, losing twenty pounds, looking twenty years younger, healing a variety of ailments including a ten-year battle with bursitis, aches and pains that she woke up with every morning, and a varicose vein that caused her terrible pain when she walked... they stopped laughing, and a few even began the diet with her.

Focus on *why* you are dining out. More than likely, you're there for the company. Focus on the social aspects rather than on the food.

You might want to bring an avocado or salad dressing with you. Also, you could bring along - like I used to do - some raw fudge in a plastic baggie. It sure helped me. After sitting through a couple of hours with people eating my favorite cooked foods, and then dessert, my raw fudge took away any deprived feelings I might have had.

I also suggest that you take along some fruit, nuts, seeds, dehydrated crackers or anything else that's quick and easy to munch on. A major reason people go off this diet is because they leave the house for the day, neglecting to bring some food along. You may think you don't need it, but please play it safe: take it anyway. If you get hungry and you're on the road, you'll be far less tempted to stop for cooked food if you've got a supply of raw and living food stashed in your car or pocketbook.

Ideally on this diet, you shouldn't have to worry about what to bring to eat. But like any new program, it takes some time to adjust, so make it easy on yourself. Plan ahead - and bring along some food until this way of eating becomes second nature to you.

If I'm out for the whole day, I usually throw some bananas in my car, or grab a bunch of grapes for the ride.

You'll get good, too, at finding raw food wherever you go. Even in a mall, there might be a pastry shop that sells apples, or an ice cream shop that may sell you a banana. Be creative!

"PAINT A PORTRAIT of life to be proud of that could not be sold for all the money on earth. Hang that portrait in your mind and understand its ever presence. Reflect on every brush stroke that makes all the mountains and valleys and rivers and skies the most beautiful in the land. Share your portrait with others but beware their brushes. Select only those whose brush will add to the beauty and structure of your masterpiece."

— **Chris Ensor**

Q. WHAT IF I'M DIABETIC OR HYPOGLYCEMIC?

A. People who are diabetic or hypoglycemic often get concerned when I tell them to eat fruit.

I've worked with many diabetics who, after one month on raw foods, are eating fruit every morning and throughout the day. If you are diabetic or hypoglycemic, you will need to add some crushed nuts to your fruit breakfast for the first week or two. You can also add some celery or greens with the fruit to slow down the sugar absorption. An even better alternative is to juice a combination of greens, like Swiss chard, kale, collards, spinach, celery, cucumber and an apple.

One client of mine was severely hypoglycemic for ten years and insisted she needed protein. She would eat a small piece of chicken at night when she started feeling light-headed, or would have some other processed food after her morning fruit smoothie to avoid feeling the effects of low blood sugar. I finally persuaded her to try a green drink in the morning, or to mix in some celery with her banana shake, or add some nuts to her fruit snacks. I wanted to get her away from cooked protein and allow her body to begin the healing process. After one week on an all raw diet she had no further low blood sugar incidents.

Elizabeth, another client, had been on diabetes' and high blood pressure medication for twelve years, along with a host of other medications. At five feet five inches, she weighed 350 pounds.

After four weeks on raw foods, she had lost 30 pounds and her blood sugar level was down from 189 to 125. It continued to go down over the next few weeks and stayed below 75 after that. Elizabeth was eating a lot of salads, nut pâtés, and dishes made with nuts and greens, and occasionally some sprouted grains. She would often have a green drink in the morning. When she did have fruit, we made a cream sauce with nuts, or a dessert with a date nut crust. Once her blood sugar was down, she began eating fruit alone. She has not had a blood sugar level increase since starting this diet more than a year ago. Today, Elizabeth eats only fruit in the mornings, and sometimes more throughout the day. She has continued to lose weight ·140 pounds to date · and has kept her blood sugar levels down.

(If you have colitis, diverticulitis, or other intestinal problems, you may need to stay away from nuts and seeds for awhile to allow your body to heal).

THE SOURCE OF SUGAR MAKES ALL THE DIFFERENCE!

Since diabetics have been told to avoid sugar, they naturally tend to stay away from fruit. But the sugar problem lies not so much in fruit, but in cooked, fat-laden, over-processed, sugar-rich foods such as condiments, sauces, pastries, candy, and many prepared store-bought foods.

Once you start to heal your body and feed it the food it needs, you will be able to eat fruit in abundance.

In *Conscious Eating*, Gabriel Cousens writes: "For diabetics and hypoglycemics, it seems that whether the food is cooked or raw is very important for their well-being. In research at George Washington University Hospital, when 50 grams of raw starch were administered to patients, the blood sugar rose only 1 milligram in one half hour before it began to decrease. With the cooked starch there was a dramatic average increase of 56 milligrams in one half hour and then a 51 milligram average drop by one hour. This is quite a significant shift in blood glucose. The major difference between the raw and cooked is the raw starch came with its own amylase and so was able to be predigested in the food enzyme stomach."

In my experience, diabetes and hypoglycemia are very quickly and easily healed with a raw and living food diet. Many people have stopped needing their medications soon after adopting this way of eating.

Q. WHAT IF I'M NOT LOSING WEIGHT?

A. Then you need to look at the volume of nuts and perhaps oils you're consuming. Whenever I put someone on this diet, he or she almost always loses 4-5 pounds (if not more) in the first week eating anything raw they choose. During the second or third week we usually have to adjust the diet by removing the extra nuts eaten as snacks or in their meals and desserts throughout the day. If you eat a meal of nuts, a dessert made with nuts; if you're snacking on nuts and dehydrated foods, or eating salads with lots of oil, all within the same day, you're getting too much fat.

You needn't eliminate dessert, or deprive yourself of anything. You just need to reduce the amount of nuts and oils you're eating.

It is better to eat numerous small meals throughout the day rather than two or even one large meal. This is how you get your metabolism working all day long. If you consume a large quantity of food in just one sitting per day - or if you eat too little - your metabolism will slow down. It will want to protect you from starvation and will try to conserve as many calories as possible. Eat smaller meals throughout the day to "keep the engine burning."

You also need to consider your level of physical activity. If you are taking in more calories than you're using up, you won't lose weight. Remember though: fruits and vegetables have fewer calories per bite than do most cooked foods. That means you can eat more of them and still eat delicious meals made from them, without having to bother with weighing out your food and eating such small amounts that you still feel hungry.

Poor food combining can also slow weight loss. Listen to your body. If you're experiencing indigestion, gas, and bloating, than consider what foods you're combining. You may not be digesting your foods properly, causing them to remain in your digestive track too long, where they ferment... possibly slowing weight loss and causing other problems, too. Refer to chapter 13 and in particular, the Food Combining Chart on page 83 for more information.

Q. WHY DON'T I HAVE TO COUNT CALORIES AND FAT GRAMS LIKE OTHER DIETS REQUIRE? WON'T AVOCADOS AND NUTS MAKE ME FAT?

A. Forgive me, but the second question always makes me sigh because it's so often asked by people who've been eating pizza, chocolate cake, ice cream, burgers and fries all their lives... and now they're afraid of an avocado and some sprouted almonds? Yet this is a valid question and I know it concerns many people.

There's a *huge* difference between cooked fats and raw fats. Studies linking fats to high cancer rates, heart attacks, kidney failure, high blood pressure, high cholesterol, angina, cardiovascular disease, and many other diseases have been done with *cooked* fats. Obesity is linked to a high, *cooked* fat diet.

Raw plant fats, on the other hand, have exactly the opposite effect. Raw fats, found in avocados, olives, coconuts, nuts, and seeds contain antioxidants. They contain oils that produce healthy joints, nerves, and bones. Raw plant fats do not cause the body to gain excess weight because, unlike cooked fats, they still contain the enzyme lipase, which is needed to digest fat. By cooking fats, lipase is destroyed, along with other important enzymes and minerals. Lipase breaks up raw plant food as it is eaten, and helps the body to digest oils in these foods. Because this food gets assimilated and digested properly, it is not causing all kinds of chronic and degenerative diseases, and it's not getting stored as excess body weight.

You will *not* get fat by eating avocados, olives, sprouted nuts and seeds, and other plant fats!

When I first started this diet I was eating two to three avocados a day and *losing* weight! I didn't have much weight to lose, but the few extra pounds just melted off, because I was eating fats in their whole, natural form with all of their enzymes intact.

AND BY THE WAY: CHOLESTEROL IS NOT FOUND IN PLANT FATS.

Foods like avocados, olives, nuts, seeds, nut butters, and

coconuts do *not* contain cholesterol. Cholesterol is found in animal products: meat, poultry, fish, dairy, cheese, eggs, and products derived from these foods.

While transitioning from a cooked food diet to an all raw diet, it's important to include high quality plant fats in your food intake. In the first few weeks, do *not*, in order to lose weight faster, eliminate fats from your diet. I've seen many people try this and they inevitably fail. You *will* lose weight eating avocados and nuts and other high fat foods on this diet, especially in the first few weeks. You may wish to adjust your diet to a lower fat intake as you progress, but don't do this too early on. Fats tend to fill you up, eliminating that "hungry" feeling and they keep cravings at bay.

"SPEEDING UP" THE WEIGHT LOSS PROCESS CAN BE HAZARDOUS

My client Janice had been doing extremely well, eating fruits, vegetables, nuts, and seeds. She started by making a lot of the recipes found in this book and then began to eat more simply. She'd have fruit in the morning, salads with avocados for lunch, salads with different veggies in them for dinner, a vegetable soup, or flax crackers with guacamole. She'd eat crackers with almond butter on them, grab some nuts if she got hungry, or, if she was "starving," throw together some dried fruits and nuts for a quick dessert.

Within three months, she had already lost 45 pounds! She only had 15 more pounds to go to reach her goal weight.

But Janice grew impatient. She wanted to "speed up" the weight loss.

So she began cutting out avocados, and then nuts. No more desserts, nut butters, or flax seed crackers. She started to eat more vegetables and less fruit (reasoning that, after all, fruits had more calories than vegetables).

Naturally, Janice started getting hungry! What's more, she tried ignoring her hunger. She could have (and should have) quelled it simply by having an avocado, a dessert, some almond butter on a celery stick, or by eating fruit until she felt full.

But she didn't. Instead, she waited until her hunger got out of control and she'd end up binging. She'd eat everything in sight: pizza, pasta, pints of ice cream. She told me she felt as if she were starving and that she needed "real food" because this diet was not filling her up.

What a cycle Janice put herself through! After binging, she'd go back on the diet, but · again, in a hurry to lose weight · she'd ignore any sort of plant fats and she'd end up starving. I reminded her about how well she'd done on the diet before throwing herself into her unnecessarily strict regime, but Janice continued this crazy cycle for a few months. Eventually she totally abandoned the diet for three weeks.

After those three weeks I got a call from Janice. She felt terrible.

All her old aches and pains had returned, along with a stuffy nose and watery eyes caused by allergies. She was, once again, suffering from heartburn. Her memory wasn't as sharp as it had been only weeks before. Her motivation was down, she felt foggy, tired and lethargic.

She also felt depressed and negative. The zest she'd had for life while on raw food was ebbing away. She realized she'd made a big mistake. After a few days back on raw and living food, she felt, once again, like a new person.

I still see Janice occasionally, and she's doing just great. When she feels the need to cut back on her food, she does so with careful consideration. She doesn't cut out the fat, and still eats everything in moderation. When she feels like she needs more food, fat, or fruit, she eats it. She's been on this diet for a little more than a year, has lost all the weight she wanted to lose (60 pounds), and has recovered from severe allergies, coli-tis, asthma, depression, and other ailments. She's a very happy person.

Please don't get me wrong: I believe in the enormous body of scientific evidence that supports the notion that if we don't overeat we are healthier. Regardless of the type of food, eating minimally has been shown to increase life span and improve health. Some of the longest living, healthiest people in the world have been known to eat sparingly.

But please allow yourself enough time to transition yourself into this way of eating! We are products of a culture that encourages overeating and far too much poor quality food. Give your body the proper raw and living foods it needs to build good health. Once you are receiving foods that truly nourish your body, it will be easier to eat less than you were used to.

RAW PLANT FOOD IS GOOD FOR YOUR LOOKS, TOO!

When I started eating raw plant fats instead of cooked fats, I noticed that my hair and nails were growing faster, healthier, shinier, and stronger. My skin grew smooth and soft. Imperfections such as lines, pimples, and large pores began to vanish.

One of the first things people notice after starting this diet is how much younger they look.

Before going raw, I wouldn't dream of leaving the house without make-up, not even if I were going to the gym! Now, a decade later, and in my late thirties, I look better *without* make-up.

Adhering to this diet is like having a natural face-lift, better yet, one that *lasts*! Sometimes I think it should be called the "Beautifying Diet." If you only try it for reasons of vanity, you'll be satisfied... and amazed at how vibrant, healthy, glowing, and younger you'll look.

So don't worry about counting calories or fat grams... and don't worry about getting FAT!

Q. HOW DO I GET BACK ON TRACK IF I DO GO OFF THIS DIET?

A. What do you do if, for some reason, you have begun to eat cooked food and strayed from a raw and living food diet and are having a hard time getting back on track? You've got to start all over. You've got to pretend that you're a beginner at this way of eating.

You need to prepare some raw food. Make more food than you think you will want or need.

Your natural tendency may be to start juice fasting or to eat minimally to lose the weight you may have gained or to get yourself "jump – started" on this diet again. But that is often a big mistake. Trying to go from eating cooked food, or worse, binging on cooked food, to a minimalist approach to eating will only lead you back into binging or into another round of bad food choices.

It is not realistic to think that you can go from eating cooked food to a minimalist diet of negligible amounts of fruits and vegetables, or just juices. You will start out with good intensions but will find yourself either starving or feeling awfully deprived which is often alleviated with a quick "fix" of cooked and processed foods.

Psychologically, the notion of surrounding yourself with a lot of food (even raw and living food) may not be appealing to you if you have been eating a lot of cooked food but now want to return to the raw food diet. But the only way to get back on this diet is to begin all over again.

Most likely it will take less than a week for you to get back on track and start feeling better.

Forget the fast. Forget the starvation route. Start at the beginning. It's the only way you'll get back to raw and stay raw.

You can do it! You've done it before, you can do it again!

Q. IS COFFEE REALLY BAD FOR YOU?

A. YES! Caffeine is nothing but bad news!

In her book, *Go for It*, Gail Olinekova writes: "Besides creating the nervous symptoms, caffeine causes other reactions which are focused on women. Painful breast lumps or cysts and

YOUR CURRENT FAILURES are not necessarily regressions. They can be means to a wiser, more fruitful path taking you in new directions leading to greater balance. They can be lenses that, no matter how fractured they seem, can reveal opportunity, sometimes fanciful, sometimes profound, that would otherwise be missed or lost. When you look at your failures only as regressions, surely they will only function as such. Change the way you look and your reality changes. Change the observing devises and the reality they observe changes. Ah, such opportunity awaits you.

— Lazaris

breast cancer are linked to caffeine. Women with histories of fibrocystic breast disease have had complete reversals in their condition when they stop using caffeine, as demonstrated in studies by Dr. John Minton, an Ohio State University surgeon. Birth defects, heart attacks, cancer and high blood pressure are linked to caffeine. Caffeine is closely related to chemicals that involve DNA, our genetic material. And through DNA cell mutation resulting cancerous tumors are formed. Caffeine also leaches Vitamins E, the B complex, and C as well as zinc and other key minerals such as calcium."

Caffeine may give you more temporary energy, but it is at the expense of your overworked adrenal glands, and that can accelerate aging. Give it up! Caffeine withdrawal symptoms can be hard to handle but only last a few days. After that you'll have more energy than that cup of coffee ever gave you!

People often think that it isn't necessary to give up coffee when they go raw since it's not really a "food." Whatever you ingest · solid or liquid · affects your body! Caffeine is a detriment to good health. It's considered by many health care professionals to be a very potent drug with serious side effects.

Q. CAN I DRINK ALCOHOL ON THIS DIET?

A. I hope you are not going raw just to lose weight or heal a particular problem, but also because you want to be the healthiest you can be. After you've been raw for awhile you'll lose your taste for alcohol. Alcohol slows your metabolism and is loaded with empty calories. Organic wine, without the sulfites added, is raw. So, if you're going to have a drink, choose this over beer or hard liquor.

Q. HOW MANY MEALS SHOULD I EAT A DAY?

A. Eat when you're hungry. When you're not hungry, don't eat.

I prefer to eat smaller meals throughout the day, instead of one or two (or three) large meals, and that's what I recommend for you. This will keep your metabolism up; you will lose weight more quickly, avoid being hungry, and keep your blood sugar levels even.

Q. I'M AN ATHLETE. CAN I GET ALL OF WHAT I NEED ON THIS DIET?

A. Please don't fall for the myths about athletes needing to "carbo load," or requiring massive amounts of animal protein. Many, many successful athletes · including runners, body-builders, tennis, basketball, and football players · are vegetarian or vegan.

More and more, athletes in every kind of sport are realizing that a plant-based diet is the best way to fuel their bodies and help them excel. To name just a few:

World Champion gymnast **Dan Millman**

"Mr. International" bodybuilding winner **Andreas Cahling**

Tennis great **Martina Navratilova**

Olympian **Carl Lewis**

Football Hall-of-Famer **Art Still**

Four-time "Mr. Universe" title-holder **Bill Pear**

Swimming World Record Holder **Bill Pickering**

World Class marathoner **Gail Olinekova**

Space restraints prevent me from listing the many, many world class athletes who eat a plant-based diet. Many of them are also raw fooders, not just vegetarians.

Raw fooder and marathon runner Gail Olinekova boasts one of the most beautiful bodies I've ever seen: extremely muscular, lean, toned, and fit. In her book *Go for It*, she reports that she achieved one of her best times in the Boston Marathon after completing a seven-day water fast. Bodybuilder Andreas Cahling is also a raw fooder. He doesn't appear to be lacking in muscle growth!

ENERGY, STAMINA, AND FOCUS

Cooking food destroys most of its vitamins, minerals, and

enzymes. Proteins, carbohydrates, and fats are in a much more useable form and are far more nutritious when raw. As an athlete, you will gain much more energy, stamina, and cardiovascular endurance on a raw and living diet. You'll also recover from injuries faster, be stronger, and improve on that all-important focus.

An alkalized body is essential for an athlete. A raw and living food diet will accomplish this. If an athlete is functioning in an acid state (and most people, including athletes, are doing just that if they're eating cooked foods), he or she cannot reach optimal health and peak performance.

I have been bodybuilding since age 15. I've been a vegetarian since the age of 16. I've experimented with raw food, on and off, since 1989, and have been 100% raw since 1998.

Many people, when seeing me work out, find it hard to believe that I'm a raw fooder. "No way can you build muscle on that kind of diet," they say.

They're wrong. I am very muscular. I have more energy, more endurance, and feel better physically and mentally than I ever have before... and I'm in the best shape of my life!

As an athlete, you may need to increase your fat intake for endurance, eat more sweet fruits for blood sugar and energy, and consume plenty of greens for protein, essential vitamins and minerals.

A lot of myths abound in the world of health, fitness, training, and athletics. But myths don't make a winner. Victory belongs to those who know - and act upon - the truth.

Q. I'M ALREADY THIN AND DON'T NEED TO LOSE WEIGHT. WHAT WILL HAPPEN TO ME ON THIS DIET?

A. What normally happens on a 100% raw and living food diet is that you lose all of your unnecessary body weight. This phenomenon is known as "losing your false body." Your "false body" consists of excess fat and toxins that inhibit the proper, healthy functioning of your "true body." Once your body is free of its excess fat and toxins, you will regain some healthy pounds, as your body achieves a stable equilibrium.

Men in particular become concerned that they are getting too thin after losing a lot of weight. Don, for example, who's nearly six feet tall, went from 265 pounds to 145 pounds while on a 100% raw and living food diet. He then started to build his body up very slowly to 175 pounds while remaining 100% raw. Today he's lean, muscular, handsome, and glowing with health!

Another client suffered from extreme eczema on her face, arms, and elsewhere on her body, along with allergies and migraine headaches. She did not need to go on this diet to lose weight - she was already very thin - but she wanted to clear up her ailments. She became so concerned about the weight she was losing that she kept going off the diet. After all, she told me, she'd always struggled to keep her weight *up* and had always had difficulties in *gaining* weight.

I tried to explain to her that even though she was thin, she still needed to purge the elements in her system that were causing her sickness. Still, the loss of weight alarmed her enough to keep her off the diet - and keep her eczema and other ailments.

Eventually, she decided she simply did not want to live in pain anymore. She took the plunge and went 100% raw. She did lose more weight and in fact got very thin, but she stuck with it. After only eight weeks her eczema was gone, along with her migraines. She remained at a low weight for about a year but then began to put on some healthy weight and soon developed a well-stabilized body. Today, she looks beautiful, has never felt better in her life, and no longer struggles with weight issues.

Whether you need to lose weight, gain weight, heal your body, or calm your mind, raw and living food puts you right where you need to be!

Q. IS THERE A DIFFERENCE BETWEEN LIVING FOODS AND RAW FOODS?

A. Raw and living foods both contain enzymes. Raw, unsprouted nuts, seeds, and grains are considered raw, and contain enzymes that are lying dormant. When these foods are soaked and/or sprouted, their dormant enzymes become active, and therefore become living foods. Fruits, vegetables, and sprouts are all living foods.

Q. I FEEL FINE EATING COOKED FOOD. WHY WOULD I WANT TO START EATING A RAW AND LIVING FOOD DIET?

A. I love what Gail Olinekova writes in her book, *Go for It*:

"People who have problems early in life (e.g. skin blemishes, varicose veins, heart flutters) are in a sense the lucky ones because a problem is indicated, and they have been given a warning so that it can be corrected. But if you are rotting from the inside and are okay on the outside, most people are lulled into a false sense of security, and it's only at forty or fifty years old, after that first heart attack, that their doctor says, 'no salt, cut out fats in your diet, get some exercise.' Why not eat like that all of your life, exercise from the beginning, and *prevent* that heart attack?"

It can take many years for our bodies to begin to break down from the dietary abuse we have heaped upon them. Our youth can cover a host of progressive, diet-related problems which, when they do surface years later, we simply assume that they are part of the "aging process."

It doesn't have to be that way!

There are many people debunking the myth of the "aging process" by following a raw and living food diet!

THE HUNZA PEOPLE...

The Hunza people, who live in the Himalayas, were once noted for their longevity. Often living well into their hundreds, they remained active, climbing mountains and hiking, among other activities. They ate sparingly, on a diet consisting mostly of raw foods such as fruit, vegetables, and sun-baked breads. They had none of the diseases so prevalent in Western culture. Breast cancer, high blood pressure, diabetes, obesity, and many other of our common disorders were unknown to them.

When Western civilization began building railroads in the mountainous areas of the Himalayas, it also introduced to the Hunza people the processed foods and junk foods we eat here in the United States. Within a year, the first case of cancer was detected among the Hunza people. Today these people have many of the same diseases common in America, and their life span has decreased dramatically.

Why wait until you get sick to make yourself healthy?

Q. I HAVE CHILDREN TO FEED, AND A FAMILY TO COOK FOR. WON'T THIS MAKE IT HARD FOR ME TO EAT THIS WAY?

A. There are ways to make it easier.

Avoid standing over a stove every night, and placing yourself near tempting cooked food at every meal.   Instead, take one or two days each week to prepare a lot of meals in advance refrigerating them or freezing them. Family members can simply heat them up or thaw them out as needed. This is far more preferable than you having to cook for them every time a meal is needed!

Start incorporating elements into their diets such as large salads at dinnertime, while at the same time de-emphasizing the major, cooked dishes.

Make big smoothies in the morning instead of greasy bacon, eggs, toast, and coffee.

By your example, and by gently introducing more raw foods into your family's diet, they may become more involved, and more supportive of your efforts.

If you have young children, it will be easier for you to improve their diets now. They may make a fuss for a few weeks, but

"THE ONLY THING that will stop you from fulfilling your dreams is you."

— Tom Bradley -

after their taste buds adapt, they'll love eating fresh fruits and vegetables. You can make this transition much easier by keeping chips, cookies, soda, and other junk food out of your house! Instead, place tempting bowls of fresh, juicy fruit on kitchen counters, on your coffee table and in the family room. Make sure you've got some delicious raw desserts in the refrigerator. You'll be surprised at how quickly your kids will start snacking on healthful food!

NOW, ABOUT THAT SPOUSE...

Your spouse can be a different story. It can be difficult living with someone who's eating your favorite cooked foods right in front of you!

It's a good idea to explain to him or her what you're doing and *why* you're doing it. And ask for help and support!

Of course, in the ideal world, your spouse would actually *join* you, however, that may not always happen.

As long as your spouse is supporting you, and maybe trying some of your raw food dishes, or just giving you words of encouragement, that's really all you can ask for.

You can't force anyone to change. But you can expect the person you love · and who loves you · to support the positive changes you are making in your life.

And remember, when you start taking better care of yourself, you will have far more to give to the people you love.

Q. IS THIS DIET GOOD FOR CHILDREN?

A. This is the very best thing you can do for your child!

I have seen the remarkable effects this diet has had on every child who has followed it. I've seen ear infections, colds, allergies, and general crankiness become distant memories when kids are switched over to a raw and living food diet. There are children that are fed only raw and living foods from birth, and have never even had an ear infection, cold, allergy, or any of the sicknesses we consider "normal childhood diseases."

"THE RAW FAMILY"

The Raw Family book chronicles the events of Russian immigrant Victoria Boutenko and her family. When they came to America, it was to live the "American Dream." They opened businesses, made money, and dined out nightly in fancy and exotic restaurants. Victoria gained 100 pounds. Her overweight husband, Igor, had rapidly progressing arthritis, and severe hyper-function of the thyroid. His doctors told him his thyroid would have to be removed, and that he would have to live on medication for the rest of his life. Victoria's children were not healthy either. Her daughter, Valya, had asthma, and Sergei, her son, was diagnosed with juvenile diabetes. Sergei writes:

"When I was about 9 years old, I started noticing disturbing changes in my health. After I gorged myself one Halloween on a pillowcase of candy, my mother found me unconscious on the bathroom floor. My mom rushed me to the doctors; who told us that I had incurable juvenile diabetes. He said that I would have to give myself shots for the rest of my life and there was nothing more he could do. My mom and I were shocked. Mother decided to go home and 'Think about it'."

While feeling strongly that this was not the right decision, Victoria didn't know what else to do. So she decided to do some research. After finding out about raw food, she began making raw meals and switched her family over to a raw diet. Within weeks, Sergei's blood sugar began to stabilize. Each family member healed his or her debilitating conditions and lost weight. Sergei overcame his condition and never needed to take any medication or have any medical intervention.

Before his mother put him on a raw diet, Sergei's grades in school were so poor that his teachers considered holding him back. He never did his homework, was hyperactive, and couldn't sit still.

Today, at age 15 and 100% raw, he's a "high school dropout." Why? Because the school work was too simple! He took a placement test and is now maintaining a B average in college.

Valya and Sergei are both amazing kids. They radiate love and vibrant health.

Q. I AM IN MY SIXTIES. AM I TOO OLD TO START THIS DIET?

A. The majority of people who contact me for help and who come to my seminars are in their 50s and 60s. It's never too late to start this diet!

This diet is especially helpful for women who are reaching menopause, because it helps eliminate its physical and emotional symptoms, such as hot flashes and mood swings.

The thought of being dependent on other people or on nursing homes for care can lead to depression and the feeling that the second part of your life may not be a pleasant time.

Raw and living food will give you a new lease on life, not just by improving your physical health but also your emotional outlook. I've seen older people go on this diet and age gracefully, gaining independence, strength, and renewed health. Both men and women report a re-awakening of sexual energy after a short time on this diet.

"My wife, Maggie, has lost over 40 pounds since starting Alissa Cohen's diet program five months ago. I never thought I would be able to make that statement because Maggie had been out of control with her eating for some time and there didn't seem to be any viable options out there for her. Looking trimmer would obviously make her feel better about herself but there was also concern about how healthy and mobile she was going to be over the remainder of her life. In just five months I have gone from having little hope to firmly believing, in fact, assuming that her weight is not going to be an issue from here on out. I am stunned at how painless the transition to the new diet has been. Amazingly, with Alissa's help, she has pulled this off while going through menopause, a notoriously difficult time to lose weight. A scientist by training, I was initially skeptical, but observing Maggie's steady progress and almost seamless adjustment has convinced me that

this approach gets results. It seems to me that Alissa's approach is realistic, flexible, sensible and that she inspires people to succeed." — Marty R.

Q. I LIVE IN A COLD CLIMATE. DON'T I NEED COOKED FOODS TO KEEP ME WARM?

A. Throughout my life, before going raw, I suffered from cold feet. When I went to bed at night, my feet would be freezing. Poor circulation, which causes cold hands and feet, vanishes on this diet.

Initially, you may feel colder on this diet, but as your body begins to heal, and your arteries become less clogged, you'll warm up. There are many people all over the world, living in cold climates, enjoying this diet. There is actually a raw and living food restaurant in Alaska! You'll find that, as your body becomes healthier, you will tolerate the cold better than ever before.

If you *do* feel chilly, add some warming herbs and spices to your foods, such as ginger, cayenne, and curry. Exercise is also a great way to increase body heat.

Don't allow the inevitable arrival of winter to become an excuse to go off of raw foods. I spent much of my adult life, after going 100% raw, in Massachusetts, where the winters are often harsh.

Your body will adapt much better to the cold if you stay raw. In his book, *The Sunfood Diet Success System*, David Wolfe writes: "The feeling of coldness when one begins a sunfood diet is typically caused by a thickening of the blood during detoxification episodes; this decreases circulation. It is also caused by an increased blood flow to the internal organs, which are finally given a chance to heal, and a corresponding decreased blood flow to the extremities."

Wolfe continues: "After you persist through the transition and detox - through the feeling of coldness - you will discover that your resistance to both cold and hot weather will increase by eating raw plant foods."

Q. SHOULD I BUY ONLY ORGANIC PRODUCE?

A. When we eat foods that are not organic, we are ingesting herbicides, pesticides, and fungicides. Over 95% of all the toxic chemical residues come from meat, fish, dairy, and eggs, according to John Robbins in *A Diet for a New America*.

But we also need to be careful with our fruits, vegetables, nuts, and seeds! The food you ingest has a profound effect on your entire system. Why would you want to ingest over 100 different pesticides that are used on commercial foods?

Beside the fact that many of these pesticides have been proven to cause cancer and other serious diseases (as if that's not enough!), foods treated with these chemicals are lower in nutrition than their organic counterparts.

Research performed at Rutgers University has shown that an organic tomato contains five times more calcium, twelve times more magnesium, and 1,900 times more iron than a commonly grown tomato. Organic spinach was found to contain twice as much calcium, three times more potassium, and eighty times more iron than its non-organic counterpart.

The same research also shows that organic foods contain over 87% more minerals and trace elements than commercially grown food.

Q. I FEEL TIRED AND WEAK. I THOUGHT A RAW FOOD DIET WAS SUPPOSED TO GIVE ME ENERGY?

A. If you are feeling weak, or as if you have no energy, your body may be going through a detox. This can happen at different times throughout the cleansing process, which can take anywhere from one week to two years, depending on how toxic you are. Normally this will happen when you first start this diet and end within the first few weeks. If it recurs occasionally, just give your body time to rest and relax. You will eventually have more strength and energy than you had before starting this diet.

Q. DO I NEED TO WORRY ABOUT MEETING MY NUTRITIONAL NEEDS ON THIS DIET?

A. If you eat a variety of foods, you will not have to worry about it at all. Living food is so nutritious, and so full of vitamins, minerals, enzymes, high quality protein, carbohydrates, and fats, that the likelihood of not getting something you needed from this diet is far less than on a cooked food diet which is *always* lacking in nutritional value.

Q. I'VE HEARD ABOUT PEOPLE WHO JUST EAT FRUIT AND CALL THEMSELVES "FRUITARIANS." IS THIS HEALTHY?

A. While there are people who consider themselves "fruitarians," this does not mean that they eat only fruit. People have tried to do this but have never been successful. Fruitarians generally eat fruit with some greens and nuts. There are many people who follow this type of diet and enjoy great health, but fruit alone is not sufficient as a long-term diet.

Q. DO YOU EVER GET BORED?

A. There are plenty of delicious raw food recipes in this book to hold anyone's interest and as you progress with this diet, you'll be making up your own!

What other diet allows you to have dessert for lunch and dinner if you want to? There are over 200 varieties of fruits: how can anybody get bored with that? How many varieties of food do you eat now? I'd be willing to bet not nearly as many different kinds as you will with raw food!

In this book, the chapter on what you *can't* eat on this diet is only about 300 words. The chapter on what you *can* eat is over 11,000!

No, I don't get bored... and neither will you!

32

TESTIMONIALS (REAL PEOPLE WHO ARE LIVING ON LIVE FOOD!)

I'M EXTRAORDINARILY GRATEFUL TO THE PEOPLE WHO OFFERED THEIR TESTIMONIALS FOR THIS BOOK, AND I HOPE YOU'LL FIND THEIR STORIES AS INSPIRING AS I DO.

"MY JOURNEY TO FREEDOM"
(JUDEEN, AGE 60)

I started my journey to health by eating only raw foods almost two years ago. When I was first introduced to this diet, I was very unhealthy. I was eating the good old American diet, including meat, bread, and that "wonderful" drink, Diet Pepsi. I was hooked on Pepsi and drank it all day long. I had recently had cancer, a total hysterectomy, and then a malignant melanoma removed from my face. I was very heavy · 275 pounds · and my blood pressure was running around 160/110. My cholesterol was high, and I had memory problems and con-stant headaches. I lived on Tums, as my stomach was always upset. I'd go through a large bottle of extra strength tums in 4-5 days. I felt this was okay since I thought they were giving me calcium. I was always getting a cold, or flu. The minute I'd recover, I'd get sick again. I choked on everything I ate. Tests confirmed that when I swallowed food, it was directed into my lungs rather than my esophagus. I also had most of the symp-toms of MS. I was tired all of the time, and depressed: despite the Prozac I'd been on for a decade. And, since both my moth-er and my sister had recently died, I was going through an enormous bout of grief.

DISCOVERING THE SOLUTION

Eventually, I visited a friend of mind who is an acupuncturist. I needed something to help me feel like I wanted to continue to live. While in her clinic, I came across a brochure on raw food classes scheduled to begin that evening. I went to that class and was hooked...I became 100% raw that night.

I also decided to stop taking Prozac: it wasn't working and it was doing more harm than good. The following week after going raw was great. I didn't need Tums, my headaches went away, and the fog in my head started lifting. My energy level started going up, and, by the end of the second week, I felt so good I hardly knew what to do with myself!

JUDEEN BEFORE

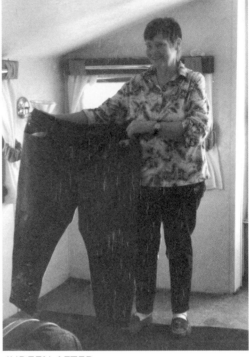

JUDEEN AFTER

DOING THINGS, LEARNING THINGS!

For the first time in two years, I felt like doing things! I was juicing carrots, celery, and beets, and drinking a pint of that every morning, and having a green salad every afternoon. I also ate fruit in the evening. After a couple of weeks I started wanting something other than greens. I was afraid I would start eating cooked food, so I bought a dehydrator. Taking the pulp from my juicing, I made crackers. By then I'd found I could make raw soups, so now I made soups, salads, and crackers. Every week I went to the class and learned more. I'd go home and experiment with all the different things I'd learned. Then I began searching the Internet for any information and recipies I could find. I read every book available on raw foods. I wanted more and more information! I shared what I'd learned with my partner, who, after a month, became raw.

EATING MORE, LOSING MORE, GAINING MORE!

I added other juices to my diet, like kale, cucumber, and bur-
dock root. My weight started dropping, even though I was eating a lot. Over a short period of time, I started changing a
great deal, both physically and mentally. I could swallow without choking. My blood pressure dropped to 110/64. My pulse
rate dropped to 60. My cholesterol dropped. The blurred
vision I'd come to accept disappeared. I wasn't stumbling anymore, and no longer felt dizzy. The MS symtoms were gone.
My physical strength was returning. I felt good mentally. The
depression had lifted. I felt so alive!

TWENTY-MONTHS LATER

It's been 20 months since I started my life change, and I am
now 105 pounds less than I used to be. Physically, I'm back to
where I was many years ago. At 60, I have more energy now
than I had when I was 35! I look better than I have in many
years. My hair is turning back to its natural color as the gray
disappears. I'm losing age spots, and still losing weight.
I haven't had a cold or flu since I started eating this way.
The only times I've felt tired and down was while detoxing: but
not sick!

My life has also changed in a spiritual way. I feel much more
connected with nature. I feel connected to all living things, and
find myself not wanting to kill bugs, or slugs in my
garden...before, I wouldn't have given it a second thought. My
consciousness about the world and everything in it has
changed! I am more open and loving with my friends, and I
really care about people more.

HOW I EAT TODAY

When I first went raw, I ate a lot of dehydrated foods and spent
a great deal of time in the kitchen. As I got further into my
journey, I stopped needing so many of the prepared foods, and
started eating more foods just as they were. Today I am still
drinking juices 4-5 times a week: I feel better when I juice than

when I don't. I have fruit in the afternoon if I'm away from home; otherwise I'll have a salad. Some evenings, instead of whole fruit, I'll have a smoothie made with berries, a banana, or mango. Sometimes I make it with almond milk, and sometimes I just use water. My salads vary from day to day, depending on what I have on hand. It might be as simple as buckwheat and sunflower greens, or cabbage. Other days I might have romaine lettuce, tomatoes, avocado, or baby greens. Sometimes I sprinkle sunflower seeds on my salad. I do eat my salads with a little dressing made from flax seed oil or olive oil, lemon juice, and some kind of garden herb such as basil. I just let my body tell me what it wants. I eat very little grains. Sometimes, if I feel really cold, I'll eat some soaked almonds and dates, which warm me right up. Now I spend only a few minutes in the kitchen each day. There are times when I might eat only oranges all day, or pears, or whatever fruit I have around.

I don't worry about what I'm going to eat, or when. If I get hungry, I eat. If I don't, I don't. When I go on a car trip, I just throw in some fruit and away I go!

Being raw has given me great freedom...and a new life!

"A GIFT OF OPPORTUNITY"
(LYNN L. AGE 35)

My journey began as a gift of opportunity.

I watched for five months as my sister-in-law, who had struggled with her own weight for years, began to gain control, not only of her food addiction, but of many other aspects of her life after starting a raw and living food diet. I marveled at the transformation she was making - both physically and mentally - and envied her strength and enthusiasm. When she told me what she was eating, my initial reaction was to dismiss the thought of trying this diet myself. It seemed very extreme.

I've always been an exercise fanatic. From a very young age, I always played sports, belonged to local gyms, and kept myself in pretty good shape. But today I realize that I had never really understood how to fuel my body properly.

I never had a weight problem until after my second son was born. Although I'd gained 75 pounds during my first pregnancy, I was able to drop the weight quickly through my - I realize now - very unhealthful diet and exercise regimen. But after gaining 65 pounds during my second pregnancy, I was unable to lose that last 25-30 pounds! I spent hours at the gym and ate terribly, reasoning at the time that the less I ate, the better.

At that time, I'd also opted to have my tubes tied...a procedure that produced many physical side effects, including severe menstrual cramping, acne, and hot flashes at the age of 34! I also occasionally experienced severe neck pain from an old injury. When my neck would act up, I would be out of commission for days, or until I sought treatment from my acupuncturist.

LYNN L. BEFORE

ENOUGH WAS ENOUGH!

When I was offered the unique opportunity to finally lose the weight I'd gained, and possibly heal myself through raw and living foods, I made the decision to take it.

I visited the local health food stores and stocked up on organic fruits and vegetables, raw nuts, honey, apple cider vinegar, and various other raw food "staples" I was told I would need. I purchased a food dehydrator, a food processor, and a juicer. I also got something money couldn't buy: the support of my husband who began the diet with me.

The major obstacle I faced was the fact that my children were not eating raw, and I was preparing all of their meals. This was especially difficult in the beginning; but I found that by eating before starting their meals, I could curb the temptation to eat cooked food.

LYNN L. AFTER

MAKING PROGRESS, GAINING ENERGY

Eventually, I felt so good eating raw that I didn't want to pick at the kids' meals. I also found that my children were eating a lot more fruits and vegetables because they saw me eating them. In the beginning, I ate a lot because I was so hungry! I tried all the different recipies given to me, and while I didn't think they all tasted that great at first, I found that the longer I stayed raw, the more delicious everything I ate became. It was as if my taste buds were being reawakened!

Within the first week of eating raw, I could already feel my energy level rising. I wasn't as tired during the day, and began sleeping much better at night. Instead of dragging myself to the gym 4 or 5 days I week, I suddenly needed to go every day, just to expend all this new-found energy! I began to notice my body beginning to respond to my workouts. I felt much stronger, and had far more endurance than I had before I went raw.

My husband and I really got into juicing. We would make huge fruit drinks in the morning, and then juice some greens later in the day. I would also have a big green salad for lunch, and loved inventing my own dressings! Whenever I would crave sweets, I would grab a handful of almonds and raisins, or spread some almond butter on a piece of celery or a flax seed cracker. There was always a way to satisfy the cravings, as long as I didn't let myself get hungry.

HOW I EAT TODAY

As time has passed, I've fallen into a fairly regular eating pattern. I eat most of my fruits before noon and then mostly greens for the rest of the day. I try to keep the amount of nuts I eat to a minimum since I'm still trying to lose weight. I have become addicted to young white coconuts, and drink the milk from one or two of them every morning. Then I save the shells for one of the delicious desserts I've learned to create! Whenever I go out, knowing I'll be away from home for awhile,

I make sure to grab a bunch of bananas or some fruit, and I always carry a bottle of water. I recently started making smoothies in my blender, using bananas, mango, strawberries, or whatever is available, and have found them to be great fillers!

POSITIVE RESULTS

I feel very fortunate to have met Alissa, and to have been given the opportunity to learn about, and experience, a raw food way of life. So many positives have come into my life since beginning this journey just three months ago. I've lost 30 pounds, but more than that, feel and look better than I have in years!

I am amazed at how soft and smooth my skin has become. The acne is gone, and I haven't had a hot flash in three months! I also feel like all the hours spent working out at the gym are finally starting to pay off. And I know this is because I have learned to feed my body what it really needs to be fit and strong.

A few weeks ago, I felt as if my neck was going to go out, as it had for years, and braced myself for a few days of severe discomfort. Instead, almost as if my body adjusted itself, the pain was gone by the next morning!

I am only three months into this new way of living, but I already feel like a different person! I've gained some valuable tools that will forever help me maintain a healthy way of life. I firmly believe that, if you listen very carefully, your body will let you know exactly what it needs to survive.

I am so glad that I finally took the time to listen to mine!

"BETTER AND BETTER!"
(LYNN P. AGE 55)

Diabetes. High blood pressure. Allergies, asthma, and skin rashes. This was my life.

LYNN P. BEFORE

At 5'2" and 298 pounds, I've been on every diet imaginable. Weight Watchers, Slim Fast, Opti Fast. High protein, low fat, you name it, I've tried it.

And while I did manage to lose a small amount of weight on a few of these plans, I couldn't stay on them and eventually gained the weight back.

I even went to an Overeaters' Anonymous meeting. There I learned some new tricks: how, for example, to hide food at work, and how to eat an entire cake right out of the box with a fork.

After thirty years of being at, or close to, this weight, and having all kinds of physical problems, I was still hopeful that, one day, I would find a diet that would help me...one I could actually stay on.

For about seven years, I'd visit my chiropractor weekly, along with a nutritionist and a therapist. I was placed on a high protein, low carbohydrate diet. The goal was to get my blood sugar down, my weight down, and to cure some of my ailments.

It never happened.

ALISSA'S CHALLENGE

A friend had given me Alissa's phone number, and during our conversations, I became more and more interested in the raw and living food diet. Since she was in California and I, in Massachusetts, I had to rely on the phone as my sole source of information from her. I'd told Alissa about my health situation, and the fact that I'd been working with three professionals for seven years without much of a change. One day, after telling Alissa that I really wished that I could heal my body and lose weight, she responded unexpectedly:

"When you really mean what you just said, let me know."

I told her that I *did* mean it. She told me that she didn't think so. I didn't know how to reply.

Then Alissa told me that if I really did mean it, I'd have to prove it. If I really wanted to change the situation I was in, she would fly out to help me. As it happened, she needed to see other people in the area and had business to attend to here. Feeling a bit shocked, I didn't say much, other than that I would "think about it."

When we hung up, the reality of the conversation stunned me. Here she was willing to come across the country to help me and I needed to "think about it?" Alissa was right. If I were really serious about getting healthy I would've jumped at the opportunity.

GETTING SERIOUS

The next morning, phone in hand, I found myself willing the time to pass quickly. But I couldn't quite wait out the three-hour time difference and so, at 9:00 AM Boston time (6:00 AM California time) I called Alissa. Brushing aside my apologies for such an early call, Alissa was delighted that I'd made the decision. I think at that moment she was actually happier than I was. I was excited, but still unsure of myself, and I was afraid. Alissa knew · and I suppose I did, too · that I was dying. I certainly knew that my life was falling apart and that I needed to do something soon or I might not get another chance.

Alissa laid out all the conditions in detail. I would immediately cut out meat, chicken and fish. In the following week, I would eliminate dairy foods. In the week following that, sugar would go. By then she would have arrived and we would eat 100% raw foods from the moment of her arrival. She would stay for three weeks.

The truth is, I didn't change my diet much at all before she arrived. In fact, I probably ate more of all the foods she'd told

LYNN P. AFTER

me to eliminate, out of sheer nervousness. But, by the time she arrived I'd calmed myself down considerably, telling myself that if I didn't like this diet, I'd drop it.

GETTING STARTED

We spent the first few days preparing a bunch of food: raw ravioli, banana cream pie, crackers, smoothies, and salads. At first, none of it tasted very good to me...and I found the green drink she forced me to drink each morning horrendous. (Who would've thought that I would come to actually enjoy that green concoction!)

I liked the fruit drinks and simple salads much better than the combinations of foods I wasn't used to. The sweetness of the fruit and the creamy salad dressings tasted much better than the "foreign" foods, such as avocados, unroasted nuts, and raw vegetables. My taste buds were so polluted that it took a while for me to actually think plain vegetables tasted good.

(Alissa was determined to get me to like those avocados. She'd sneak them into my meals every chance she had!)

We also began an exercise routine. The only problem was, I couldn't move much. In fact, I could barely walk. Taking out the trash left me huffing and puffing. I couldn't even make the 200 yards to the corner of my street. I couldn't breathe and my legs ached terribly. But Alissa never gave up on me.

My house was a complete disaster. Two of the rooms had so much stuff piled up that walking through them was impossible, and the rest of the house wasn't much better. Together, we began sorting through things and clearing stuff out. Alissa told me I couldn't possible think straight amidst all the clutter and that if my house was this messy, my mind must also be.

Before Alissa arrived, I would sit up until two or three in the morning, watching TV and eating junk food. Alissa promptly removed all my TV sets. She told me to clean, read, socialize, get on my computer and find out about raw food and health, or to be creative and start taking pictures and making jewelry again, which I so loved to do.

FACING THE MUSIC

I needed to face some issues about what being overweight and unhealthy meant for me. I had set up a whole life based on my inability to do things for myself. I had people who would help me, so I could enjoy being lazy. While I laid on the couch in the afternoons and evenings, someone else ran my small retail business. I had friends who were also out of shape and unhealthy. We would get together, talk all about our diseases, and then go out to eat together.

Alissa urged me to start thinking and living my life *now* the way I wanted it to be, as if I were already a healthy, fit and happy person. So I started to do that.

I stopped the commiserating sessions with my friends. I started to be more active in my business. I started doing little things, like picking up around the house and changing my own light bulbs. I stopped procrastinating and relying on other people so much.

I STARTED TO CHANGE MY LIFE

Within a month and a half, my blood sugar levels were down to normal. My doctor took me off the diabetes and high blood pressure medication I'd been on for 21 years! As she put it: "I don't know what you're doing, but whatever it is, keep doing it!"

I started swimming again. I continued to walk, and began to have more energy to do other things, too. When we couldn't be together, Alissa and I talked on the phone. I continued to stay raw.

From the first day she walked into my life, I have been 100% raw. Imagine that! I, who couldn't stay on a diet for even a few weeks, now eat 100% raw and living foods!

I've lost 95 pounds so far. I've healed my diabetes, high blood pressure, high cholesterol, and skin problems. My memory is better and I'm thinking much more clearly.

When I first started this diet, I ate mostly vegetables, nuts, and seeds with a small amount of fruit. Alissa prepared a lot of green drinks and salads for me, and if I ate fruit, she would top it with crushed up nuts or some veggies to slow down the sugar since I was a diabetic. Now, fruit is my favorite food! Who would have thought that? Not me! And it only took a few months.

HOW I EAT TODAY

Since I'm not big on food preparation, I keep my diet simple. Usually I have a bowl of cut up oranges in the morning, or a smoothie. Then I'll eat some crackers (I make big bagfuls every month) with spinach dip or cashew cream cheese. I may also have some almond butter on crackers, or veggies, or a piece of fruit, or a juice. For dinner, I sometimes make corn chowder, pea soup, or something quick that I can blend up. When I have salads, I'll mix up a vinaigrette or raspberry dressing - it only takes a few minutes. At night, if I'm hungry, I'll have some banana ice cream with fudge sauce. Sometimes I make up my own desserts with dates and almonds for the crust, and what-ever ground up fruit I've got on hand for the filling. It always comes out great!

STAYING RAW IS THE KEY

I know I'll continue to eat this way, and lose even more weight, because I now love the food. And I know what happens if I deviate from this diet.

Within the past seven months, I cheated a couple of times. It was really very strange! The food didn't taste nearly as good as fruit smoothies or bowls of oranges do. Worse, I could feel, if not immediately then definitely by the next morning, the after-effects cooked food had on my body. I would wake up tired, my face puffy, my joints sore, and definitely not in a good mood. I didn't feel like getting out of bed at all, and when I did, I had no energy. I felt as if I'd been drugged.

These episodes shocked me, but also confirmed that this diet is the healthiest way to eat. The fact that the positive results came so quickly was a big plus for me. Once I started losing weight and healing my body in such a short period of time, I was more and more inspired to continue.

Before going raw, I wasn't sure I'd make it through the next couple of years. Now I feel like my life is just getting better and better. And I know, as long as I stay raw, it will only get better still.

"I COULDN'T BELIEVE THE SCALE!" (RUSS, AGE 38)

When my scale told me I weighed 320 pounds, I didn't want to believe it. It was too difficult. I'd been a top athlete in high school, and in incredible shape. But once out of high school, I

RUSS BEFORE

RUSS AFTER · with the raw girls!

married young, and worked very hard at two jobs to support my family. I neglected myself by overeating and not working out. Eventually, I got divorced and gained even more weight. Finally, I decided to try and lose some.

On my own, I dropped to 290 pounds. But after that, no matter what diet I tried, my weight stayed the same.

SEVERE DIVERTICULITIS, AND A LOT OF PAIN

A severe case of diverticulitis kept me in serious, daily pain. To treat this condition, surgeons removed a piece of my intestine. The pain medication I was taking didn't help. When I asked the doctors about healing this problem, they could only suggest cutting out more of my intestine, and staying on medication for the rest of my life. Nutritionists would make dietary suggestions, such as "eat more fiber," and "cut out fats." Nothing seemed to help. To top it all off, I also had excruciating pain in my back and neck. I finally had to go on disability because I could no longer function as I needed to.

At age 36, I felt like an old man. I was frustrated, and got no real answers, no real programs, to live pain free and heal my condition.

FRUITS, VEGETABLES, AND SEEDS???

I had initially heard about the raw and living food diet through my girlfriend. At first I just didn't think it was for me. Fruits, vegetables, nuts, and seeds??? I'm a big guy · six feet · and was used to eating a lot of food. I liked my bagels, danish, and coffee for breakfast, and my meat and other hearty meals for lunch and dinner! But my girlfriend kept asking me to try the diet, and, after watching her transform her own body with it, I decided to give it a try.

Well, I couldn't believe it! I began losing weight · 40 pounds in three months · had an amazing amount of energy, and my back and neck pain vanished. But what really astonished me was that, after just four days on this diet, I was pain free! No more intestinal pain! I could hardly believe it!

EVEN MY DOCTOR WAS AMAZED!

I told my doctor that I was no longer taking pain medication, since I was no longer in pain. She asked me for Alissa's phone number so that she could find out more about this diet, and begin referring other patients to her.

As soon as I began eating this way, I realized that it was the easiest way to eat... and even more important, that it is filling and delicious! If I can be full and satisfied on this diet, any-body can!

My taste buds have changed, and instead of craving danish or bagels, I crave juicy fruits like grapefruit and oranges. I like to keep my diet simple, even though there are plenty of won-derful raw recipes.

HOW I EAT TODAY

Typically, I like fruits, especially citrus fruits, and all kinds of salads. Usually I eat five oranges, four grapefruits, four bananas, and a huge green salad by noon. My salads have all kinds of greens in them, olives, tomatoes, and onion, with a light vinegar dressing. Then I'll eat some vegetables in the afternoon, like celery, tomatoes, or carrots. My girlfriend will sometimes make Spinach Dip, Cashew Cream Cheese, or a Raw Pizza. Sometimes I'll eat out at the raw restaurant near our home. They have great desserts and meals. But a lot of times I'll just have another salad with all kinds of veggies.

PAIN FREE AND HEALTHY

I never thought I could be content eating these kinds of foods. But everything changes when you start eating this way. You begin to appreciate these foods and actually crave them. I've seen people from all walks of life - including myself! - recover from medical conditions they've had for years. Within weeks of starting this diet their doctors have taken them off their medications. Even if you are at the top of your health goals, this diet will take you to a whole new level of physical and mental fitness. I believe it can work for anyone, and can heal any condition.

This no longer feels like a "diet" to me. It's now just the way I eat, allowing me to live pain free and healthy.

"I THINK I'VE BEEN HUNGRY ALL MY LIFE." (MAGGIE, AGE 58)

As a child of alcoholics, I hungered for companionship and love, but fell short. I learned to fill that empty hole at my core

MAGGIE R. BEFORE

with the easiest and quickest of medications: food. The most reliable drug of choice, food is quick, easy...and dangerous.

One of the benchmarks of an addiction is the amount of risk one is willing to take to medicate cravings. With a food addiction, the addict doesn't have to be isolated to indulge in his or her behavior. After all, everybody has to eat.

As a result, the risks are internalized and denial, ingrained.

When Alissa approached me regarding a raw food diet for weight control, I was in a deadly dance with food. My cravings were constant. Shame was being fed by my inability to find a way out of the addictive life that lay ahead of me, like so many chocolate chips on the road to old age. While facing no immediate health problems, the psychic toll was becoming an extraordinary burden.

RAW AND LIVING FOOD: LOGICAL BEYOND BELIEF

Diet Coke is the perfect metaphor. It appeases the cravings but fosters the behavior. I did not need still another round of starvation, gritting my teeth until I could bite into the next half of a bagel. The chemistry of my food was going to have to change.

And there it was, raw and living food: logical beyond belief.

I have eaten, primarily, a vegetarian diet for the past 30 years. For the past 17 years, I've worked as a produce buyer in a natural foods cooperative. How, then, could I have had such an unhealthy relationship with food? The keyword is "relationship." My involvement with food went much further than sustenance.

MAGGIE R. AFTER

During my first two months of eating raw and living food, I read nothing related to the diet. I relied on my instinct, and on Alissa, for guidance.

HOW I EAT TODAY

My approach is to eat as simply as possible. Fruit smoothies in the morning, avocado and tomato at midday, salads for dinner, flax seed crackers for snacking. For me, desserts push buttons since they replicate my old way of eating. There are so many raw dessert recipes, but, for me, they are like that proverbial Diet Coke. I do not include them in my diet.

AN EXTRAORDINARY GUIDE

Alissa is an extraordinary guide. She combines patience and compassion with a willingness to truly hear and learn about each individual she encounters. She deals with everything from simple behavior, to dietary choices, to addiction issues with care, wisdom, and grace. Bringing raw and living foods into the lives of people is a mission she lives, adapting concepts that are workable throughout life.

In today's culture, overweight people can find many systems of support for weight loss. For me, the issue is not maintaining "control" over my weight. My focus is on living healthy, alive in mind, body, and soul. Alissa has given me the tools, a plan, and the inspiration to make my life everything it was meant to be. I believe she has given me a way to save my life.

She is magic.

"CHANGING MY VIEW OF THE WORLD" (STACIE, AGE 46)

In January, 1997, I found a lifestyle that changed how I ate, and my view of the world. It has transformed me physically, mentally, and spiritually.

As a young child, I suffered from allergies, ear aches, headaches, and sore throats. My ears, eyes, and throat itched, my nose and eyes ran, and I was unable to pronounce words correctly because I was so blocked up.

I was allergic to animals, dust, grass, trees, flowers, molds, and lots of foods. I craved all those foods and ate them extensively. I was never without a box of Kleenex, particularly from

STACIE BEFORE

May through October. Snowy weather brought some relief.

Allergy tests revealed so many positives, the specialists couldn't guarantee any results, even with double-doses each week for a year. Thankfully, I wasn't subjected to that.

As a first and second grader, I was plagued with headaches so severe, they left me spending days lying on the couch, holding my head, rocking in pain. Nothing helped.

FAST FORWARD TO 1981

That year I began working for a computer components company. I wasn't made aware of the chemical dangers inherent in such work. After eight months, I was hit with a mysterious ill-

STACIE AFTER

ness. I was diagnosed with rheumatoid arthritis. The doctors didn't know how to treat it. They told me to rest and to take aspirin. I spent the next two months with cold, wet towels draped on my body. It took four months to feel normal again, and able to return to work. I continued to work for the company for a year and a half.

Eight months later, I began to have headaches again. I ate five bottles of aspirin in two weeks, with no results. One morning the pain was so intense, I couldn't get my hands up to hold my head without screaming from the intensity. Rushed to a doctor, I was told that my organs were shutting down. I was told to cut out sugar, dairy, fried foods, and meats. I was told I could not digest certain substances, and that I had toxic poisoning and that I was suffering from malnutrition.

I didn't look malnourished. In fact, I was a few pounds overweight and had been trying to lose them. Because I ate such a small amount of food, with no nutritional value, my body was holding on to every bite. I began to view my foods differently, but was still resistant to vegetables. I did like fruits, and those became my main source of sustenance.

UNABATING PAIN

Within a few months, I began experiencing intestinal cramping so severe that a few times I almost passed out. Once, too weak to call for my husband, I had to drag myself across the floor to where he was in the house. He took me to the hospital. The doctors sent me home, saying everything was normal. This was the start of a pattern.

Month after month, during my menstrual cycles, I would roll and cry through four to six hours of pain, and a day or two of exhaustion and aches. After a few months, the pain moved into my right shoulder. Now the real fun began.

After two or three days before the real pain, I would feel a type of nausea move through my entire body. I imagine a person on chemotherapy might feel this sensation. The nausea wasn't confined to my stomach. I could truly feel my arm, or leg, or even my ear becoming nauseated. The apprehension of what was to come became overwhelming. I began losing the function of the upper right side of my body.

Like a knife that had been heated in fire, a pain plunged into and ripped across my shoulder blade. I would spend the next five days sitting, without daring to lean back, in my recliner. Intensely cold, I twitched, withered, and cried the whole time. I had to be helped up to use the bathroom. I would eat or drink nothing during this time. My digestion had shut down and even water made me ill. The pain's intensity kept me from sleeping. I kept my arm clutched to my side, as any movement resulted in a sharp, stabbing, ripping pain. I could only whisper, as even breathing was a painful movement.

After five days, I was able to get out of the chair. I was so weak and tired. I would stand and slowly wander through the house. My family would see me get dizzy, and tell me to sit. I couldn't face that chair any longer.

I WANTED OUT

All this time, month after month, year after year, I wanted to die. My family thought I was dying. When these episodes would occur, my young children would run and hide, crying "Oh, no! Mom's sick time! She's dying." I began saying "I want to die so much." Friends would urge me to hang on, saying that perhaps tomorrow there would be a cure for me. I didn't care about tomorrow. I felt I needed to die today, but wasn't able to even function enough to take my own life. I found myself thinking about ways to do it, to end my life, of ways that would minimize the effect on my family. For a while, I didn't want any help. I wanted out.

"GO FIND WHATEVER GIVES YOU RELIEF"

By this time I'd seen 37 doctors and gone through even more therapies. Many were good, but not nearly good enough for what I was experiencing. I continued to search out doctors and submit to further testing. Nothing showed up in any of them, and finally, they were good enough to tell me: "We don't know what's happening to you. Go find whatever gives you some relief."

I had always had an interest in medicine, although having a family early on put that interest on the back burner. I began to visit hospitals, pouring through research books, looking for articles about the effects of lead, to which I'd been exposed at work. A few doctors agreed with my theory, but again, tests showed nothing. Finally I found a doctor who tested my hair samples. He found lead.

DEALING WITH LEAD POISONING

Now that I knew what was wrong with me, and how it had happened, I spoke with a few attorneys. I learned it would be a long, expensive fight. I'd already been through enough fighting within myself. I decided it was time to empower myself further. I needed to be in charge of my body and my mind. I came across a beautiful book: *Love, Medicine and Miracles*, by Bernie Segal, M.D. This book gave me the hope to live. I decided to put my efforts and energy into my health, rather than in legal battles.

Natural therapies felt best to my body, and I started to find many wonderful naturopathic doctors who understood my needs. We all worked together with a number of therapies simultaneously. While I made good progress, the daily pain and limited use of my right side continued. My illness had taken its toll on my marriage: my husband and I divorced.

BEGINNING TO CLEANSE

In 1996 I met a man - an iridologist - who eventually became my boyfriend. He suggested an herbal cleanse to release toxins and waste. Later, he suggested that I not cook my food so much. We cleansed together for one week on a salad of three vegetables and an apple cider vinegar dressing. My body released a lot of old stuff. We decided to continue, adding more fresh, living foods daily and lightly steaming veggies for dinner. At times, we'd eat our usual snack foods. As my diet changed me and some supplements cleansed me, I was at times seemingly sicker.

After a month, we decided to treat ourselves to our favorite Thai food for dinner. I was pretty ill. I could tell how much work my body was going through to process such a heavy lump of food.

I quickly saw the benefits of living foods.

TRANSITIONING AND HEALING

We continued our new way and transitioned over the next year. I learned how to make raw and living versions of our favorite foods, so we didn't really miss anything. I didn't realize the impact of this lifestyle, or know how big the raw and living foods movement was going to be. I just instinctively knew it was the truth, and my body proved it. I was told by a number of doctors that a raw food diet would be hard on my system. I told them that my daily pain was much harder!

My pain lessened on a daily basis, although I would still go through some time "in the chair." This was major progress! My mind became clearer. I loved the cleansing process and started short fasts. I worked with energy and mind techniques to get past the pain. People noticed my alertness and more positive attitude. They said I had a glow, and looked younger, or somehow different. I pushed my body further and slowly became stronger. I gained the ability to perform most daily routines.

100% RAW AND LOVING IT!

Within nine months, the intense days "in the chair" stopped. I am, today, back in the gym lifting weights! This, after my doctors told me that certain nerves were gone and would not heal...and to think I'd once believed them!

Since, at one time, my allergies had been so severe that I couldn't even be around people whose clothing held cat residue, my children were understandably flabbergasted to discover that I now own two cats. (They also eat raw.)

Once, I would spend my summer days looking outside through closed windows: the smell of pollen was sickening. Today, I put my nose directly into flowers and enjoy their aroma!

Since going raw, I haven't had so much as a cold.

I am more in touch with all of my senses, and with my connection to this universe. I am making a huge ecological contribution to this planet. My food choices save on plastic and paper packaging, chemical processing, the fuels needed by the trucking industry, road wear and tear, and on and on and on.

I have been feeding myself only raw and living foods for five years. My body and mind function together, making me more positive, joyful, and enlightened. I have unlimited energy, great strength, youthfulness, and no pain. At age 46, I feel 26. When I tell people I have grown children and three grandchildren, their mouths drop open!

It has been a long road to health. I am so happy to be alive!

"I'D REALLY HIT ROCK BOTTOM."
(CHRISTINE, AGE 37)

I'd really hit rock bottom. As a bridesmaid in my sister's wedding, I'd gained so much weight that the woman at the dressmaker's shop had to sew extra panels into my dress!

I'd seen the dress a year earlier, and thought it was beautiful, especially when I'd imagined it on me as a thin woman. I had determined that I would lose 100 pounds before my sister's wedding. After all, I had a year to do it, and I had that vision of myself looking great in the light blue, satin, bare-shouldered dress.

Well, weeks worth of "I'll start my diet next Monday" came and went, and all of a sudden, it was a year later, and there I was, walking down the aisle in that dress...with the extra panels sewn in.

You see, for quite awhile I had hidden my body pretty successfully under big shirts, and my family and friends really didn't know how really overweight I'd become in the past two years.

The day remains a kind of blur to me, even now. I was numbed by the knowledge that I'd been exposed. My relatives were shocked, and some of them asked my parents what had happened to me.

I'd like to say that I went on a diet the day following the wedding, but I think I pigged out that day at the wedding brunch! I knew I was out of control. *Everyone* knew I was out of control!

I ASKED MY FRIEND ALISSA FOR HELP.

"Please help me," I asked her over long-distance phone calls. At that time, Alissa was living in another state. "I can't do this alone, I've never been this fat!" Finally, she came out to stay with me and help me start my diet.

I'd always wanted to go raw after seeing Alissa do it. She'd inspired me for years, but her way of eating just seemed a little extreme to me. I knew I was a food addict. Could I stick to a diet like this?

The first week was exciting. It was difficult, and I definitely went through food withdrawal. But the energy I felt was immediate! The vitality I felt came with the promise of a future I'd craved for so long!

At 233 pounds, I had no energy. I was tired and exhausted every single day. I socialized and had fun, but it was always in spite of my weight. I would say to myself: "I'm going to dance all night and I don't care what anyone thinks!" I was recently divorced, not dating much. I found once I got over 200 pounds, I became invisible to men.

CHRISTINE BEFORE

A MONTH AND A HALF INTO THE DIET...

... I was jogging every day, sleeping soundly, and waking up with boundless energy. And I'd lost 35 pounds! Yet I was eating so much food! I kept calling Alissa, telling her "I am not going to lose weight! I'm eating too much food!"

But every week I lost weight on the most delicious and satisfying food I'd ever eaten!

The food I'd eaten before starting this diet was delicious too...but in a different way. I was always hungry. No matter how much I ate, the feeling of fullness would go away, and quickly be replaced with insatiable hunger. I was addicted to pizza, bread, cheese, butter, and pasta. Anything high in carbohydrates and high fat, I craved. I was always chasing a high with food that never got satisfied.

After the first week on the raw and living food diet, your taste buds adjust, and you really start tasting and appreciating the incredible flavor of a juicy mango, or a delicious green salad! And the most exciting thing for me was - and still is - that the food is so satisfying. When I'm full, I'm *full*!

The cravings for carbohydrates and fat are gone as long as I stay on this diet. When I go off, they reawaken, and it is very difficult for me to go back to raw. I really think that 100% raw is the best way for me because it keeps me thin, at peace with food and lets me really enjoy my life. I have a capacity for joy in my life that I'd never had before. Everything feels better.

CHRISTINE AFTER

100 POUNDS LATER...

I have now lost over 100 pounds and feel fantastic! For the first time in my life, I feel free of the constant struggle I'd always had with food. My disposition has completely changed, too. I feel happy, and positive, and far better able to deal with any situation that comes into my life. As soon as I would go off of this diet, I would feel that old sadness and depression creeping back into me within a couple of days. I'd feel negatively toward people. I'd feel impatient. Yet within days of getting back on raw food, all of that would disappear.

I thought at first that this was just my imagination, that food could not have that much of an effect on my emotional well-being. But I've tested this out many times...it does!

I am now committed to staying raw. I believe it is the only way to live my life and be as happy as I can possibly be!

HOW I EAT TODAY

Usually for breakfast I eat 3-4 oranges and a couple of bananas. Around mid-morning I'll drink coconut milk. At mid-day, I always have a huge salad with all kinds of greens and veggies: spinach, Swiss chard, kale, tomatoes, mushrooms, onions, carrots, etc. At night, sometimes I'll enjoy a piece of raw pie I've made, such as Blueberry Cheesecake or Banana Carob. I like to eat dessert for dinner! The beauty of this diet, for me, is that I can eat raw desserts and they are better than cooked desserts because they are guilt-free and delicious! Sometimes I'll make some raw lasagna or live hummus and eat that. My diet varies, and I tend to eat lighter, simpler food during the summer.

SPREADING THE WORD

I have shared this diet with family and friends, and most of my family and many of my friends are raw now! It feels so good to be able to give the gift of health to the people you care about! I don't have to do much to convince people to try this diet: in fact, they often approach me. When I see people I haven't seen in awhile, they are astonished at how I look. It's not just the weight loss, but the glow in my face, and then energy they say I project. They also comment on the texture of my skin, which has changed dramatically! I look and feel younger and more vibrant than when I was a teen-ager!

LORETTA BEFORE (far right)

"THE FOUNTAIN OF YOUTH!"
(LORETTA, AGE 71)

I am 71 years old, and although I have always felt younger than my age and have kept active and healthy throughout most of my life, I have often struggled with my weight. For the past 50 years, I have been on and off a lot of diets. And although I

LORETTA AFTER

never had more than 30 pounds to lose, my weight always fluctuated, and it was always a battle to keep the excess pounds off.

So I eventually became resigned to being at least 25 pounds overweight. I also had bursitis in my shoulder, and a varicose vein in my leg that bulged out, becoming increasingly painful and making it difficult for me to even walk.

NOT EXACTLY A "NEW" DIET, BUT STILL...

I have two daughters who have been vegetarians for many years, and had turned to the raw and living food diet. While they each live in states other than mine, they had spoken to me many times about what, and how, they were eating. So, while this diet wasn't new to me, I never thought *I* would want to eat this way. I had a very active social life which revolved a lot around food! My husband and I ate out often, and would go out to eat with friends frequently. I didn't think that I would be able to continue to live my life the way I had been, or keep up my social life if I were on this kind of diet.

Eventually, though, I started to feel worse from my varicose vein, painful shoulder, and extra weight. I started to educate myself more about this diet and talked with my daughters about how they did it. Soon after that, Alissa was in my area. I decided to spend a few days learning how to eat this way. Together, we made delicious meals, and she taught me how to easily incorporate this diet into my daily life.

SUCCESS CAME EASILY!

I couldn't believe how easy this diet was! I can easily keep the social life I am used to, and continue to eat out with friends and family. The changes in my life have been remarkable! It has now been six months. I've lost the 25 pounds and have kept it off, effortlessly! My varicose vein has completely disappeared, and I am lifting weights and walking every morning...without pain! The bursitis hasn't flared up since I started this diet, and I am able to use my shoulder and arm again, without any pain. In fact, my husband and I just took up golfing, and we've been on the links 4-5 days a week!

TURNING BACK THE CLOCK

I feel with this diet I'm turning back the hands of time. I've noticed that the lines in my face are smoothing out, that my skin is glowing and healthy looking, and my hair and nails are growing more. I have more energy than I have had in years, and am feeling younger and younger with every day on this diet. The only way I can describe it is that I feel like I am reversing in age!

HOW I EAT TODAY

I really don't miss eating cooked food at all. I don't even miss my morning coffee! I usually have some fruit in the morning, 4-5 oranges sliced up, grapes, or grapefruit. If I feel hungry around mid-morning, I'll have a banana shake or a smoothie. I usually have a large salad sometime during the day, or some cut up fruit. My favorite meal is portobella mushrooms with avocado topped with Cashew Cream Cheese. I also like to shred zucchini and make a tomato sauce for it: it tastes like spaghetti! I like to make fudge, too. It tastes wonderful when you want something sweet. Sometimes I'll take some fudge or an avocado out with me if I know I'm going to be out for a long time, just in case I get hungry. And sometimes I'll prepare different raw dishes for dinner and serve them to my husband. He doesn't even know they're raw! He just thinks it's some delicious new recipe I've discovered!

NEW TASTE BUDS

A couple of times, after starting this diet, after cooking my husband's dinner, I've succumbed to the aroma of the cooked food and ate some. I felt instantly tired and sluggish...and the cooked food never tasted as good as I'd imagined it would.

Today, I like my raw food much better than that processed,

cooked, dead food! I feel like my taste buds must have been asleep for many years (or poisoned or polluted) to think that cooked food tasted good! This diet has reawakened my sense of smell and taste for all the wonderful, fresh, pure, whole foods that we have on this planet! This diet has given me back my energy, and stamina for so many things in life. I am thinking more clearly, and my memory is so much better now.

Alissa is right. This is the fountain of youth!

"I'VE BECOME MY OWN VISION!" (NANCY, AGE 55)

On New Year's Eve in 1999, I came down with the flu. After running a temperature for two weeks, I was in bed and unable to leave the house for six more. The flu finally went away, but left me still in extreme pain.

I couldn't sleep for more than two hours without waking up, screaming in pain. The smallest of movements were excruciating. After months of testing and doctors, a rheumatologist diagnosed me with sleep apnea, fibromyalgia, severe arthritis, irritable bowel syndrome, herniated disks of the upper spine, and vascular disease.

NANCY BEFORE

HOW COULD THIS BE HAPPENING TO ME???

Before I got sick, I was a jazz dancer, taking lessons daily. I swam thirty minutes a day, jogged regularly, studied Latin dancing, trained in kick boxing, and worked out on a Nordic Track and Cross Trainer. At 40 I placed in a triathlon. In my younger years, I was on the team that broke the long distance medley swimming record and I was the first woman lifeguard on Cape Cod, Massachusetts.

Suddenly, at age 54, I was unable to sleep, work, focus, and was in constant pain. My team of doctors · rheumatologist, sleep specialist, psychiatrist, and neurologist · put me on experimental pain killers that helped me to sleep but reduced very little pain. It also put 20 pounds on me within two

NANCY AFTER

weeks...and I was already 15 pounds overweight since I hadn't been exercising.

My marriage floundered. My husband didn't believe I had fibromyalgia, and kept telling me if I would lose weight I'd be able to walk. Needless to say, with my world falling apart, I became very depressed.

STILL, I TRIED...

I joined *Weight Watchers*, but realized immediately that it wasn't what I needed. Then one day a raw food restaurant opened in my suburban Boston town. I started stopping in quite often. My fingers had swollen to three times their natural size and I could no longer wear my wedding ring. The restaurant owner told me about the advantages of wheat grass and thought it might help. When I drank it, I could immediately feel the circulation return to my hands and feet. Within two weeks, I was able to wear my rings again. The restaurant owner gave me Alissa's card and suggested I contact her.

When I met Alissa, I was 35 pounds overweight, depressed, and in constant pain. Walking was a problem, and my hands had lost most of their strength. Alissa invited me to a seminar planned for the following week. She told me that if I liked what I heard, she would work with me.

100% RAW!

Although my doctor had told me that a change in nutrition would probably not help me, I felt differently. And following the seminar, I decided to go 100% raw!

For me, the hardest thing to give up was coffee. The medication made me cloudy in the morning, and coffee was my crutch. Today, I don't miss it at all.

I began this diet by having huge smoothies in the morning with bananas, berries, and oranges. For lunch I would eat a large salad with dehydrated falafel balls with tahini salad dressing, sun burgers, or hummus, and a shot of wheat grass. For dinner, I would have the leftover falafel, or some Nut Loaf,

Curried Carrot Soup, or a tomato or mushroom soup. I would snack on fruit, dates, raisins, almonds, and dried papaya. By eating this way for the first couple of months, I lost some weight and started to feel better.

REGAINING CONTROL...AND HOPE

Soon, I was able to walk more than 15 minutes without feeling severe pain. Just last week, I walked around Boston for 35 minutes, sat down for a minute to rest, and then walked another 35 minutes. My husband was amazed!

The next day I gardened and organized my outdoor furniture.

Alissa suggested that I cut out some of the dehydrated foods, a lot of the oil, and some of the nuts I'd been eating. My food portions had been gigantic. Because I used to work out 2-3 hours each day, I never gained weight and was accustomed to eating large quantities. And, let's face it, I've got an addictive personality. Coming from a family of foodaholics, my tendency is to eat when depressed and to use food to fill up loneliness.

HOW I EAT TODAY

I eat fruit for breakfast: a papaya, grapefruit, oranges, or bananas. For lunch, I enjoy large salads with guacamole and a shot of wheat grass. My dinner menu usually consists of soups and salad, with some hummus, burgers, or avocado slices. Sometimes I make avocado, tomato, and sprout sandwiches on flax crackers, or I may just have a green drink. If I snack, it's on fruits, juices, and sometimes a raw dessert.

Before going raw I was always hungry and grazing on food. On this diet I feel completely satisfied. I've lost the rest of the weight I wanted to lose, and am back to doing so many of the things I'd thought I had lost forever. I spend hours in my garden, take long bike rides every morning, and practice yoga. I go out with friends, socialize, and in general, am having a great time. I drive from the Boston-area to New York to see my family, and the five-hour drive causes me no pain at all!

Just before I'd gotten sick, I received a brand new set of skis. Finally, just last week, I was able to actually use them!

My body is healing, and my mind is so much clearer. I am so grateful to God for connecting me to Alissa. She has such a charismatic personality. Her firm but kind guidance has been incredible. Her essence is pure and sincere. Her smile lights up any room. Alissa has taught me to have a vision: one of health and hope. That vision is who I am today: a happy, hope-filled, positive person who is no longer depressed and in pain, but enjoying life to the fullest.

"MY RAW TRANSFORMATION" (SHAZZIE, AGE 31)

Being brought up in the north of England in the 1970s, I was full of white bread, meat, chips (fries) and a bit more meat.

SHAZZIE BEFORE

SHAZZIE AFTER

Living in my own dream world, I ate very little of what was put in front of me as it tasted disgusting. I often fantasized about the bananas which where rationed by my mum as they were so expensive. Mum was so worried that I wasn't eating correctly that she made me take a thick green multi-vitamin and mineral liquid. Ugh, mum!

AS A TEENAGER

I became a vegetarian when I was 16, just after realizing that pain and suffering isn't a great thing to inflict on our animals and that karma is probably for real. As I stopped eating meat I started eating cheese, cheese and more cheese (as well as crackers and pasta). Although I didn't feel any worse on this diet, it just didn't feel right and I couldn't live on it for long.

A year later I gave up eggs, and then I finally managed to give up milk. I desperately wanted to be a vegan for ethical reasons but had to overcome the cheese addiction. I managed it two years after first turning vegetarian.

AS AN ADULT

I slipped in and out of depression, was a bit of a hermit, found myself a social life, danced a lot and, at the age of 25, started drinking alcohol. My diet remained vegan, but as more vegan convenience foods were being developed (soya cheese, soya meat, burgers, grills, etc.), my diet became worse. Eventually, most of the food I ate came out of tins or packets.

EVERYTHING STARTED DETERIORATING

As my mental and physical health deteriorated I kept bumping into living foods. But it wasn't the right time for my heart to embrace this way of life. I was obviously not prepared for the massive changes it would impose on my life. I wasn't ready to meet my power.

Coming from weak stock, I'd always felt that I was runt-like. But as time went on I started to find survival on a day-to-day basis increasingly difficult. I:

Was constantly tired: unable to sleep, but then unable to wake, felt jet-lagged all the time;

Had colds and flu: I had always suffered two week stretches of colds or flu about 4 or 6 times a year;

Was emotionally unbalanced and depressed with feelings of hurt, anger and disappointment, very apathetic;

Had difficulty breathing, a really runny nose, cellulite, was overweight, whole right-hand side ached, cystitis;

Had a short attention span (daydreamer), difficulty under-standing simple stuff such as left and right and map reading;

Felt that people took my energy and I was powerless to stop it, and felt exhausted by the presence of some. I also felt the pain of others so much it hurt. I leaked my energy and absorbed the energy of others in totally inappropriate ways.

After gradually putting on weight over the years, there was now a surprising 11 stone (154 pounds) of me struggling to fit into size 12 (UK) clothes. I flatly refused to ever buy a size 14 - that would mean I'd been defeated. I had a permanent frown, my face was baggy and puffy - in fact, I was puffy and squashy all over. Internally I was no better - I had a pulse of about 90 and my blood pressure had started creeping up. I wondered how I'd got like that, and whether it was my destiny. I thought about most other women, and how overweight they are - and thought maybe that's just what happens to you as you get older. At the age of 29 everything was heading south - my skin, my chin and my spirits.

I HIT ROCK BOTTOM

Work was taking its toll on me, I had a permanent pain in my stomach which I'm sure was an ulcer, I always wanted to throw up, and most days I could only eat boiled rice with vegetables.

One day towards the end of a very stressful year, I think I had a nervous breakdown - how exactly do you know when you won't go to the doctor? I even resigned from my job (which I didn't end up leaving). Nothing was right. Yes, I had a nice house, a lovely boyfriend, a well-paying job, some very dear friends and a family who loved me, but nothing was right. Why, when I had so much, did I have so little inside? Why was my heart and spirit so empty? I didn't even understand how these problems were real - after all, I wasn't in a wheelchair or an asylum, but I truly felt like the world had ended. I couldn't get any lower. One day I was standing in the car park at work crying and my boyfriend at the time said that he couldn't take much more of this, he didn't know how to help me. The truth was, I couldn't take any more either. I gave myself a good talking to: "Either do something about this state of your life or kill yourself. You are not going to continue living like this any longer."

Well, I didn't kill myself...

I FOUND WHAT I WAS LOOKING FOR

Shortly after that time I read many health books which gradually put me on more and more raw and unprocessed food whilst simultaneously reducing coffee and wheat. At work I went on confidence and assertiveness courses. I also had reflexology, lots of massages, acupuncture and osteopathy. These positive actions did me so much good. This very tight ball of wool was slowly beginning to be unraveled. I went on a diet and lost some of the bulk which I'd been carrying. For the first time in my life, things were looking up. I'd tasted life and I wanted more.

A BOOK CHANGED MY LIFE

Then my boyfriend bought me a book about eating all raw. I read it while we were in Scotland, and as I turned every page my jaw just kept hitting the floor. I was blown away by the information in that book. At last I was reading something that made complete sense to me. It was telling me what I had always felt but I could never make sense of before.

The one thing that stands out in the book is the final sentence at the end of each chapter: "Cooked food is poison." As soon as I saw it, I knew that was it: I was being poisoned! No wonder I felt like I was dying. I was toxic since before I was even conceived, even since before my mum was conceived! Every cell in my body was made up of substandard material and with these shaky foundations there was no wonder I'd been crumbling.

I WENT RAW

I immediately went raw. I first of all noticed my skin turn so soft and spot free. Facial lines disappeared, the tone of my skin became more even. I lost a lot of weight and friends thought I had an eating disorder, but I'd never felt better. I had a real lust for life and wanted to do something with my new-found energy.

I was ready for more change, and now strong enough to want new challenges! I started my own design company,

Rawcreation Ltd. (www.rawcreation.com), and did lots of rebranding work for "The Fresh Network," the UK raw food network. I made so many new friends because I'd documented my transition on my web site (www.shazzie.com).

I started practicing Astanga yoga, which helped with all the spiritual changes I was going through, as well as giving me tummy muscles to die for!

I put some weight back on after at the end of this year, and people stopped telling me that I was too thin. My diet consisted of many smoothies, salads, fruit and sometimes a few more complicated recipes. I was in love with durian, bananas, persimmons and figs. I desperately wanted to be out in nature as often as possible, and often left my desk just to go and run through a near-by meadow. I sensed freedom for the first time in my life. I could breathe!

IN THE SECOND YEAR

I stopped the world. I was just a bit dizzy from all my changes and needed to get to know myself again. I moved to Spain and spent days, weeks and months painting, lying by the pool in the sun, meditating, practicing yoga. I loved living there, on my own, overlooking the mountains and orange groves. The feelings of being raw deepened, it was now part of me, not just something I do. All floaty feelings disappeared. I started to feel more grounded, more at peace with myself and the world. I became tolerant of others, and found love in everything. I wrote "Shazzie's Detox Delights" -100 raw recipes based on my first raw 6 months.

Much of my life was spent living in the sun, often wild and free, skinny-dipping in rivers, and tasting the ocean each time as if it was the first. I was a walking meditator totally dedicated to a cause: getting my life back. I ate much more seasonally than the year before, and loved the Spanish oranges, melons, cherimoyas, persimmons and figs.

IN THE THIRD YEAR

Well, this is where the story ends, as I'm only just beginning my third year. I wonder how it can be more fantastic than the last two, but I know it will be. Life for me, as a raw girl, is on an upward spiral of love, devotion, happiness, joy, open-heartedness and maybe a bit more love.

WAS IT REAL?

I can't fully remember how I used to feel. The aches and pains, the need to sleep during the day, the fear of waking up are all replaced by the exact opposite: I feel so young and flexible, my sleeping patterns are totally regular, and I love new mornings with new challenges. Within my first raw year, my life turned into a fantasy life - wishes come true every day. That poor girl who suffered for so many years is long gone, she's at peace now: nobody is her enemy and she's safe. She's home.

"THE CONSTANT STRUGGLE WAS WEARING ME OUT." (SHEILA, 47)

I'd tried every possible way to get rid of my severe sinusitis. I was beginning to resign myself to the fact that I would have to live with the brutal migraines and the stuffed up nose that went along with it. I was also overweight, desperately trying to stay in my size 12 pants and not move up to a size 14.

The constant struggle was wearing me out. I had a bad knee that kept me from exercising, and that was one of the excuses I would use not to lose weight. At age 46, I didn't think that my physical body would improve, or that my mental outlook about getting older and sicker would change.

THEN ALISSA CAME TO VISIT

And everything was different after that!

Alissa was in Florida giving a seminar. After looking at the

SHEILA BEFORE

before and after pictures of the people she had helped, and after hearing what she had to say, and after tasting the raw food she'd prepared, something inside me told me that I needed to give this a try...or miss out on a huge opportunity.

I'm not one for diets. Actually, I've never really dieted. I have a family, a husband who is a big meat-and-potatoes person, and a very busy job that leaves me little time for cooking, or even thinking about food. After hearing how quick and easy this diet is, and tasting how delicious the food was, I figured I could fit it into my lifestyle. I worked with Alissa for a few days, learning how to prepare different meals, and learning about the diet. It all seemed so simple! I couldn't believe that this diet could do all that she claimed. Boy was I surprised!

HOW I EAT TODAY

I usually have a banana shake in the mornings, which takes all of 2 minutes to whip up. I'll take a bunch of fruit with me to work. At lunchtime, I'll have a huge salad with avocado, and sometimes the leftovers from the night before, such as a dessert, or the rest of a raw meal. For dinner, I'll make some raw pasta, Eggplant Pizza, Mock Tuna, Cabbage Rolls, Sushi, or some soup. These are all quick meals, taking only minutes to prepare. I'm always throwing together a raw dessert, as these also only take a few minutes to make. Once in awhile, I'll make other dishes, such as meatloaf, crackers, chips, and other dehydrated goodies. These are also very quick and easy to make, but need to stay in the dehydrator overnight. I try to keep it simple, and eat a lot of fruit and salads, but never feel deprived because I can always whip up something for lunch or dinner that satisfies me. When I first started, and even now, the fact that I can eat dessert and snacks keeps me from feeling like I'm on a diet at all!

SHEILA AFTER

NO MORE SINUSITIS!

Within three months, I went from a size 12 to a size 7, eating all the food I wanted to eat, like Ice Cream Sundaes, Apple Pie, and Chocolate Mousse! My excruciating knee pain completely disappeared. I'm rollerblading and biking with my daughter again, after years of giving all that up, and I'm feeling more positive and happy about my life and where it's going. But best of all · and almost unbelievable to me · is the fact that I no longer suffer from migraines, a stuffed up nose, or any symptoms from the sinusitis I'd been living with for the past 10 years!

This diet has given me back my life! Instead of feeling like I'm declining with age, I feel like I'm getting younger and healthier every day! I have lost weight before, but have never looked so healthy. My skin is smooth, and, I swear, it's tighter and firmer than before.

Alissa's abundance of energy and zest for life is contagious. I never thought I could be like that, but she has shown me that anyone can obtain the radiance she possesses. Through eating a raw and living food diet, anything is possible. I truly believe that!

"THANKS, MOM!" (JOHN, AGE 12)

I had allergies for a number of years. Then I transitioned to raw foods, and my allergies are gone 100%.

I had hay fever, and was horribly allergic to pollen and even dust. I had to have a special air filter just to be able to sleep. Every spring and fall I had a runny nose, sneezing fits, and watery, itchy eyes. After awhile I would develop a hacking cough. But now with raw foods I don't have those symptoms anymore.

My mom was doing raw foods for her own health reasons, and she tried to transfer them to my diet a little bit at a time, like sneaking avocados into my smoothies: bleeeeeech!!!

Then she tried out some recipes on me from her raw food books. We found some that I really liked (and some I really disliked). After awhile of being 50% raw, my palate changed more, and I wasn't as addicted to cooked foods.

I heard about other people's success with the raw diet. At first I thought it was all a crackpot thing. But this made me think it was really real. And then I changed to 70% raw by adding more raw into the meals I already ate. Here's an example:

I loved angel hair wheat pasta with tomato sauce and tofu. We used raw zucchini pasta instead of the wheat pasta. Then eventually I realized I didn't feel good with the tofu. So after awhile we took out the tofu and made the sauce raw also. We took other meals that I normally ate and replaced them, too, like with raw "pizza," raw hummus, raw "tuna," Sun Crackers, and Sunflower Seed Pâté.

HOW I EAT TODAY

Here are common meals for me.

For breakfast: fruit and "chocolate" (raw carob) smoothies, with hemp seeds, avocado, or young coconut; or soaked oat groats blended for "oatmeal" with cashew milk.

For lunch: fruit and nut salads, and Apple Crisp.

For snacks: Raw Banana Raisin Cookies, Raw Fudge, and fresh fruit

For dinner: the things mentioned earlier, and raw guacamole, all with a salad and raw olives.

I make sure I always have something raw and good with me when pizza and candy are around. When people see my unusual meals, at first they think it's very strange. But after they taste the food, they think that I am very lucky that I get to eat this way.

When people ask me what I eat and why I eat this way, I tell them what I am allergic to, and they say: "What do you eat if you don't eat wheat, sugar, dairy, and chocolate?"

But there is so much good food to eat on this diet! On the

raw food diet, I feel much better. I am more able to do my sports, and my athletic abilities and stamina are stronger. I am so glad that I didn't go on medication and other drugs and that I found this healthier way to live!

"I WANTED A LIFE CHANGE" (LEO, AGE 34)

I started the raw and living food diet because I wanted a life change. I saw the results my sister had with it and was amazed: losing 75 pounds in four months! I'd ballooned up to 265 pounds and felt awful. I'd lost weight before, but couldn't seem to keep it off. I was finding it very hard just to get out of

LEO BEFORE

bed in the morning. Simple tasks, like playing with my children, were a lot harder with all that excess weight. I didn't even feel like going out at night, because I didn't feel good about myself. I realized that I didn't need a diet: I needed to change my lifestyle. I decided to go raw.

TWO MONTHS LATER...

In two months, I've lost 30 pounds and I feel fantastic! My energy level has never been higher. I work out 3-5 days a week, and my workouts have never gone better. I seem to have boundless energy when I do cardiovascular exercise, and I can lift weights without any pain the next day. I bounce out of bed in the morning, ready for action, because I'm not weighed down by all the bread and pasta I used to eat.

SOMETHING WONDERFUL

When you go raw, your body transforms itself into something wonderful. You can see a glow in the face of anyone who's raw. I believe you see this glow, because this is the way God meant for us to eat. God didn't put cooked food in the Garden of Eden. He put fresh fruit and vegetation!

LEO AFTER

   I haven't been sick all year. I like people more than I used to. I want to socialize more, because I've got all this special energy I'm receiving from the live enzymes in raw and living food.

A NATURAL HIGH

You actually feel naturally high with this diet. I'm now one of the top salespeople in the country for the large corporation I work for, and the way I feel right now has played a big part in my success. I feel good about myself, which is the first step to success!

   A lot of the guys at work made fun of all the fruits and vegetables I was eating at my desk when I first started this diet. Now, a lot of them are doing it with me! I am continuing to lose weight quickly, and look forward to losing all my excess weight. But I'm not planning to go off this diet when I reach that goal.

Because this is no longer a diet. It's my way of life!

"A NEW LEASE ON LIFE" (MARIANNE, AGE 59)

The raw and living food diet has given me a new lease on life. At age 59, I found myself with post-menopausal weight gain I no longer wanted. As an acupuncturist and holistic health practitioner, the idea of eating enzyme-rich raw and living food sounded logical to me.

Alissa's encouragement, along with the varied and delicious recipes she provided, made my transition to raw and living food easy and fun. I began most days with a large blended fruit smoothie, at least 20 ounces. I found it was fulfilling, and sat-

MARIANNE BEFORE

MARIANNE AFTER

isfied my appetite all morning. I would often have a large vegetable salad for lunch, sometimes with guacamole or raw pâté. I would keep bananas, apples, carrots, celery, and some pecans and cashews in my office in case I got hungry or worked late. I never really needed much else.

When I first began this diet, I ate more than I do now. I realize that my body was cleansing and learning to regulate itself at the same time. I also found that I was waking up a few times during the night, then going back to sleep. After two weeks, I was sleeping soundly and waking easily each morning, raring to go! I was ready to exercise and to begin my workday with renewed ambition.

WONDERFUL CHANGES!

Within a few weeks, I noticed that my skin was smoother and that the weight was melting off. My necklace lines (the deep creases at the front of my neck) were disappearing. My eyes had lost their puffiness. My eyesight improved. The whole world looked brighter, and, as a great plus, my cellulite was melting away. I was thrilled!

Energy and stamina I'd thought I lost forever came back. Three months after I went raw, my husband and I went to a party and I ended up dancing all night. My husband had to sit down and rest, but I never even felt tired! It was wonderful!

Within a few months I'd lost 25 pounds, and have kept it off for over a year. I look younger, and feel younger. I no longer have to pull myself up off the couch: I bounce right up! The raw and living food diet is truly a gift that I will always be grateful for.

"AFTER FIVE MONTHS RAW" (RACHEL, AGE 31)

After years of compulsive overeating, yo-yo dieting and trying probably every fad diet out there, I finally stumbled across the

RACHEL BEFORE

raw foods movement. At the time, I was suffering from gall-stone symptoms, and was on a quest to learn how to naturally alleviate the pain, and rid my body of the stones.

Thankfully, someone introduced me to raw foods while on this quest to heal myself!

I had never heard of anyone living solely on raw, living foods. Intrigued, I read as much as I could find on the topic. While gathering information, I came across Alissa's website (www.alissacohen.com). I e-mailed her to tell her that I wanted to be on her "before and after" page someday, when I had an "after" picture to send her. She sent me a kind reply, telling me she would gladly post my "before and after" pictures, as long as I lost my weight on raw and living foods. The seed was planted!

I so badly wanted to rid myself of the symptoms I was suffering. In my late twenties, I felt like an old woman. I struggled with many minor but irritating health issues, including: psoriasis, bursitis in my hip, lower back pain, pain in the gallbladder area, daily acid reflux, insomnia, panic attacks, shortness of breath after minor exertion, a feeling of pressure in my head like it was going to burst, tenderness in my legs (they hurt if even touched lightly), and my weight of 263 pounds. Many of these symptoms scared me. And I was really tired of being fat!

THE STRUGGLE TO STAY RAW

Yet, I simply could not stay on raw foods for any length of time. None of my health problems or the strong desire to heal myself were compelling enough to keep me raw. I tried - and failed - several times. I would eat raw for a month or so, and my symptoms would disappear. I would wake up without the bloated feeling I'd become so accustomed to. My face wouldn't be swollen like it was when I was eating junk food. My feet didn't hurt when I took my first few steps after waking up in the morning. I was needing less sleep and gaining more energy.

Needless to say, every time I went raw I was encouraged by the results. But then, at some point, I would feel that I just *had* to eat something cooked!

And, after succumbing to cooked food, I wouldn't even want to *look* at raw food for days. The thought of eating raw actually made me angry!

The great feelings I had while eating raw foods immediately left me after I ate cooked food. And I would quickly regain the weight I had lost. I had been an emotional eater since high school · maybe even before. I was addicted to junk food and to cooked food. I believe my past relationship with food so strongly influenced me, that I could not easily break my habits and make such a drastic change in lifestyle.

THE SOLUTION: "RAW IN PROCESS!"

Finally, after a year and a half of trying raw foods and failing, I contacted Alissa again. I wrote that I was going to try once more, and repeated my hope to one day be on her "Before and After" page. I had no idea how I would achieve it, but I was determined to become one of her success stories.

She wrote back with a fabulous idea: "Raw in Process!" I would send her a "before" picture that she would post on her website, and follow up by sending another picture of myself each month. I could also send her a journal if I wanted to.

I was so excited! This was just the motivation I needed to go for it! I would have accountability with Alissa (and, incidentally, all the people who visited her site each day).

The accountability factor really has been key to being able to stay raw for any length of time. My family and friends also continue to give me much encouragement and support. I now realize how beneficial a support network is!

I never could have imagined being raw for even one month, much less five. Thanks to Alissa, I now feel I can be raw for life! I'm not "there" yet, but I've made such progress! In just over 5 months, I have lost 65 pounds and have gone from size 22-24 to a size 14-16. The weight is falling off, and most of the symptoms I mentioned earlier are gone. The only stubborn

RACHEL AFTER

problem is the psoriasis on my scalp...although, there too, the scalp patches are starting to go away. The psoriasis on other areas of my body is totally gone.

Now, I have so much to look forward to in life! Eating raw and living foods is enabling me to achieve a dream I have had to do sacred dance again. Doors are opening in life that would have remained shut, had I not followed this path.

I am so thankful to God for His love for me; to my family and friends for their enthusiastic support; and to Alissa for all of her encouragement on this journey to life in The Raw!

Note from Alissa: I've included portions of Rachel's unedited journal here. I hope you enjoy following her journey. She's an inspiration to me, and to the many people who visit my website.

RACHEL'S WEB JOURNAL (EXCERPTS)

DAY 2 I found my ankle bones tonight! I haven't been able to see them for months at least, probably longer. The swelling is going down after only two raw days. Amazing! Tonight I had a major headache.

- Juice of several kale leaves, 1 lime and 2 green apples
- 2 flax seed candies
- 1 avocado w/juice of a lemon
- 3 bananas
- handful kumquats
- a dab of cashew butter w/honey
- couple of soaked almonds
- a tomato

DAY 4 I know I shouldn't, but I get on the scale every day. I can't believe I have already dropped 8 pounds in 4 days! No headache today. My body is getting rid of mucous.

- Juice of 5 carrots and 1 apple
- 1 cracker with veggie dip
- part of a cherimoya (I let it get too ripe! Drat!)

- 3 more crackers
- 2 bananas
- a bunch of crackers with the veggie dip and a tomato
- a bite of cookie
- more crackers with cashew butter

DAY 9 Had a busy day out of the house, not too much time to think about eating. I actually managed to have 3 meals today. I normally just eat a little here and there throughout the day. I'm not necessarily going for the 3 meals a day thing. Who made that up anyway?! Felt full for a long time after my salad at lunch, probably because I ate some olives, oh yeah, I just remembered the mushrooms! As soon as I say I don't want to eat a certain food, there I go eating it! Funny. They were the little marinated mushrooms (mm) and I ate plenty of them (10-15??) (I still can't think about eating plain mushrooms!) The olives (and probably the mm) have lots of salt which I am avoiding just fine at home. OK, I m going to try and avoid the olives and mm next time I eat out. I don t want the salt, plus I'm not sure the olives are raw anyway. No headache today. Had some very mild acid reflux, I think from the salad today. I just drank some extra water. It was nothing like the acid reflux I would get before going raw.

- Juice of 5-6 carrots and 1 apple
- Big salad at souper! salads w/oil and vinegar (romaine lettuce, spinach, grn and blk olives, mm, red onion, cucumber, radish etc.)
- 3 valencia oranges w/a lg handful of walnuts (this was YUMMY together!)

DAY 10 I had an earache today in my left ear. Are all these detox symptoms?

- 2 bananas
- 1 avocado wrapped in an untoasted nori sheet

- 3 valencia oranges with 1 handful of walnuts
- pine nuts (a tablespoon??)
- a mango
- a few nibbles of recipes I am making/dehydrating for tomorrow

DAY 11 Alissa, I sure am feeling very grateful for you today! Just wanted you to know that I am beginning to feel the temptations! We had dinner with a friend tonight and our apartment is totally wrecked because we are packing and are moving in a few days. So, we ate out at the pool. Hubby grilled hamburgers. (I am not quite ready to present a raw meal to company, but that will come in time!) I had bought chips for them to eat. One of my downfalls is Cheetos. I will have to get that bag out of the house. It was a weird feeling to have to exercise control over my body to not reach out for those chips! I felt like something outside myself was going to cause me to eat the Cheetos. Isn't that how I've always been, though. Letting outside influences define my behavior? Someone "makes" me mad (it's really MY choice to get mad or not) and I eat. I feel disappointed, I eat. I feel happy, I eat. Do I ever just work through my feelings without eating? That is my goal! I have let FOOD define me, EATING define me, FAT define me. It's no wonder I feel so powerless! I have given away so much authority over myself, not only to people, but to things. God, help me. I do want to be free from this! I feel like I am strength training right now, that I am building up the muscles of self control. It scared me a little how much I wanted those chips, but I don't have to feel scared! No one is forcing me to eat them! I am in control. I also have started trying to think differently about food in general, how it is supposed to taste, look, smell etc. I want to wash my mind of the cooked ways and expectations! Part of this is from trying to make recipes that are supposed to resemble a cooked item. It's most always a disappointment to me when I eat it because even though it may be good, it tastes or feels nothing like what it was supposed to resemble. Like mayon-naise, for example. I tried a recipe in a raw book for mayo. It was tasty but NOT mayo, not even fake mayo! Then I think, well why do I want to eat mayo anyway? I don't need it! The best part about the dehydrated food I ate tonight was the fresh, living food I put with it, like the sliced tomatoes and the romaine lettuce. Now to what I ate today! I had dehydrated a some stuff from one of my books. It was time consuming and worth it. I suppose! I had made provision for myself to have my raw food at dinner and I'm glad I did that. My dinner was very filling and satisfying. It was a lot of work though and I want to eat simpler. It's fun to try new things though!

- frozen blueberries

- 1 banana

- a small dehydrated nut patty with the sauce I made to go with it.

- raw sandwich made from dehydrated grains, etc., for the bread, nut patty for the "meat", tomatoes, lettuce, pickle slices, and the mayo made from pureed veggies, nuts and spices.

DAY 13 I realized today that I feel so much more at peace on raw foods. I was having some symptoms in my body before going raw and they have left. I felt that something was not right with my heart but I could have been having panic attacks. Didn't know which one. But, I am not having them now and I don't even worry about my heart now. I feel the problems were food related anyway. I no longer have the intense pounding in my chest from overeating junk. I just generally feel lighter! Another thing I realized today is that it is nearly impossible to overeat raw foods. My body seems to know when to stop eat-ing. I get a really strong signal and this is a new thing for me! I never got that satisfied feeling eating junk food. I'm liking eating this way more and more every day!

- salad with oil and vinegar, walnut pieces

- pine nuts (small amt-1 T maybe??)
- a goo of 6 dates mixed with sesame seeds and honey
- grape tomatoes with some rinsed capers (I didn't enjoy the capers like I did before I went raw. I'm going to toss them!)

DAY 17 Had a very hard day today with cravings. Kidneys still ache.

- juice of 6-8 carrots and 1 apple
- Strawberry/blueberry smoothie with almonds, water and honey
- (I can't find where I wrote what else I ate on this day, if I did eat more. I'm sure I did since I was having cravings!)

DAY 23 Good day! Had a dream last night that I ate fried chicken from the bone! It happened twice in my dream. Again, I was SO glad I was only dreaming! I don't know why I dreamed of chicken—I hate eating chicken off the bone-it grosses me out!

- few bites pineapple
- few baby carrots in Avo-Walnut Dip
- slice of dehydrated veggie (can't remember the name!) in avo-wal dip
- 1 olive
- 1 romaine leaf w/Avo-Walnut Dip
- avo-dip with carrots
- watermelon
- few bites chopped tomatoes
- 8 jal. stuffed olives
- avo-wal dip (it's gone now :)
- nibbles of recipes for the dehydrator
- few oatmeal cookies
- walnuts in honey and cinnamon

DAY 24 Had such a moody day today! Not peaceful at all. I should have started my period today but didn't. Not surprised with the drastic changes my body must be going through.

- Juice of beet, beet greens, bit of ginger, celery, red pear and more stuff I can't remember.
- pine nuts
- few walnuts
- 1 oatmeal cookie
- 4 olives
- avo mayo dip with flax "bread" YUM!

DAY 27 Struggling with thoughts of the future. Will I be able to stay raw? I'm scared that after I lose weight I will be tempted to revert to my old ways. For now, I'll quit worrying and and take it one day at a time!

- some watermelon
- 2 oatmeal cookies

MONTH 2, DAY 29
Total pounds lost: 22
Inches lost from: neck (-1/4), arm (-1/2), bust (-1), waist (-1 1/2), hips (-1 3/4), thigh (-1 1/4)

I weigh 241. So I lost 22 lbs in a month! I am fighting off discouragement after seeing my 1 month pics. I can't wait till my arms hang straight down beside my body!
Pretty uneventful day.

- Plums for 2 meals (6 in all)
- Guacamole for dinner
- 2 jal. stuffed olives
- 10 or so black olives

DAYS 34-35 Too busy to log my eating. I did stay raw which did build discipline in me. This is the first time I have been away from home for a few days since going raw. There were plenty of times I wanted to eat junk. I did stock up on black olives, which I love. So that helped. I also successfully burned myself out on them and I consider that a good thing! The thing that helped me stay raw, besides of course being on this Raw in Process page, was having plenty of fresh fruit, veggies, raw nuts and dried fruits available to me. I had NO excuse to eat anything but raw! On the last day, we ate at Joe's Crabshack and I asked for a special salad. The waiter was so pleased with the salad he had told the chef to make as well as being pleased that I liked it! That was cute. I didn't t feel intimidated by all the women on the beach who had beautiful bodies. I felt at peace knowing I would be there someday! Also my max size was 24. That was my largest size jeans. Now I can fit into 18-20 and that is a happy feeling. I was bummed after my 1 mo pics, but I went to Alissa's site and looked at my pics side by side and could see a difference. I didn't get to this weight in a month!! I'm feeling the strength today to stay in it for the long haul. I give many thanks to God and to Alissa for helping me on this journey.

DAY 39 We went to our dear friend Diane's house for dinner. She was so sweet to have raw food for me! It is a great feeling to have support of friends on this journey. I am into my size 18 jeans. When I started this 39 days ago, I was in size 24 jeans! Wow. I have inquired about sacred dance classes. This is something that is in my heart to do; I used to dance when I was smaller. I am excited about dancing again! Classes start in Sept and the great thing is that I know I will be able to dance unselfconsciously by then! I feel like I am beginning to enter life's arena. I have been an observer way too long.

- Peach smoothie with walnut milk
- Dehydrated zucchini and yellow squash chips dipped in nut butter

- 3 green olives (I am finally burned out on them! Woohoo!)
- watermelon, few slices kiwi
- salad w/lemon juice for dressing
- blueberries

DAY 47 Great day! Nice to feel un-obsessed with food for a change.

- green soup with pine nuts
- nut/date bars
- a few pickled peppers, a pickle, some sliced jalapenos
- taste of seed cheese

WEEK 8, DAY 50
Total Pounds Lost: 30
Total Inches Lost: 13.25

We are on vacation now with hubby's family. All carnivores (omnivores, technically) of course. This should be an interesting trip! I got in a hot tub for awhile and was so amazed at how I felt. Back in Oct. when I was a junk food junkie and carnivore, the whole 9 yards, we house-sat for a family with a hot tub. I got in for a short time and felt SO ill. It took till morning for me to feel normal again. I was so pleased to be able to stay in this hot tub for awhile and feel nothing but great!

- Banana
- Salsa and guac (for 2 meals)
- A few bites of a raw nut meal bar

DAY 52 Had an amazing experience at a steak and seafood restaurant. The only thing I could order on the menu was a guacamole-pico de gallo salad with crab. The waitress insisted they had to bring the crab out since I was paying for it. I told her I did not want it in my face. She said Oh no, it will be on the side. She didn't get it I guess! She said someone else might want it! Anyway, I made sure to tell her I wanted nothing cooked in my salad. She seemed to finally get it. When she brought it out, there was a tiny mound of guac and pico on romaine lettuce. But it was covered in white stuff! She could tell I was eyeing the dish and she quickly pointed out there was no crab meat in the dish. I said, but what is this white stuff? Dressing? She said yes and I told her I could not eat this, I don't eat anything cooked. So I refused the dish. She semi-frantically told me she could do anything I needed to make the dish edible. I didn't think she could and told her I just would-n't eat and it was OK. Then my nephew said, don't you get sick if you don't eat? I had almost had it by then and answered an adamant NO. He said, Well, I do. The waitress was very nosey, curious I mean, and asked me questions about my diet almost every time she came to the table! Normally this would be fine; I like telling people about the raw foods diet. But she did not want to know for information sake. She kept asking stupid questions like can't you eat meat? It was clear that I was caus-ing her pain by not eating meat! I told her I'd rather be skinny and eat raw foods than eat meat. She pointed to her slim self and said I eat meat! Well, yea for her! I don't think she has ever been 263 pounds. Then my MIL said, oh, she will again when she gets to where she wants to be. HAHA! Whatever. The waitress kept making comments about how it was torture for me to see all the wonderful food around me. Admittedly, some of the food did look good, but it was not torture. I was hungry though!! My family kept asking me if I wanted their food. I would have had some of the salad, but it already was drenched in dressing! One member said, do you want my broc-coli? It's barely steamed! Another offered me their kale leaf garnish! HAHA ·

- 2 nectarines
- 2 bananas ·
- fruit/seed/nut mix
- guac and salsa w/pico de gallo and lettuce

Day 53 We drove home today. I can tell I had stuffed some resentment over my family being so weirded out about my eating. I got a little aggressive in a conversation and immediately realized that I was not really angry about the subject at hand, but about everyone's questions and attitudes about eating this way. Once my (skinny) SIL made a comment about how I was starving myself. Then hubby said, she eats all the time! Like that made it better! Haha! My family really was not that bad about it and their questions were sincere. I just got tired of the questions and comments. Do you eat oils? Do you want an ice cream, oh, I forgot you can't have that. Are you getting full enough on fruits and vegetables? I could never do that, I don't have the self discipline and on and on. They all suffer allergies and other physical ailments and it was frustrating for me to know that they would keep on relying on meds to cope. They are not open to changing their habits. I did not even try to convince anyone to try raw foods. I didn't see the point.

- Fruit/nut/seed mix
- Salsa w/guac, jalapenos, lettuce and pico de gallo
- Few olives
- Few bites of a raw brownie
- Essene bread in olive oil

DAY 56 Today was a heavenly raw day! I tried 4 new recipes and 3 of them were awesome! I made a Berry Pie, cinnamon rolls and a mush resembling the flavor of taco meat. This is a great thing for a former SAD eater. A new friend who read my journal said it looked like I don't eat very much. I explained to her that part of being kind to myself and being grace-based (vs performance-based) on the raw diet is that I don't force myself to write down exactly how much I eat every day or when I eat it. That would totally stress me out. Maybe it is too reminiscent of those Weight Watcher days!!! ARG!!!! I really do eat till I am satisfied. And today, after these new recipes, I thought, How will I stop eating this? It's SO good! But I found that the meal made of a mixture of raw foods (like the taco mush) has the same ability as the mono meal to trigger satiety. Yea!

- 6-7 olives (at 3AM !)
- about 8 olives (at about 3PM)
- a bowl of taco mush with guacamole
- a cinnamon roll
- a piece of Berry Pie
- about 8 olives

DAY 58 At different times today I felt like I was having to remind myself not to reach out and grab some cooked food (non-food). It was weird. We had company and so lots of cooked food and junk was easily accessible. I stuck with my food and do not feel deprived. I am loving how energetic and generally good I feel. Also, as an aside, my cholesterol in May 2002, after 2 or 3 weeks raw, was 123! In October 2001, my cholesterol was 222!

- Carrot/kale juice
- Piece of Essene bread with olive oil
- Taste of seed cheese
- Bowl of salsa with guac and pine nuts
- More pine nuts (total for the day prob about 1/8 cup or so)
- Small piece of Berry Pie
- Nibbles of Essene bread and olive oil
- Salad with seed cheese
- A few olives

DAY 61 Why I do not eat much on certain days, I do not know. I just did not feel like eating much. Some things sounded good to me but I didn't want to make the recipes. I had other things to do anyway like working on the house. Sometimes I feel I don't eat interestingly enough. Then I think who am I living for anyway? Who cares what I eat as long as I like it. I do eat what I want at the time. Unless I am drinking carrot and kale juice! Then I am forcing myself to consume something good for me. I am not into greens as much as I need to be. I like them OK, but I forget to eat them. They just are not my favorite food. I got to talk to a friend of a friend today about the raw food diet. That was fun! Mary Beth, I hope you find the answers you are seeking! The raw food diet is wonderful.

- A bunch of olives (maybe a generous cup??)

- Pine nuts (probably 2-3 tablespoons)

- A taste of seed cheese

- A walnut (couldn't NOT list it, LOL)

- Some currants

MONTH 2, DAY 62
Total Pounds Lost: 36 (measurements taken from day 64)
Neck: (-1/4) Arm: (-1/4) Bust: (-3.25) Waist: (-3.25) Hips: (-3.50) Thigh: (-2.50)

Today marks 2 months raw! Yea! Every month when I take pics I get disappointed. I think, don't I look better than this??? Isn't it time my arms hang straight by my side??? LOL I know I did not get to be this size overnight and it will take time to shrink. I really am OK with that. I just have to be honest and say I get disappointed when I see how slow the progress is. More than disappointment though, I feel a burning desire to keep going!! I look forward to next month's picture and think how much better it will look compared to the before picture. This little motivating factor really spurs me on. I am so thankful for Alissa's help and encouragement and for the opportunity I have through her to be accountable by sending in my pictures. It really is a powerful visual motivator. I can't believe the difference in my face already. Wow.
We had some relatives over today. They LOVED the raw Berry Pie I made. Even my MIL said I could eat like you do if I get to

have stuff like this!! She was so surprised at my raw Berry Pie (not my own recipe). I guess she thought I ate salad all the time. Hehe Oh! We took the family to Krispy Cream tonight. I used to frequent that place. I wonder how long it'll take to get all that KK lard out of my system! Anyway, I felt so smug and had to smile knowing that most of them would leave the place feeling ill and I would feel great! That's exactly what happened!

- Nectarine/banana/strawberry smoothie
- Piece of raw strawberry pie
- Salad (it even had kale in it!) with pine nut basil dressing
- Guacamole with salsa and pico de gallo

DAY 68 I continue to be amazed at how I cannot overeat even the yummiest raw foods! I NEVER remember feeling so satisfied on cooked foods. Stuffed, YES! But not that feeling you get when you've had just enough. I used to marvel at skinny people and how they could throw away half a burger. I finally know how they must feel and how they are able to quit eating when they are full. I love this!

- Few bites Banana Ice Cream w/walnuts and dates
- Carrot/apple juice
- Couple bites of Carrot Cake cookies
- taco mush on romaine lettuce with guac
- guac, salsa and pine nuts
- raspberry/banana/carob ice cream w/dates and walnuts
- small saucer of nuts and dried fruit
- olives
- bite of honeycomb and honey
- t bee pollen
- pickled okra

DAY 69 Felt sluggish and bloated after all the combinations I ate yesterday (plus, I know the vinegar in the okra is not great for the body). Someday maybe I will manage looking into proper food combining. Right now I am in the stage of not wanting to be confused with the facts. I don't want to be troubled with too many rules right now. I know myself... I would crash and burn if I tried being perfect at raw foodism.

- Salad plate of "taco mush" w/guac
- Couple of small romaine leaves stuffed with guac and taco mush
- Walnuts
- Couple bites frozen dates
- 3 plums

DAY 70 Sometimes I get tired of the comments I get about my eating. We were going to a wedding party and I asked our friend and hostess if there would be anything raw there. She thought for a minute and apologetically answered no. I asked if it would be OK for me to bring something and let her know if not, that I would eat before the party. It was fine to bring something. She asked me "Now what is it you are doing?" I told her and she said, in a worried tone "And things are going alright for you?" Yes, great! I said (maybe she didn't notice I had dropped about 40 lbs?) This lady is a firm believer in the myth concerning complete protein. She's entitled to her beliefs. I was gearing up that evening to fend off any enemies. I was having a really hard time feeling meek, or imagining myself answering kindly. Surprisingly, it was a pleasant evening. I brought a Greek salad and I know I ate the best tasting food at the party! I even got to share about raw foods with an interested, not-offensive-about-it person. I hope I become a little less tightly wound the longer I am raw.

- Guac and salsa with pine nuts
- Dried apple slices
- Huge Greek salad! YUM (cucumber, bell pepper, red onion, tomato, olive oil, olives, a little vinegar

DAY 73 My complexion is looking so much better. In fact, all my skin seems smoother and healthier. I was wondering when my face was going to clear up! For awhile it seemed my complexion was getting worse. I'm sure as detox continues, I will still have times where my complexion does not look good. I pigged out today. Some days I am prone to emotional eating still. Even though I cannot stuff myself on raw foods (THANK GOD!!), I still can eat when I am not really hungry or when something is getting to me emotionally. Thankfully this does not happen nearly as often as it did when I was on the SAD.

- nuts/seeds/fruit mix
- olives
- salad
- pistachios/macadamias
- dried apples
- dried mangos
- slice of artichoke heart
- a sheet of sushi nori

WEEK 12, DAY 85
Total Weight Loss: 42 lbs
Total Inches Lost: 18.75

I dropped 2 more pounds this week but NONE of my measurements changed! I can't figure that out. Maybe my scale was lying? My clothes even felt bigger so I don't know what is up... I finally got over my prejudice against turnips and made Alissa's Raw Ravioli recipe (It's listed on her site). It was SO yummy, I kept eating them as I made them and hardly had any left for dinner. Plus I only made 1/4 the recipe since I didn't think I liked turnips. I am making them again today. We have small group tonight at our house and they will be eating spaghetti. I am going to tempt them with the ravioli... I bought more turnips so we will have plenty! I noticed today at the grocery store how my thinking is changing. I am actually becoming more ecologically minded. I am so happy about this! I used to wonder about those people who came to the grocery store with their own canvas bags to use to carry their groceries out. Now I am actually going to do it myself! I know that is a small thing to many, but it is a start for me. I heard someone say that most people are poisoning the planet hundreds of times a day; whatever we can do to stop this in our own lives is good (OK, that's a paraphrase). I guess what I'm trying to say is that small beginnings are good!

What I ate today:

- generous portion coconut cream pie (I tweaked it a bit)

- 1/4 recipe of Alissa's Raw Ravioli (YUM!!!)

- few olives

- another generous portion of J's pie

DAY 100, August 13, 2002

YEA! 100 days raw. I kept remembering that throughout the day and would get a little lift.

- young coco, pineapple, strawberry and date smoothie

- olives

- pistachios

- a bite of honeycomb

DAY 102, August 15, 2002

I made chips tonight. These were fab! Someone on the raw-foodsupport.com BB posted their recipe for vinegar and salt zucchini chips. Sorry but I had to use white potatoes. They were SO good! Not something to eat every day, but a really good food to have when those wicked cravings hit. And with the spiral slicer (Alissa sells them!) you can get the potato slices (or whatever veggie you are using) SO thin that it only takes a matter of a couple hours in the Excalibur dehydrator on the lowest setting to have crispy chips. I feel like I am trying to sell something. Well, I am! Raw food is awesome and I hope anyone and everyone reading this will give raw, living foods a try! I don't care if you are a partaker of the SAD (Standard American Diet)... or if you are a junk food addict like I was. Try raw. It just makes sense on so many different levels.

OK, I feel talkative tonight... I guess I've been quiet too long. I have been experiencing too much stress at home... in my relationship with my son. Now I can see the light at the end of the tunnel and I feel a little more talkative. So let me tell you something about my 100th day that I just didn't feel like typing out at the time. I went shopping and was in a hurry. Didn't find what I wanted in one store and the only other store around was Avenue, which is for plus sized women. Now why hadn't I ever discovered this cool store while I could still fit into their clothes?! Actually, I did fit into their 14-16, which was their smallest size. BUT! I could not bring myself to buy anything from that store. Not on my 100th day. Not ever again. I am not that anymore. I had to keep telling this to myself when I saw clothes I could have worn even last month. That is not me anymore. I have to be careful with myself. I think that in buying something from a plus-sized store I would have been sending myself a negative message on some level. I have lived in those stores for so long (and loved them!! don't get me wrong!) but at 100 days, shouldn't I make a break!? I did. And I'm not going back.

I feel so out of touch with my body and where I am now. Not that I have achieved my goal! I am still working toward something higher (or lower, I should say). But I have just noticed that I don't have a sense of awareness about my body. And I didn't have it when I was a size 22-24 either. That is how I was able to get to that size! By not being aware. So now that I realize I am still not aware, it is a little scary. How do I become more aware and in touch with my body? I know I am making progress because I am feeding myself good things... I am not overeating as bad as I used to. But I'm just wondering about this body awareness issue. Is this common for people with eating disorders?

One more thing I have just felt like saying/admitting. Some cooked food still appeals to me. I won't list it here in case someone like me is reading this (if someone mentioned a food that sounded good to me, I used to not be able to rest till I got some)! I remember what Alissa told me early on about temptation to eat cooked food (a paraphrase): Do not even dwell on the thoughts about that food! Don't even start thinking about how good it would taste or feel to have that food! As soon as the thought enters your mind, make it leave! Very good advice!

- Young coco, pineapple, orange smoothie
- 2 Brazil nuts
- part of an avo with pine nuts and Italian dressing (olive oil, apple cider vinegar, lemon juice, garlic, Italian seasoning and cayenne)
- 3 raw ravioli
- 2-3 olives
- few pieces dehydrated turnip slices (they aren't getting crunchy!)
- about 10-15 dehydrated vinegar and salt potato slices (apple cider vinegar, olive oil, sea salt—got this idea from the raw BB—so very yummy)
- carob candy (how much? enough! YUM!)

Exercise:

- Callanetics tape-the one for beginners. My only comment is: **OOOUUUUCCHHHHH!!!!!!!**

DAY 104. August 17, 2002

I consider this a success... I am finally able to cook things for hubby that I used to REALLY like. I haven't been able to do this till after my 100th day. It feels good to be this free!

- 1 slice of pie
- a bowl of raw potato chips-nibbled on them throughout the day — TOO MUCH SALT!
- 1 plum
- what else?

DAY 126, Monday, September 9, 2002

I woke up today with strange pains in the upper part of my stomach. I have only had these kind of pains a couple of times before and they are really awful! I also felt nauseated and had diarrhea all day. What a way to feel when you are leaving for a trip! I fasted all day because I was never hungry and the thought of food made me sick. I also did not exercise today, of course!! Spent the night in Wichita.

DAY 154, Tuesday, October 8, 2002

I have lost 65 pounds so far! I am really loving this! I know some of you like to know how many inches I've lost... I will try and post that soon!

DAY 156, Thursday, October 10, 2002

I am running out of clothes I can wear. I don't want to buy new ones because I won't be wearing them for long. Today I tried on a pair of size 12 pants and everything fit except the waist... I couldn't button it. But I was so excited to know I am close to being a 12 again! People ask me what my goal is. I tell them I don't really have one in mind, that I am going to let my body decide where it wants to end up. I don't want to stress about getting to a certain goal and then be depressed if I don't make

it. I do have a hope though of being a size 6-8. That would be miraculous! I am not really in touch with what is happening in my body and that scares me. The weight has come off so quickly that I am not able to really grasp it. I am scared of gaining weight again in the future. To help myself with this fear, I plan on keeping my goals in mind. For instance, last Sept. the sacred dance class I was signed up for was cancelled. Next Sept. it will be offered again. I am going to be keeping that in mind so that I will be less tempted to go back to my old ways. I so badly want to take this class! I also hope to have the raw community on the Internet for accountability... to occasionally post my pictures. Somehow accountability really works for me! I know that having accountability with Alissa through this journal (and thus having accountability with those who read these words) has made all the difference in keeping me raw. I'm grateful to all of you!!

RECIPES

PIZZA! *(pg.406)*

CALZONE *(pg.390)*

ENCHILADA! *(pg.387)*

CARROT PECAN BURGER ON A BURGER BUN WITH JICAMA FRIES AND HONEY MUSTARD SAUCE. *(pg.385)*

NORI ROLLS *(pg.404)*

**ANGEL HAIR PASTA
WITH MARINARA**

(pg.395)

PIZZA BREAD USED AS A WRAP (pg.352)

**BBQ CHICKEN
FINGERS**

(pg.414)

WATERMELON SOUP

(pg.356)

STRAWBERRY CRÊPES

(pg.379)

POTATO SALAD

(pg.447)

CORN CHIPS

(pg.347)

CANNOLI

(pg.492)

DATE NUT TORTE

(pg.483)

CHOCOLATE CAKE WITH WHIPPED CREAM AND TOPPINGS *(pg.511)*

ALMOND BUTTER AND RAISIN COOKIES WITH ALMOND MILK *(pg.531)*

SPROUTING

SPROUTING IS EASY...ANYONE CAN DO IT! AS IS THE CASE IN
JUST ABOUT EVERY FACET OF THIS DIET, KEEP IT SIMPLE.
I USED TO USE SPECIAL SPROUTING JARS, SPROUTING
SHEETS, MESH SCREENS...AND FOUND THE WHOLE PROCESS
RATHER TEDIOUS. TODAY I JUST USE LARGE BOWLS AND
PAPER TOWELS.

WHY SPROUT AT ALL?

There are some very good reasons to soak and sprout.

Soaking nuts, seeds, grains, and legumes removes their natural enzyme inhibitors: phytates and oxalates.

Sprouting greatly increases the nutritional value of these foods and makes them far more digestible because their protein is broken down into amino acids, their starches are changed into simple sugars, and their fats are converted into soluble fatty acids.

Sprouting increases the enzyme content of these foods. Even though they are raw, their enzymes are lying dormant. Sprouting activates them. If you do not sprout them, your body has to use its own enzymes to break up these foods.

Soaked and sprouted nuts, seeds, grains, and legumes are highly nutritious and produce an amazing amount of nourishment that otherwise would not be available. In sprouted wheat for instance, vitamins are increased tremendously: Thiamin (B1) increases by 30%, Niacin increases by 90%, Vitamin B2 increases by 200%, Pantothenic acid increases by 80%, and Biotin, by 100%! Amino acids increase greatly as well, and because of this predigested state, the body does not have to work as hard to digest this highly concentrated source of protein.

Many people are convinced that sprouts are the perfect food...and with good reason! Packed with vitamins and minerals, their proteins, carbohydrates, and fats are broken down into a useable form. Sprouts are bursting with energy from all of the enzymes they contain. And when you sprout seeds, nuts, grains, and legumes, they become more alkaline.

IT'S SO ECONOMICAL!

It's almost unbelievable. A teaspoon — *one teaspoon* — of alfalfa seeds yields about *two pounds* of sprouts! All for just a few pennies.

I usually buy one-pound bags of mung beans, lentils, buckwheat, alfalfa seeds, sunflower seeds, and pumpkin seeds...at about a dollar or two per bag. If only one teaspoon of alfalfa yields two pounds of sprouts, it's easy to see how economical the process becomes.

THE BASICS:

The process can take anywhere from several hours to four or five days.

Place your seeds, nuts, grains, or legumes in a large bowl. Cover them with enough water so that when they expand, they'll still be covered. Check the chart for the appropriate soaking time. (I usually soak mine overnight.)

When the soaking time is done (for me, usually the next morning), drain them, and keep them in the same bowl without the water. Cover with a paper towel. (Or if you prefer, use mesh or wire screens.)

Continue to rinse and drain the seeds, nuts, grains, or beans for a few days — two to three times a day unless otherwise indicated. Make sure that between rinses, they are kept out of water and drained. Sprouts should be kept moist but well-drained.

Make sure they get fresh air and are not in direct sunlight (unless indicated, in order to increase chlorophyll content).

Certain nuts, like almonds, need only be soaked for twenty-four to forty-eight hours, rinsed, and then kept in water in the refrigerator. Most sprouts will keep for four to five days.

TROUBLE-SHOOTING

If you are having trouble getting beans, seeds or grains to sprout, you may have soaked them for too long. Or, they may have been old and dead before you began the sprouting process. Make sure you buy them at a place with a high turnover rate so that you know they have not been sitting on the shelf for a long time.

Buckwheat, wheat berries, and garbanzo beans tend to mold easily; rinse these more often.

SPROUTING, IN SIX EASY STEPS

1. Soak

2. Drain and rinse

3. Cover with some sort of loose protection (such as a paper towel)

4. Set aside to grow

5. Rinse and drain two or three times a day

6. After a few days, check to see if sprouts are done. When they are, rinse, drain and refrigerate.

YOUR "SPROUT CHART"

There are many, many types of nuts, seeds, grains, and legumes that you can sprout. This chart illustrates some of the more common types. The figures given are *not* exact; they will vary depending on the seed, climate, and environment. With a little experimentation you'll get the hang of it in no time!

Product	Dry Amount	Soaking Time	Sprouting Time	Yield	Additional Comments
Alfalfa seeds	3 tbls	5 hours	4-5 days	4 cups	Place sprouts in direct sunlight on the last day of sprouting to "green" them and increase their chlorophyll content.
Almonds	3 cups	24-48 hours	———	4 cups	Almonds just need to be soaked for 1 –2 days and then kept in the refrigerator in water. Change water daily. Will keep for 5-6 days.
All other nuts – walnuts, macadamia, etc...	3 cups	6-8 hours	———	4 cups	These nuts will not sprout. They just need to be soaked and then used or kept in the refrigerator for a day or two.
Amaranth	1 cup	3-4 hours	1-2 days	3 cups	Rinse 3-4 times a day. These small seeds sprout very quickly.
Barley (hulled)	1 cup	6 hours	12-24 hours	2 cups	Rinse 3-4 times a day.
Buckwheat (hulled)	1 cup	6 hours	1-2 days	2 cups	Rinse 3-4 times a day.
Clover	3 tbls	5 hours	5 days	4 cups	Place sprouts in direct sunlight on the last day of sprouting to "green" them and increase their chlorophyll content.
Fenugreek Seeds	4 tbls	6 hours	4-5 days	3 cups	The longer the sprout the more bitter it becomes.
Flax Seeds	1 cup	6 hours		2 cups	Flax seeds will soak up a large amount of water so make sure you give them enough to absorb. They do not need to be sprouted just soaked.
Lentil	3/4 cup	8 hours	3 days	4 cups	Rinse 2-3 times a day.
Garbanzo Bean (Chick pea)	1 cup	12 hours	3 days	4 cups	Rinse 3-4 times a day.

Product	Dry Amount	Soaking Time	Sprouting Time	Yield	Additional Comments
Millet	1 cups	5 hours	12 hours	3 cups	These small seeds sprout very quickly. The sprout will be very small on these.
Mung Beans	1/3 cup	8 hours	4-5 days	4 cups	Rinse these sprouts vigorously to remove the hulls after sprouted.
Pea	1 cup	8 hours	3 days	3 cups	
Pumpkin seeds	1 cup	6 hours	1 day	2 cups	You don't have to wait for these to sprout. You can use them after soaking.
Quinoa	1 cup	3 hours	1-2 days	3 cups	
Radish	3 tbls	6 hours	4-5 days	4 cups	Place sprouts in direct sunlight on the last day of sprouting to "green" them and increase their chlorophyll content.
Rye berries	1 cup	6 hours	2-3 days	3 cups	Rinse 2-3 times a day.
Sesame seeds	1 cup	4 hours	1 day	1 cup	Only hulled sesame seeds will sprout.
Spelt	1 cup	6 hours	1-2 days	3 cups	Can be used as a substitute for wheat.
Sunflower seeds	1 cup	6 hours	1 day	2 cups	You don't have to wait for these to sprout. You can use them after soaking.
Teff	1 cup	3 hours	1-2 days	3 cups	
Wheat berries **Note:** Use the soft wheat berries for bread and crackers and hard wheat berries for wheat grass.	1 cup	8 hours	2-3 days	3 cups	Rinse 3-4 times a day.
Wild Rice	1 cup	12 hours	2-3 days	3 cups	Make sure you use <u>wild</u> rice.

DEHYDRATING

YOUR DEHYDRATOR ELIMINATES THE NEED TO COOK THE LIFE OUT OF YOUR FOOD! AND YOU'LL ENJOY WONDERFUL CRACK-ERS, COOKIES, CHIPS, AND OTHER DELICIOUS MUNCHIES IN THE HEALTHIEST MANNER POSSIBLE!

DEHYDRATING DRIES FOOD at a temperature high enough to remove water, but low enough to keep your enzymes intact. The process results in desirably crunchy, crispy, and sometimes hard food. But because temperatures are held below 112 degrees, the vitamins, minerals, and enzymes are preserved.

TIMING CAN BE A BIT TRICKY...

It all depends on the thickness and water content of your food. Fresh fruit, for example, will take longer than certain grains or seeds. And a loaf, such as a nut loaf or a loaf of bread, will take longer and may still be soft in the center then slices of sweet potatoes for chips. Although recipes in this book give estimated dehydrating times, the key word is "estimated." Again, with a little experimentation, you will become a master!

...BUT DEHYDRATING IS EASY!

Just place whatever you are dehydrating — burgers, breads, crackers, nut and veggie loaves, cookies, whatever — on the mesh dehydrating screen...just as you would place them on a cookie sheet. If your food is too large, or too high, you might have to remove the tray above the food to give yourself extra space.

Consider buying Teflex sheets with your dehydrator. These liners will allow you to dry watery and thinner foods — pureed fruit, ground veggies and seeds for crackers — without the food seeping through the mesh screens. Plastic wrap serves the same function, but the Teflex sheets are reusable and easier to handle. Whenever possible, use the mesh dehydrator screens alone because it allows the airflow to surround the food, resulting in faster drying times.

(Note: in recipes calling for the use of a dehydrator, I specify where a Teflex sheet is needed.)

Set the thermostat for *no higher than 110 degrees!* (I usually keep mine between 95 and 105 degrees.)

Periodically check the food's texture for desired doneness. You can dehydrate foods just until they're firm and chewy, or until they're crisp and hard. You be the judge. After you make a given recipe a few times, you'll know what texture you prefer. Keep track of the timing and make notes for future reference.

In most cases it's a good idea to flip the food and transfer it off the Teflex sheets onto the mesh sheets about halfway through the dehydrating time. Again, this allows for faster drying. To do this simply place a dehydrator screen with a mesh screen on top of the food you want to flip. Place both hands on the sides of the sheets, and turn them upside down (so that the bottom sheet is now on top.) Remove the sheet and mesh screen, and slowly peel the Teflex sheet off the food.

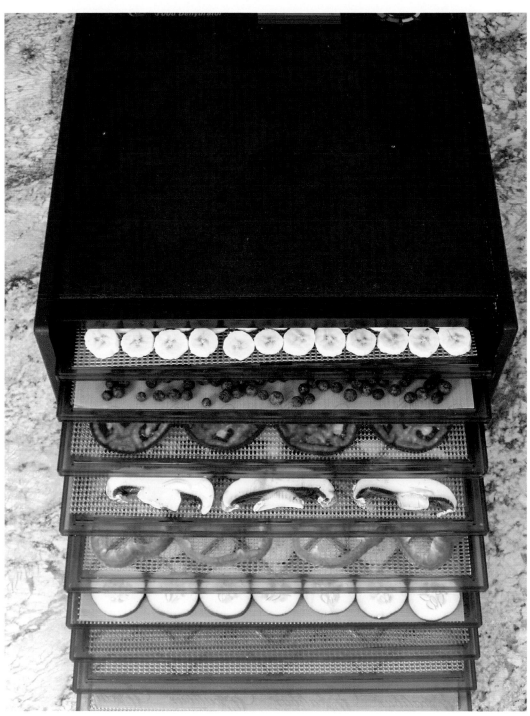

9 tray Excalibur Dehydrator

RECIPES

INTRODUCTION

You'll notice that in preparing raw food dishes, even if you follow the directions precisely, the finished product may come out a little differently every time. This is because fruits and vegetables vary each time in ripeness, texture, and size.

Take the avocado, for example. Even the slightest reduction in size — say, a quarter of an inch smaller, may result in a different taste than the last time you used an avocado in the same recipe, for smaller size allows more of the other flavors to permeate the dish. Or, if your avocado is riper, your meal may taste sweeter and/or creamier.

Once you experiment with a recipe once or twice, you will become adept at spotting any potential problems and will be able to remedy the situation with easy alternatives.

Use the freshest produce available and always try to use organic. Because you are not going to conceal the flavor of foods by cooking them, you want the food you start with to have the best flavor possible.

Since I know that many readers may not own a Vita-Mix or a juicer that homogenizes, I've used a food processor to test all of these recipes and they all work. That said, some recipes would certainly benefit from the use of a Vita-Mix or a homogenizing juicer. For example, some of the desserts and soups will be creamier if the Vita-Mix is used. And the breads will have a "doughier" texture if the ingredients are homogenized through a juicer. Pâtés will be smoother if a homogenizing machine is used, but with the addition of a little water and longer blending time, a food processor will work just as well.

Many recipes call for diced or minced ingredients. This method is advised in order to enable you to measure the food properly. Once you get used to preparing raw food dishes, you'll be able to just "eyeball it." Most of the time, I just toss all the ingredients into my food processor all at once, thus saving me lots of time. There are some specific recipes calling for minced, diced, or shredding vegetables because of the texture required for those particular dishes, those will be specified.

After preparing a recipe, you may want to add more spices or flavorings, such as sea salt or lemon. Suit your own taste!

Don't be afraid to experiment and/or substitute ingredients. I suggest, though, that you try the recipe exactly as specified the first time, sample it, and find out what you like about it and what you don't like about it. Then, you may alter it to suit your taste buds. Even though you think you might not like a specific raw vegetable, you may be pleasantly surprised because of the way it is used in these recipes. Here's a classic example: a close friend of mine *hates* turnips — some childhood trauma associated with them — and swore that she would *never* eat anything I made if it contained turnips. This same friend *loves* my ravioli...which is made with turnips. (I think I might have conveniently forgotten to mention that to her!)

A FEW MORE TIPS:

When making flax crackers, you can either soak the whole flax seeds or grind the dry flax using a Vita-Mix or a coffee grinder. (The food processor will not grind whole flax seeds)

If a recipe calls for onion or celery in the food processor, just cut the onion or celery into large enough chunks so they can be broken up easily. Don't worry about dicing them, or making them too small.

Certain grains, such as buckwheat and barley, are easy to sprout, therefore don't let recipes calling for buckwheat or barley intimidate you...it can be done in a day and a half. Just soak them overnight, and then let them sit in a bowl and sprout the following day.

I specify soaking the sun-dried tomatoes in most of these recipes. I do not give a specific amount of time for these. Just soak them until they are soft. This can take anywhere from 1 to 3 hours or overnight if you prefer.

When soaked fruit is called for in a recipe, this is to insure the optimum in creaminess or smoothness. If you find you don't have time to soak the fruit, or simply forget to soak them, that's okay...the result just might not be as creamy or smooth.

Although certain nuts and seeds are healthier and easier to digest if soaked, you should only soak the nuts in these recipes if directed to do so, otherwise the recipes may not come out as expected. If you have not planned ahead and do not have sprouted nuts and seeds, you can still make the recipe, most of the time with fantastic results. I don't want you to have to wait 2 days to make any of these recipes because you don't have sprouted nuts and seeds on hand. In the future, after making raw food for a while and getting a feel for how many ingredients you use and what you like to make on a regular basis, you will always have a bowl of soaked and sprouted almonds and dates in the fridge, or some other ingredient that is one of your staples, like sunflower seeds, dried tomatoes, etc...

You can make your own sandwiches easily with lettuce stuffed with pâtés, leftover burgers, and so on.

When a recipe in this book calls for coconuts, I have used white, baby Thai coconuts, unless otherwise specified.

When a recipe calls for 4 cups of sprouted Rye, Wheat, Barley, etc... that means 4 cups of <u>sprouted</u> grain that is measured <u>after</u> the grain is already sprouted, not before!

If you don't like using honey, try substituting dates in some of the recipes. Sometimes just date water (water in which dates have been soaked) will work best.

Remember, although it is not repeated with every recipe, everything used in these recipes is RAW! Any juices, honey, all nuts, carob powder, etc... are always raw!

APPETIZERS AND SIDE DISHES

ALTHOUGH MANY OF THESE APPETIZERS COULD BE USED AS ENTRÉES, THESE DISHES ARE ONES THAT ARE MORE OFTEN SEEN AS AN APPETIZER OR SIDE DISH, SUCH AS THE TYPICAL BROCCOLI AND CHEESE, MASHED POTATOES AND GRAVY, NACHOS, OR STUFFED MUSHROOMS.

PESTO STUFFED MUSHROOMS

Served warm out of the dehydrator, these are heavenly! These taste like a soft, breaded, cooked, stuffed mushroom.

18-22 button mushrooms, washed and stemmed

STUFFING:

1 cup walnuts

1/2 cup pine nuts

2 cups basil

1/2 cup olive oil

3 cloves garlic

1/2 teaspoon sea salt

1. Place mushroom caps top side down on a plate.
2. Blend all stuffing ingredients in a food processor until smooth.
3. Scoop a small amount of stuffing into each mushroom cap.
4. Dehydrate at 105 degrees for 5-6 hours, or until soft.

MASHED POTATOES AND MUSHROOM GRAVY

These "mashed potatoes" are great with a topping like the mushroom gravy to give them more flavor.

MASHED POTATOES:

2 cups soaked cashews

2 cups water

1 head cauliflower

WHITE BUTTON MUSHROOMS- A particularly rich source of riboflavin, mushrooms are also one of the best sources of niacin around. They are also an excellent source of copper, which is necessary to assist iron in making red blood cells.

CAULIFLOWER - Like cabbage, broccoli, and some of its other relatives, cauliflower is filled with phytonutrients which can help to detoxify cancer-causing agents and impede tumor growth.

1/4 medium onion

1 teaspoon olive oil

Sea salt and pepper to taste

MUSHROOM GRAVY:

2 cups crimini mushrooms (you can substitute portobellas)

2 Tablespoons Bragg Liquid Aminos

1 Tablespoon water

1 small clove garlic

1/2 teaspoon sage

Sea salt and fresh pepper to taste

FOR MASHED POTATOES:

1. In a food processor, process the mashed potato ingredients until they are well blended. (This should look a bit grainy)

2. Remove from processor and place in a bowl.

FOR GRAVY:

1. In a food processor, blend the mushroom gravy ingredients until smooth.

2. Pour mushroom gravy over mashed potatoes.

BROCCOLI AND CHEESE

If you dehydrate this long enough, the broccoli will begin to soften. This is a tasty side dish with a beautiful orange and green appearance.

3-4 cups broccoli, chopped into large bite size pieces (not diced)

CREAMY CHEDDAR CHEESE:

1/2 cup pine nuts

1/2 cup macadamia nuts

1/2 cup sunflower seeds

1 1/2 cups red bell pepper

1/2 lemon, peeled

2 cloves garlic

1 Tablespoon Bragg Liquid Aminos

---

1. Place the broccoli in a plate or bowl.
2. Blend the cheddar cheese ingredients in a food processor until creamy.
3. Pour the cheddar cheese sauce over the broccoli.
4. Dehydrate at 105 degrees for 5-6 hours or until desired texture for broccoli is achieved and cheese is warmed.

AVOCADO CHUTNEY

An amazing medley of flavors to tantalize the taste buds!

1 large avocado, diced

1 cup whole corn kernels

1 small onion, finely chopped

1 red bell pepper, diced

1/4 cup olive oil

4 cloves garlic, minced

1 lime, juiced

2 teaspoons cumin

2 teaspoons chopped oregano

1 teaspoon chili powder

1 Tablespoon cilantro, diced

Sea salt and pepper to taste

---

1. Combine the avocado, corn, pepper, and onion in a medium-sized bowl.

2. In another bowl, combine the olive oil, lime juice, cumin, garlic, chili, oregano, cumin, and cilantro.

3. Mix the second combination of oils and spices into the avocado mixture.

EGGPLANT ROULADE

These appetizers look like the little puff pastry hour d'oeuvres that are popular party fare. These bite-sized pieces are lovely served as is. However, I prefer them dehydrated, as this will make them crispy and a bit more flavorful. The down side is, they are not as pretty when they are dehydrated as the inside gets black through the drying process. Try half dehydrated and half fresh and judge for yourself. These have a very spicy, Indian flavor.

WRAPPER:

4 large eggplants

FILLING:

1/2 cup spinach

8 crimini mushrooms

2 avocados

1 onion

1 slice red onion

1 Tablespoon almond butter

1/2 lemon, juiced

1/4 cup nutritional yeast

1 teaspoon cayenne (or less)

1 Tablespoon Bragg Liquid Aminos

Sea salt and pepper to taste

SECOND LAYER OF FILLING:

1 cup sundried tomatoes, soaked

6 dates, pitted and soaked

1 Tablespoon onion

FOR WRAPPER:

1. With a vegetable peeler, slice the eggplants into long, thin, bacon-like strips. Make these as wide as possible.

2. Soak the eggplant slices for 5-10 minutes in a bowl of sea salted water, and then place on paper towels to dry.

FOR FILLING:

1. In a blender, combine the filling ingredients and blend until smooth.

FOR SECOND LAYER OF FILLING:

1. In a food processor, blend the second layer filling ingredients until fairly smooth.

TO ASSEMBLE:

1. Place the strips of eggplant on a flat surface. Place a layer of the filling along the length of the eggplant strip, leaving at least 1/2 inch at the end.

2. Place a thin layer of the second layer filling on top of the filling in the eggplant strip.

3. Roll the strips up into round circles.

4. Place on a plate or in the dehydrator if you wish and dehydrate at 105 degrees for 4-6 hours.

APPLE SAUCE

Unlike cooked applesauce this is fast, easy and delicious! You
can leave some of the apples in pieces if you prefer a chunkier
texture to a smoother one.

4 apples

2 Tablespoons honey

1/2 teaspoon cinnamon

1/4 teaspoon vanilla

1. Slice the apples into large chunks. (There is no need to peel
   the apples)
2. Place the apples and all other ingredients into a food processor and blend until smooth.

AVOCADO CUPS

Elegant and simple. The avocado meat is scooped out of the
shells, mixed with herbs and spices and then placed back into
the shells for a lovely presentation.

2 avocados, diced

2 tomatoes, diced

1/2 cucumber, diced

1 bunch chives, diced

1 clove garlic, minced

4 Tablespoons olive oil

1 Tablespoon apple cider vinegar

1/2 teaspoon Bragg Liquid Aminos

Dash of cayenne

1. Halve the avocados and pit. Remove avocados from their shell leaving the shell intact.

2. Combine the diced avocados, tomatoes, cucumber and chives in a bowl.

3. Place this mixture into avocado shells.

4. Combine the apple cider vinegar, olive oil, garlic, Bragg Liquid aminos and cayenne and pour over the avocado halves.

MARINATED PORTOBELLAS IN GINGER VINAIGRETTE

I used to marinate portobellas and then grill them until they were soft and full of flavor. By marinating and dehydrating these mushrooms it brings about a similar taste and the same soft, delicate texture.

5 large portobella mushroom caps

GINGER VINAIGRETTE:

1/2 cup olive oil

1/4 cup Bragg Liquid Aminos

1 Tablespoon fresh ginger

1-1 1/2 Tablespoons lemon juice

1 clove garlic

---

1. Wash and stem the mushroom caps.

2. In a blender, combine the ginger vinaigrette ingredients and blend until smooth.

3. Place mushrooms and vinaigrette in a large bowl and marinate for at least 1 hour.

4. Place caps stem side up on a mesh dehydrator screen and pour a bit of the remaining vinaigrette in the base of the caps.

5. Dehydrate at 105 degrees for 4-6 hours or until soft.

NACHOS

The perfect party dish! The cheese in these nachos acts as the base for this dish, like corn chips. This involves putting a few quick and easy recipes together.

NACHO CHEESE (BASE):

2 cups macadamia nuts

1 1/2 cups red bell pepper

1 cup orange pieces (about 1 orange)

4 cloves garlic

1 lemon, juiced

2 Tablespoons Bragg Liquid Aminos

GUACAMOLE:

2 avocados

1/4 cup onion

1/2 - 1 tomato

Sea salt to taste

Pinch cayenne

Cilantro (optional)

SPICY REFRIED BEANS:

2 cups sprouted chickpeas

1 cup walnuts

2 avocados

4 Tablespoons lime juice

2 teaspoons olive oil

1 garlic clove

4 teaspoons cumin

1/4 -1/2 teaspoon cayenne pepper

Sea salt and pepper to taste

CHILI SAUCE:

2 tomatoes

1 lime, juiced

1 clove garlic

1 Tablespoon Bragg Liquid Aminos

1/2 Tablespoon cumin

1 teaspoon jalapeno pepper

1 teaspoon chili powder

1 teaspoon oregano

1/8 teaspoon sea salt

FOR NACHO CHEESE (BASE):

1. In a food processor, combine cheese ingredients and blend until smooth and creamy.
2. Remove from processor and place on a Teflex sheet on top of a mesh dehydrator screen.
3. Spread batter into a thin sheet about 1/8 inch thick.
4. Dehydrate at 105 degrees for 7-10 hours. Flip cheese and peel off Teflex sheet and onto a mesh screen after 5-6 hours.
5. Remove cheese from dehydrator and cut into small squares (2 x 2 inches).

FOR GUACAMOLE:

1. Place onions, tomatoes, cilantro, sea salt and cayenne in a food processor and pulse chop until chunky.
2. Peel and pit avocados and cut into large chunks.

3. Place avocados in food processor with other ingredients and pulse chop to desired consistency.

FOR REFRIED BEANS:

1. In a food processor, combine refried beans' ingredients and blend until smooth.

FOR CHILI SAUCE:

1. In a blender, blend the chili sauce ingredients until smooth.

TO ASSEMBLE:

1. Place a dollop of guacamole on top of each cheese square.

2. On top of the cheese square and guacamole, place a dollop of refried beans.

3. Pour a spoonful of chili sauce over each of these piled nacho squares.

Note: For spicy nacho cheese, add jalapenos.

MISS HAMLIN'S CRANBERRY SAUCE

CRANBERRIES · Cranberries and their juice can help urinary tract infections by preventing bacteria from sticking to the urinary tract and causing infection.

Special thanks to a good friend of mine for this recipe. This sauce is always a hit at holiday dinners!

12 ounces cranberries

4 apples, peeled and chopped

8 ounces raisins, soaked

1. In a food processor, blend the cranberries with 2 of the apples.

2. Remove from processor and fold in the remaining 2 apples and raisins.

KIM-CHI

You can often buy this popular dish raw and without sugar...but
it's just as easy to make and it's much fresher! Eat this Kim-Chi
as is, serve over burgers or loafs, or use in collard or cabbage
roll-ups to spice up the dish!

1 medium to large sized napa cabbage, shredded

2 cups carrots, shredded

1/2 cup red bell pepper, diced

1/2 cup onion, shredded

1 Tablespoon apple cider vinegar

1 Tablespoon ginger, minced

1 teaspoon honey

1/4 teaspoon red chili flakes (or more if you like it really hot!)

1 Tablespoon sea salt

Mix all ingredients together in a bowl and allow to sit overnight
or at least a few hours for the flavors to mingle.

MARINATED ASPARAGUS AND TOMATOES

Asparagus is not something I use all of the time. But marinated in this dish with bright red, juicy tomatoes, it's a delicious
beginning to any meal and a colorful addition to any raw table.

1 pound of asparagus

2 tomatoes

GINGER VINAIGRETTE:

1/2 cup olive oil

1/4 cup Bragg Liquid Aminos

1 clove garlic

1-1 1/2 Tablespoons lemon juice

1 Tablespoon fresh ginger

———————————

1. In a blender, mix the vinaigrette ingredients together and blend well.

2. Cut the stems off of the asparagus and slice the tomatoes. Place both in a long, casserole type pan or dish.

3. Pour the ginger vinaigrette over the asparagus and tomatoes and let marinade at least a few hours, or overnight.

CUCUMBER WHEELS

CUCUMBERS - Their high silica content is beneficial for the hair, skin, and nails. They make your skin glow and help clear acne. Cucumbers are also excellent diuretics.

Very pretty! You can vary their color and design by your choice of topping, i.e. pâtés, pesto, etc...

2 large cucumbers

1 recipe Hummus

———————————

1. Peel the cucumber with a vegetable peeler from top to bottom, leaving narrow strips of skin in between, giving the cucumbers a "striped" look.

2. Slice the cucumbers into 1/2 inch slices.

3. Place the cucumber slices on a plate and top each with a spoonful of hummus.

Note: You can dress this up by placing a thin sliver of carrot on top of the hummus. Try topping with other vegetables as well, such as diced scallion, an olive, etc...

MARINATED GREENS

Although I usually prefer to eat foods the day I make them, this is much better the next day. The greens will "wilt" as if they were cooked, instead of just tasting like a salad. Use any variety of greens for this dish: kale, collards, e.g. I like using spinach and Swiss chard.

8 cups greens

MARINADE:

1/3 cup olive oil

1/4 teaspoon sea salt

1 clove garlic

1 Tablespoon fresh ginger

1 Tablespoon Bragg Liquid Aminos

1/2 cup water

Pinch of cayenne (optional)

---

1. Cut greens into large, bite-sized pieces.
2. Blend the marinade ingredients in a blender until well blended.
3. Pour marinade over greens and mix well.
4. Cover and let sit for at least a few hours, or preferably overnight.

SWISS CHARD - High in Vitamin K which is best known for its role in bone health and blood clotting.

MARINATED ONIONS

Remember those French Fried Onion Rings in a can, used in green bean casseroles? These taste just like them!

3-4 onions

Enough Bragg Liquid Aminos to soak the onions

1. Slice the onions very thin and separate into rings.
2. Marinate the onions in the Bragg Liquid Aminos for at least 10 minutes, longer if possible.
3. Drain, and lay onions out on Teflex sheets on top of a mesh dehydrator screen.
4. Dehydrate at 105 degrees for 10-12 hours or until crispy.

SPICY FRIES

Let these sit for a few hours, or overnight, and they'll take on the look and texture of fast food French Fries.

1 jicama, sliced into long, thin strips

1/4 cup honey

1/4 cup olive oil

1/8 teaspoon chili powder

1/8 teaspoon cayenne

1 lemon, juiced

1. Mix all ingredients except the jicama in a large bowl.
2. Marinate the jicama in this mixture for a few hours.
3. Drain and serve.

CHEESE AND CRACKER PLATTER

To create this smashing party platter, you'll need a variety of different cheeses, dehydrated and non-dehydrated and an array of crackers.

---

1. In the center of a large sheet, place the non-dehydrated cheese (or cheeses) in pretty bowl(s).
2. Surround the bowl(s) with your dehydrated cheeses and crackers randomly, creating an attractive display.
3. Decorate the sheet with red grapes.

DIPS AND SPREADS

WHETHER YOU'RE ENTERTAINING A CROWD OR ENTERTAINING YOURSELF THESE DIPS AND SPREADS WILL BE THE LIFE OF YOUR PARTY!

ONION DIP

My client Christine made this gem up. Bring this dip to a
"cooked food" party and no one will ever guess the difference.
I never tell my cooked food friends that this is raw, and they all
love it... it tastes just like sour cream and onion dip!

2 cups macadamia nuts

3/4-1 cup water

1 teaspoon sea salt

1 cup onions, diced

1. In a Vita-Mix, blender or food processor, blend macadamia
   nuts, water and sea salt until smooth and creamy. Start with
   3/4 cup water and add more only if needed to make mixture
   blend. Keep this as thick as you can and make sure it's as
   smooth and creamy as possible when done.
2. Remove from Vita-Mix, blender or food processor and add in
   the onions by hand. Mix gently and chill.

Notes: Make sure you add in the onions *by hand*, after blending
the nuts and water. For variety, try adding diced scallions.

SPINACH DIP

It's a toss up between guacamole or this, my favorite dip!
Eat this as is or serve with crackers and/or veggies.

4 cups spinach

1 large avocado or 1 1/2 small avocados

1/2 Tablespoon lemon juice

SPINACH - Reduces heavy menstrual bleeding. Reduces fatigue.

1/2 teaspoon Herbamare seasoning salt

Blend all ingredients in a food processor until smooth.

Note: Adjust Herbamare to taste or try adding sea salt instead of Herbamare.

INDIAN SPINACH DIP

I was so excited when I discovered that just by adding spices to my favorite dip, I could create a dish just like an Indian meal, palak paneer, which I used to love!

4 cups spinach

1 large avocado or 1 1/2 small avocados

1/2 Tablespoon lemon juice

1/2 teaspoon Herbamare seasoning salt

1/2 clove garlic

1/4 teaspoon curry

1/8 teaspoon fresh ginger

Dash chili powder

Dash cayenne

Dash cumin

1. Blend all ingredients in a food processor.
2. Serve as is, or warm in a dehydrator for a few hours at 105 degrees.

DILL CREAM CHEESE DIP

Wonderful on top of Essene bread, or as a dip for crackers and vegetables.

1 cup cashews

1 cup water

1/2 -1 cup fresh dill

Herbamare seasoning salt

1. Soak the cashews in the water for at least two hours.
2. Pour half the soaking water into a blender and slowly add the cashews.
3. Blend, adding water as needed, until all the cashews are used. Keep this thick by adding one or two cashews at a time until the blender is no longer able to turn over.
4. Add dill and Herbamare and blend.

GUACAMOLE

My daily staple!

2 avocados

1/2 - 1 tomato

1/4 cup onion

1/4 cup cilantro (optional)

Sea salt to taste

Pinch cayenne

1. Place onions, tomatoes, cilantro, sea salt and cayenne in a food processor and pulse chop until chunky.
2. Peel and pit avocados and cut into large chunks.
3. Place avocados in food processor with other ingredients and pulse chop to desired consistency.

AVOCADO - Highly nutritious! They are rich in vitamins, minerals, and oil. Avocados help lower LDL (the bad cholesterol). They help heal peptic ulcers and inflammation of the digestive system. Avocados help

to promote beautiful skin! To speed up the ripening process, place avocados in a bag with apples or bananas and do not refrigerate.

Note: For a chunkier texture, mash the avocados into the tomato onion mixture by hand.

BANANA-AVO DIP

One of my first raw recipes — simple, smooth, and sweet!

1 banana

1 avocado

1 small clove garlic

_____

Blend together in a food processor or blender until smooth.

HUMMUS

Tastes just as delicious as the hummus served in the finest Greek restaurants! You can change the flavor of this hummus by adding different vegetables, e.g.: red peppers = "Red Pepper Hummus," carrots = "Carrot Hummus," and so on.

4 cups sprouted chickpeas

1 cup tahini

1 cup onion

1 cup olive oil

1 cup lemon, peeled

1/2 bunch parsley

1 Tablespoon Bragg Liquid Aminos

1/8 teaspoon sea salt

Place all ingredients in a food processor and blend until smooth.

ZUCCHINI HUMMUS

Some find this easier to digest than the chickpea hummus. It's not as thick, but it's very tasty.

5 cups zucchini, peeled and chopped

1/2 cup tahini

4 cloves garlic

1/2 cup lemon juice

1/4 cup olive oil

1/2 teaspoon paprika

1/8 teaspoon cayenne

1 1/2 teaspoons sea salt

Place all ingredients in a food processor and blend until smooth.

GUS'S PESTO

Hearty, heavy, and intense! I use this for my stuffed mushrooms and as a filling for peppers and tomatoes.

1 cup walnuts

1/2 cup pine nuts

2 cups basil

1/2 cup olive oil

3 cloves garlic

1/2 teaspoon sea salt

Blend all ingredients in a food processor until well blended and smooth.

MISS ACKERLY'S PESTO BUTTER

This is sooooooo creamy and rich! Perfect for spreading or dipping.

1 1/2 cups pine nuts

1/2 cup basil

1 garlic clove

1 teaspoon olive oil

1/4 teaspoon sea salt, or more, as needed

---

1. Place pine nuts, basil, garlic and sea salt in a food processor. Begin blending while continuously adding a small amount of oil. Add only enough oil as needed to blend.
2. Add additional sea salt as needed to taste, as this is what will bring out the flavor.

Note: The idea is to make this as smooth and creamy as possible while using the least amount of oil.

PESTO LIGHT

With more vegetables and fewer nuts, this is the "light" version of the heavy pesto. This pesto is wonderful with fresh vegetables or crackers. It is also used in the Pesto Lasagna and the Pesto Pasta.

1/2 cup pine nuts

1/2 cup fresh cilantro

1/2 cup fresh basil

4-5 cloves garlic

3 Tablespoons Bragg Liquid Aminos

2 Tablespoons lemon juice

2 cups tomato, chopped

1. Place all ingredients, except for the tomato, in a food processor and blend until blended but still chunky.
2. Add tomato and pulse chop a few seconds until well blended but not soupy.

BLACK OLIVE TAPENADE

This reminds me of the garlic and herbed oil served at Italian restaurants. The addition of fresh mint leaves gives it a wonderful flavor. Serve with crackers or breads.

24 black olives

1/2 cup olive oil

1/4 cup parsley

1/4 cup basil

OLIVES - Contain good oils! They cleanse the liver and gallbladder increasing secretion of bile. Help lower LDL bad cholesterol.

2 cloves garlic

2 Tablespoons lemon juice

2 Tablespoons mint leaves

Sea salt and pepper to taste

_____

1. Place all ingredients except olives in blender or food processor and blend until smooth.
2. Add in olives and blend until only little bits of olives are visible.
3. Chill and serve.

Note: Make sure you use black olives or this may not taste right.

SALSA

This is so good that I usually double the recipe! If you've got a favorite salsa ingredient not listed here, feel free to add it.

4 tomatoes, chopped

2 scallions

2 cloves garlic

1/2 cup parsley

1/2 cup cilantro

1 Tablespoon cider vinegar

1 Tablespoon olive oil

1 Tablespoon lime juice

1 teaspoon cumin

1 teaspoon sea salt

Jalapeno to taste

1. Place the lime juice, jalapeno, cilantro, parsley, garlic, cider vinegar, olive oil, cumin and sea salt in a food processor and blend until well ground.
2. Add in the scallion and tomatoes. Pulse chop until everything is diced and blended.
3. Add more jalapeno or sea salt if needed.

Note: Let this sit for a few hours in order for the flavors to blend.

MANGO SALSA

Luxuriate in a taste of the Caribbean!

MANGOS - Rich in nutrients and good for the kidneys.

2 mangoes

1 lime, juiced

1 clove garlic

1 teaspoon green chili pepper

1. Blend all ingredients in a food processor except one mango.
2. Place mixture into a bowl.
3. Dice remaining mango into small pieces and add to mixture, stir.
4. Chill and serve.

PINEAPPLE SALSA

Pineapple with a kick!

2 cups pineapple chunks

1/3 cup cilantro

1 small clove garlic, minced

1 Tablespoon lemon juice

1 Tablespoon jalapeno, finely diced

Mix all ingredients together by hand.

AVOCADO SALSA

My friend (and fellow avocado lover!) Collette, treated me to this on my last visit to her home.

2 avocados

1 medium tomato

1 medium red onion

1 small red bell pepper

1 teaspoon ground coriander

1 teaspoon ground cumin

3 Tablespoons chopped cilantro

2 cloves garlic

2 Tablespoons lime juice (or to taste)

1 Tablespoon olive oil

Dash cayenne or chopped jalapeno

Sea salt to taste

Pepper to taste

1. Finely chop the onion.

2. Cut the avocados in half; remove the seed and carefully peel.

3. Finely chop the avocado flesh; place in a medium-sized bowl and toss lightly with lime juice.

4. Cut the tomato in half horizontally. Squeeze gently to remove seeds (optional); chop fine.

5. Remove seeds and membrane from pepper; chop fine.

6. Finely chop the cilantro and garlic (and jalapeno, if desired).

7. Combine all ingredients with avocado.

8. Add coriander, cumin, olive oil, sea salt, and pepper. Toss together so avocado does not become mashed.

Serving suggestion: Serve with raw crackers or on a salad.

BROCCOMOLE

A distinctively tasty dip.

1 1/2 cups broccoli

1 green bell pepper

1/2 tomato, diced

1 1/2 Tablespoons lemon juice

1 Tablespoon chives

1 Tablespoon honey

1/8 teaspoon garlic powder

─────────────

Blend all ingredients together in food processor until smooth.

PEPPER DIP

Enjoy this dip's light, garden fresh flavor.

1 red bell pepper

1 green bell pepper

1 tomato

1 avocado

1 1/2 cups broccoli

1/4 cup onion

2 teaspoons jalapeno

1/4 teaspoon sea salt or to taste

———————

Blend all ingredients in a food processor until smooth

Serving suggestions: Serve with crackers or vegetables.

CUCUMBER DIP

Light and refreshing!

1/2 cup cashews

1 cucumber

1/2 avocado

1 teaspoon olive oil

2 Tablespoons dill

1/2 teaspoon Herbamare seasoning salt

———————

Blend all ingredients in a food processor until smooth.

RAW CHEESES, DAIRY, AND CREAMY SAUCES

EAT THESE "CHEESES" RIGHT AFTER YOU PREPARE THEM...
OR, FOR A REAL "SLICE OF CHEESE" EXPERIENCE, DEHYDRATE
THEM!

CREAM CHEESE

Hard to believe that this would taste like cream cheese using just water and macadamia nuts, but it does! And the texture is perfect.

4 cups macadamia nuts

2 1/2 – 3 cups water

1. In a Vita-Mix or blender, blend nuts with enough water to turn over. Start with 1 1/2 cups of water, adding more as needed. (Make sure you keep this as thick as possible).

2. Place mixture in a small bowl, covered with cheese cloth, and let it sit at room temperature for at least 6-8 hours.

3. Store in refrigerator.

NACHO CHEESE

Corn chips? Nacho cheese? Guacamole? Sour Cream? Is this supposed to be a *diet*?

2 cups macadamia nuts

1 1/2 cups red bell pepper

1 cup orange pieces (about 1 orange)

4 cloves garlic

1 lemon, juiced

2 Tablespoons Bragg Liquid Aminos

1. Combine all ingredients in a food processor and blend until smooth and creamy.

2. Remove mixture from processor and place on a Teflex sheet on top of a mesh dehydrator screen.

3. Spread batter into a thin sheet about 1/8 inch thick.

4. Dehydrate at 105 degrees for 7-10 hours. Flip cheese and peel off Teflex sheet and onto a mesh screen after 5-6 hours.

Notes: For spicy nacho cheese, add jalapeno.

Serving suggestions: Serve in slices on crackers, use it for nachos, or break it up over salads.

AMERICAN CHEESE

This will resolve those cheese cravings!

BRAZIL NUTS - Packed with dense nutrients, especially selenium! One Brazil nut can supply twice the RDA of selenium, which prevents free radical cell damage.

2 cups Brazil nuts

1 1/2 cups red bell pepper

1 whole orange

4 cloves garlic

1 lemon, juiced

2 Tablespoons Bragg Liquid Aminos

1 teaspoon ground yellow mustard seed

---

1. Place nuts in a food processor and grind into a fine powder.

2. Add remaining ingredients and blend until smooth and creamy.

3. Remove mixture from processor and place on top of a Teflex sheet on a mesh dehydrator screen.

4. Spread batter into a thin sheet about 1/8 inch thick.

5. Dehydrate at 105 degrees for 7-10 hours. Flip cheese and peel off Teflex sheet and onto a mesh screen after 5-6 hours.

Serving suggestions: Serve in slices on crackers, break it up over salads, or use in other recipes.

SWISS CHEESE

This cheese tastes exactly like real Swiss cheese... without the holes!

1 cup cashews

2 Tablespoons nutritional yeast

1 Tablespoon lemon juice

1/4 cup water

_____

1. Blend all ingredients in a food processor.

2. Remove mixture from processor and place on a Teflex sheet on top of a mesh dehydrator screen.

3. Spread batter into a thin sheet about 1/8 inch thick.

4. Dehydrate at 105 degrees for 7-10 hours. (After 5-6 hours flip cheese and peel off Teflex sheet and onto a mesh screen).

MOZZARELLA CHEESE

Now you've got the perfect, delicious filling for those favorite recipes of yours!

Use this in the Calzone and for the Lasagna.

1 cup macadamia nuts

1 cup cashews

2 Tablespoons Bragg Liquid Aminos

1 1/2 Tablespoons lemon juice

1/4 to 1/2 cup water

1. Blend all ingredients in food processor, starting with just the 1/4 cup water.
2. Add more water as necessary to keep mixture thick but able to turn over.

Note: This cheese can be dehydrated (see instructions with the other cheeses) but I usually use this as is in other recipes.

CREAMY CHEDDAR CHEESE

This is the perfect pizza cheese! It's also wonderful for pouring over vegetables. There is no need to dehydrate this cheese.

1/2 cup pine nuts

1/2 cup macadamia nuts

1/2 cup sunflower seeds

1 1/2 cups red bell pepper

1/2 lemon, peeled

2 cloves garlic

1 Tablespoon Bragg Liquid Aminos

Blend all ingredients in a food processor until smooth and creamy.

RICOTTA CHEESE

This is a blander cheese. I made this to go with specific recipes that would normally call for a ricotta type cheese. It is mild in flavor and not overpowering allowing the other flavors in a recipe to come through (such as in the Lasagna).

1 cup macadamia nuts

1 cup almonds

1/2 lemon, juiced

1/4 cup orange juice

1/4 cup water

Blend all ingredients in a food processor until creamy.

MAYONNAISE

Although thinner than real mayonnaise, it tastes like the genuine article! To make this thicker, just chill it for a few hours.

3/4 cup almond milk

2 Tablespoons avocado

1 1/2 Tablespoons cider vinegar

3/4 teaspoon sea salt

3/4 cup olive oil

———————

1. Blend first four ingredients together in a blender.
2. Slowly add the oil and continue to blend until smooth.

SOUR CREAM

This is a little sweeter than real sour cream. But it's scrumptious served with the enchiladas or any other dish that would normally call for a side of sour cream!

1 1/2 cups cashews

1 Tablespoon cider vinegar

1 teaspoon white miso

1/2 cup water

1/2 teaspoon sea salt

———————

Combine all ingredients in a blender until smooth and creamy.

WHIPPED CREAM

Three variations! The grape juice adds a terrific taste, but there may be times when you just don't have it on hand.

2 cups cashews

3/4 cup whole orange

2 dates, pitted

or

1/2 cup cashews

1 cup grape juice

1/4 teaspoon vanilla

or

1 cup soaked cashews

1/2 cup water

1/2 teaspoon honey

———————————

For any/each of these recipes, just blend all ingredients until smooth!

PINEAPPLE NUT CREAM

Top your fruit with this sweet cream for an elegant dessert.

3/4 cup almonds

2 cups pineapple

1 1/2 cups cashews

———————————

1. Grind almonds into a fine powder.
2. Add remaining ingredients and blend until smooth.

APPLE NUT CREAM

Rich, thick, and delicious over fresh fruit.

3 apples, peeled and cored

3/4 cup cashews

1 Tablespoon tahini

3/4 cup water

———————

Blend all ingredients in a food processor until smooth.

ALL RECIPES IN THIS SECTION REQUIRE A DEHYDRATOR. BREADS CAN TAKE A LONG TIME TO DEHYDRATE, DEPENDING UPON THE THICKNESS AND TYPE OF GRAIN USED. YOU CAN INTERCHANGE ANY OF THESE RECIPES. FOR INSTANCE, YOU CAN MAKE THE MUFFINS INTO A BREAD, OR THE BREAD CAN BE FLATTENED OUT FOR CRACKERS. IF YOU DEHYDRATE THE CRACKERS AND CHIPS UNTIL COMPLETELY DRY, THEY WILL KEEP FOR A LONG TIME OUT OF THE REFRIGERATOR

BREADS, CHIPS, MUFFINS, AND CRACKERS

IN SEALED BAGS OR CONTAINERS. SINCE BREAD AND MUFFINS RETAIN MOISTURE, THEY NEED TO BE REFRIGERATED.

THERE ARE SO MANY VARIATIONS ON RAW AND LIVING BREADS. EXPERIMENT FOR YOURSELF, USING GRAINS SUCH AS BUCKWHEAT, WHEAT, AND RYE. THEN ADD ANY VEGGIES, FRUITS, OR NUTS OF YOUR CHOICE.

THE SAME HOLDS TRUE FOR CRACKERS. YOU CAN ADD ANY KIND OF VEGETABLES AND HERBS TO FLAX SEEDS TO MAKE DELICIOUS CRACKERS. ONCE YOU TRY A FEW OF THESE RECIPES AND GET THE HANG OF THE PROCESS, YOU MIGHT TRY INVENTING YOUR OWN.

CORN TORTILLAS

Yes, real raw tortillas! Immediately out of the dehydrator, they're soft and chewy so you can roll them around your favorite fillings. I use these for the enchiladas. It's important not to let these get too well done otherwise they'll be hard and crispy and will not be flexible enough to roll. Just let them "bake" enough so they are not soupy and you can shape them.

4 cups frozen corn

1/2 cup whole flax seeds ground (not soaked)

1/2 cup orange juice

1 clove garlic

1/8 teaspoon sea salt

1. Place all ingredients in a food processor and blend until smooth.
2. Place mixture on a Teflex sheet on top of a mesh dehydrator screen. Spread about 1/8 inch thick and dehydrate at 105 degrees.
3. When tortillas are solid enough to turn (after about 3 hours) flip onto mesh screen and dehydrate until other side is solid (another 1-2 hours or so).
4. Remove from sheet and fill with your favorite fillings.
5. Roll up and place back in the dehydrator for 2-8 hours, depending on the filling.

Note: When you flip the tortilla after the first 3 hours, it's ok if it's still mushy. It will solidify in approximately two hours. Remember, the key to this recipe is not to let the tortilla get too crispy before you roll it.

I use frozen corn for this recipe as fresh corn gives the tortillas an undesirable flavor and texture.

BURGER BUNS

Finally! Something to hold all those raw burgers, pâtés and sandwich ingredients that actually mimics the real thing! These look and taste like real buns if you shape them round and full and sprinkle them with sesame seeds.

You can also make bread, crackers, and pizza crust out of this dough. The thinner you roll out the dough (as you would for crackers or pizza) the faster it will dehydrate.

BUCKWHEAT - Has a high pro-portion of all eight essential amino acids and especially lysine at 6.1 percent greater than any of the cereal grains. Additionally, buckwheat con-tains up to 100 percent more calcium than other grains. Buckwheat is botanically not a grain but a fruit. It is considered a grain though because of the way it looks and tastes. Use only raw buck-wheat, not toasted (kasha) or whole buckwheat groats.

2 cups sprouted buckwheat

3/4 cup soaked whole flax seeds

3/4 cup carrots

1/2 cup olive oil

1 teaspoon curry

1 teaspoon fresh rosemary (or 1/2 teaspoon dried)

1 teaspoon fresh thyme (or 1/2 teaspoon dried)

1 clove garlic

1 teaspoon sea salt

Sesame seeds (optional)

1. Grind the carrots in a food processor until they are diced.
2. Add in other ingredients and blend well until dough-like
3. Form into buns and place on mesh screens on dehydrator screens. Sprinkle with sesame seeds, if desired. Dehydrate at 105 degrees for 24 hours.

Note: These should be firm but not hard.

BANANA BREAD

My grandmother used to make the best banana bread! We would eat it hot out of the oven and smother it with cream cheese. I couldn't give that up!

Because of the lack of dry ingredients, this bread may take longer to dehydrate and it will be softer and moister then most other breads when finished.

3 cups sprouted wheat berries

3 bananas

1/2 cup dates, pitted and soaked

1/4 teaspoon cinnamon

1. Blend all ingredients well in a food processor.
2. Place on a Teflex sheet on top of a mesh dehydrator screen.
3. Form dough into a loaf and dehydrate at 105 degrees for 18-24 hours.
4. Turn loaf after 10 hours.

Serving suggestions: Top with "Cream Cheese."

SPICY MONKEY BREAD

A different twist on the banana bread, you'll find this heavier and denser.

1/2 cup walnuts

2 cups sprouted wheat berries

3 bananas

1/2 cup dates, pitted and soaked

1 teaspoon vanilla

1 teaspoon cinnamon

1/2 teaspoon nutmeg

1. Grind walnuts in a food processor until fine.

2. Add the rest of the ingredients and blend well.

3. Remove from processor and place on a mesh dehydrator screen.

4. Form dough into a 2 inch high loaf and dehydrate at 105 degrees for 16-24 hours.

5. Turn loaf after 8-10 hours.

Note: Make sure the bread is not mushy in the middle. Breads can take a long time to dehydrate depending on the thickness and type of grain used.

BLUEBERRY BREAD

This bread couldn't be easier to make. The blueberries are responsible for this bread's scrumptious flavor!

2 cups sprouted wheat berries

1/2 cup dates, pitted and soaked

1 cup blueberries (fresh or frozen)

1. In a food processor, combine the wheat sprouts and dates and blend until dough-like.

2. Remove from food processor and place in a bowl. Fold in blueberries.

3. On a mesh dehydrator screen form dough into a 2 inch high loaf and dehydrate at 105 degrees for 16-24 hours.

4. Turn loaf after 8-10 hours

Note: Make sure the bread is not mushy in the middle. Breads can take a long time to dehydrate depending on the thickness and type of grain used.

CARROT RAISIN BREAD

Reminiscent of the carrot raisin manna bread I ate so much of when I first became a vegetarian. This is a very pretty looking bread.

2 cups sprouted wheat berries

1/2 dates, pitted and soaked

1/10 teaspoon nutmeg

1/10 teaspoon cinnamon

1 cup shredded carrots

1/2 cup raisins (soaked for 1/2 hour)

1. In a food processor, combine the wheat sprouts and dates and blend well.

2. Add the nutmeg and cinnamon and blend until dough-like.

3. Remove from food processor and place in a bowl. Fold in the carrots and raisins.

4. On a mesh dehydrator screen form dough into a round loaf and dehydrate at 105 degrees for 16-24 hours.

5. Turn loaf after 8-10 hours.

Note: Make sure the bread is not mushy in the middle. Breads can take a long time to dehydrate depending on the thickness and type of grain used.

ZUCCHINI BREAD

I love this bread, courtesy of *Living in the Raw* by Rose Lee Calabro.

2 cups sprouted wheat berries

1/2 cup pitted dates

1 cup zucchini, grated

1 cup raisins

1 teaspoon vanilla

1 teaspoon cinnamon

1/2 teaspoon nutmeg

1/4 teaspoon cardamom

1. Process wheat and dates through a Champion Juicer using the solid plate. (If you use a food processor instead of the juicer, make sure that you blend the wheat berries and dates well.) Place mixture in bowl.
2. Add the remaining ingredients and mix well.
3. Form into two loaves of bread. Place on a dehydrator screen with a Teflex sheet, and dehydrate at 105 degrees for 4-6 hours.
4. Turn bread over, and remove Teflex sheet. Continue dehydrating for 4-6 hours or until desired moisture is obtained.

CINNAMON RAISIN BREAD

Pepperidge Farm Cinnamon Swirl? Well, pretty close!

You can form the dough into 'bread' slices instead of a loaf for easier sandwich preparation.

1 cup walnuts

5 cups sprouted barley

1 cup dates, pitted and soaked

1 teaspoon cinnamon

1 cup raisins

1. Grind walnuts in a food processor until fine.
2. Add the rest of the ingredients except for raisins and blend until dough-like.
3. Add raisins and mix into dough.
4. Remove from processor and place on a mesh dehydrator screen. Form dough into a 2 inch high loaf and dehydrate at 105 degrees for 16-24 hours.
5. Turn loaf after 8-10 hours.

Note: Make sure the bread is not mushy in the middle. Breads can take a long time to dehydrate depending on the thickness and type of grain used.

RYE BAGELS

These bagels are dense and hearty, with a strong rye flavor. They are so incredible served with the Cream Cheese or Onion Dip!

2 cups sunflower seeds

4 cups sprouted rye berries

1 teaspoon minced onion

1 1/2 teaspoon sea salt

1/3 cup caraway seeds

---

1. Grind sunflower seeds in a food processor until fine.

2. Add the rye berries, onion and salt and blend well.

3. This will be hard to blend so you can add a little water as you go. Start with a tablespoon at a time and add up to 1/2 cup water. Be sure not to add too much, as this dough should remain very thick.

4. Remove from processor, add in caraway seeds by hand and place on a mesh dehydrator screen. Form dough into a 4 inch round bagel with a hole in the middle (use about 1 cup of dough for each bagel) or into a 2 inch high loaf and dehy-drate at 105 degrees for 16-24 hours.

5. Turn bagels or loaf after 8-10 hours.

Note: Make sure the bread is not mushy in the middle. Breads can take a long time to dehydrate depending on the thickness and type of grain used.

ELAINA'S CORN BREAD

Elaina Love is a Master Chef and Instructor for the Living Light Culinary Arts Institute. She holds retreats and individual train-ing sessions around the world.

Elaina has contributed some of her fabulous recipes for this book.

1 1/2 cups dry golden flax seeds ground into meal OR soaked 4-8 hours and ground in a Vita-Mix blender (blend dry seeds first before getting your blender wet)

2 cups soaked raw almonds (1 1/4 cups before soaking) soaked 4-8 hours OR 3 cups almond meal leftover from almond milk and 1/2 cup oil

2 cups raw cashews OR 1 cup raw cashew butter

1 cup pine nuts

1 10 ounce bag of frozen corn OR 10 ounces of corn fresh off the cob

1/4 cup raw honey

2 teaspoon Celtic sea salt

2 cloves garlic

1: Put almonds in the blender with enough water to cover, and blend until creamy. Use a celery stalk as your spatula to keep things moving in the blender.

(Alternate Step 1: Put 3 cups almond meal in a large mixing bowl with 1/2 cup melted coconut butter or olive oil.)

2: Blend cashews as you did the almonds or add the cashew butter to the bowl.

3: Blend pine nuts, corn and honey or maple syrup in the blender until creamy. You can stop blending while the corn is a little chunky if you like. You may need to add a little water to blend.

4: Put all ingredients together in the bowl and mix well. Let sit for 15 minutes.

5: Spread the batter onto a 16 x 16 dehydrator screen covered with a Teflex sheet. Make the bread about 1/4" thick. Score into 25 squares with the edge of your spatula or a butter knife. You should fill at least 2 sheets

6: Dehydrate at 105 degrees for about 3 hours. Flip the bread and take the Teflex off.

7: Dry for another 3 hours or until bread is still very moist and is easy to lift up.

Store in the refrigerator for up to 1 week.

MORNING MUFFINS

This recipe also makes a great bread. It has a solid texture and is delicious topped with apricot jam or nut butter.

1 cup sunflower seeds

1 cup almonds

1 cup sprouted wheat berries

1 Tablespoon honey

2 teaspoons cinnamon

1 teaspoon vanilla

1/8 teaspoon sea salt

1/2 cup raisins

1. Grind sunflower seeds and almonds in a food processor until fine.
2. Add in wheat berries, honey, cinnamon, vanilla, sea salt and blend well. Add in a couple of Tablespoons of water to help bread 'turn over' if needed.
3. Remove from food processor and stir in raisins by hand.
4. Place on a mesh dehydrator screen. Form dough into small muffin shapes.
5. Dehydrate at 105 degrees for 10-16 hours depending on size of balls and degree of firmness.

APPLE CURRANT MUFFINS

Apples and raisins give these muffins a wonderful, old fashioned breakfast flavor.

1 cup walnuts

2 cups sprouted wheat berries

2 bananas

3/4 cup dates, pitted and soaked

1/2 teaspoon vanilla

1 teaspoon cinnamon

2 cups grated apple

1/2 cup raisins

---

1. Grind walnuts in a food processor until fine.

2. Add the sprouted wheat berries, bananas, dates, vanilla, and cinnamon and blend well.

3. Remove from food processor and stir in raisins and apples by hand

4. Place on a mesh dehydrator screen. Form dough into small muffin shapes

5. Dehydrate at 105 degrees for 10-16 hours depending on size of balls and degree of firmness desired.

SWEET POTATO CHIPS

You can make chips using a variety of different vegetables, but sweet potato chips are a favorite of mine. Here are a few different ways I like to prepare them. Experiment on your own, using different dressings and marinades.

THE SIMPLE SWEET POTATO CHIP

I like this plain chip recipe because it only takes a few hours to make mounds of chips! They're a great alternative to crackers for dipping.

Sweet potatoes (one medium sweet potato yields about 3 large dehydrator screens of chips).

1. Peel, then slice the sweet potatoes in a spiral slicer, mandolin, or any other machine that will make thin slices. You can use the food processor but this tends to make thicker chips. I prefer thinner chips, but experiment for yourself to see what you like best.
2. Spread the sweet potatoes on mesh dehydrator screens.
3. Dehydrate at 105 degrees for 4-5 hours or until crispy.

CHEESY CHIPS

These remind me of the popcorn I used to make in my early vegetarian days. I'd sprinkle on yeast for extra vitamin B, and a "cheesy" taste.

2 sweet potatoes

1/4 cup water

1/4 cup Bragg Liquid Aminos

1/2 - 1 cup nutritional yeast

1. Peel, then slice the sweet potatoes in a spiral slicer, mandolin, or any other machine that will make thin slices.
2. Combined the water and Bragg Liquid Aminos in a large bowl.

3. Marinate the sweet potatoes in the water and Bragg Liquid Aminos mixture for at least 5 minutes.

4. Drain the chips, and then lay them flat on a dehydrator screen.

5. Dust the sweet potatoes with the yeast. I like them heavily coated for a real cheese flavor.

6. Dehydrate at 105 degrees for 8-10 hours or until crispy.

HOT CHIPS

Make 'em as hot or mild as you like by altering the amount of chili or cayenne pepper.

2 sweet potatoes

1/4 cup olive oil

1/4 cup lemon juice

1 teaspoon cayenne pepper and/or chili powder

1. Peel, then slice the sweet potatoes in a spiral slicer, mandolin, or any other machine that will make thin slices.

2. Combine the olive oil and lemon in a bowl.

3. Coat the sweet potato chips with the mixture by placing them in the bowl with the olive oil and lemon.

4. Drain the chips and lay them flat on a dehydrator screen.

5. Sprinkle with the spice mixture. The amount you use will depend upon the degree of "kick" you want.

6. Dehydrate at 105 degrees for 8-10 hours or until crispy.

ALMOND BUTTER SWEET POTATO CHIPS

These chips are very sweet, more like a dessert!

2 sweet potatoes
1/2 cup honey
1/2 cup almond butter

1. Peel, then slice the sweet potatoes in a spiral slicer, mandolin, or any other machine that will make thin slices.
2. Combine honey and almond butter in a small bowl.
3. Lay sweet potato slices on a dehydrator screen.
4. Put a small amount of the almond butter and honey mixture onto the chip and roll it up.
5. Dehydrate at 105 degrees for 8-10 hours or until crispy.

Note: The almond butter and honey will keep these chips more moist then the others.

ZUCCHINI CHIPS

Use these for dips instead of crackers.

4-6 zucchini

1. I usually slice these through a food processor. They tend to come out too thin and stick to the dehydrating screens if they are sliced through a spiral slicer or mandolin, but you can experiment with the size.
2. Spread the zucchini on mesh dehydrator screens.
3. Dehydrate at 105 degrees for 8-10 hours or until crispy.

ITALIAN ZUCCHINI CHIPS

4-6 zucchini

Italian Dressing (Page 471)

1. I usually slice these through a food processor. They tend to come out too thin and stick to the dehydrating screens if they are sliced through a spiral slicer or mandolin, but you can experiment with the size.
2. Put the Italian dressing in a bowl with the sliced zucchini and let marinate for at least 1 hour.
3. Drain the chips. Lay them flat on a dehydrator screen.
4. Dehydrate at 105 degrees for 14-18 hours or until crispy.

Note: These marinated chips will get even harder and crispier once you remove them from the dehydrator and let them cool.

BABY RAW'S SEA SALT & VINEGAR CHIPS

My niece, Brooke, made these up a week after going raw to satisfy her craving for potato chips.

3-4 potatoes

Apple cider vinegar (enough to cover potatoes in a large bowl)

Sea salt

For this recipe I usually use 3-4 potatoes. You can use as many as you like.

1. Peel, then slice the potatoes in a spiral slicer, mandolin, or any other machine that will make thin slices.

2. Place potatoes in a large bowl with enough apple cider vinegar to cover them and let soak for 10-15 minutes.

3. Remove potatoes from the vinegar and place on a mesh dehydrator screen.

4. Sprinkle the sheets of potatoes with sea salt and dehydrate for 5-10 hours or until crisp.

FLAX SEED CRACKERS

FLAXSEEDS - Supply an essential fatty acid (ALA). ALA is converted by the body into the type of omega 3 fatty acids found in many fish. The richest sources of lignins, which provide fiber, flaxseeds prevent constipation.

The basic cracker: I love these! They are simple, yet tasty and great for dipping or topping with avocado, tomato and onion. After you make these once, you can vary the amounts of garlic and ginger and lemon to suit your taste.

2 cups whole flax seeds (soaked in 2 cups water for 4 hours or overnight)
2 cloves garlic
1/2 lemon, juiced
2 Tablespoons Bragg Liquid Aminos
1 Tablespoon fresh ginger

1. Place all ingredients in a food processor and blend until well combined, and until the garlic and ginger are completely ground.

2. Remove from processor and place on a Teflex sheet on top of a mesh dehydrator screen. Spread batter into a thin sheet about 1/8 inch thick (or less... I like to make these very thin: the 'goopy' substance from the flax seeds holds these crackers together even if they have holes).

3. Dehydrate at 105 degrees for 10-16 hours, depending on degree of crispness desired. Flip crackers and peel off Teflex sheet after 7-8 hours.

Note: When you place whole flax seeds in the food processor with the other ingredients, the flax seeds will stay whole. This is suggested just to grind the other ingredients and to blend the flax seeds into the mixture.

GOLDEN CARROT FLAX CRACKERS

These crackers are very pretty, and the golden flax gives them a lighter taste.

1/2 cup sunflower seeds

2 cups whole golden flax seeds (soaked in 2 cups water for 4 hours or overnight)

3 large carrots, shredded

2 stalks celery, diced

1/4 cup parsley, chopped

1/4 cup onion, diced

1/4 green pepper, diced

1/4 cup red cabbage, shredded

---

1. Place sunflower seeds in a Vita-Mix, food processor or coffee grinder and grind into a fine powder

2. Remove from processor and place in a bowl.

3 Add the remaining ingredients to the bowl with the sunflower seeds and blend well.

3. Remove from bowl and place on a Teflex sheet on top of a mesh dehydrator screen. Spread batter into a thin sheet about 1/8 inch thick.

4. Dehydrate at 105 degrees for 10-16 hours, depending on degree of crispness desired. Flip crackers and peel off Teflex sheet after 7-8 hours.

VEGGIE FLAX CRACKERS

Chips with multicolored beauty! The perfect chip to make when you're having company. Loaded with vegetables, these crackers are packed with nutrition!

2 cups whole flax seeds (soaked in 2 cups water for 4 hours or overnight)

3 cups cilantro

2 cups broccoli, chopped into small pieces

2 cups celery, diced

2 cups spinach, torn

1 cup sun dried tomatoes, soaked

1 orange bell pepper, diced

1 carrot, shredded

1/4 teaspoon sea salt

---

1. Place flax seeds in a food processor with cilantro, tomatoes, and sea salt. Blend until the cilantro and tomatoes are well ground. Place mixture into a large bowl.

2. Place all other ingredients into the bowl with above mixture and stir until well combined.

3. Remove from bowl and place on a Teflex sheet on top of a mesh dehydrator screen. Spread batter into a thin sheet about 1/8 – 1/4 inch thick.

4. Dehydrate at 105 degrees for 10-16 hours, depending on degree of crispness desired. Flip crackers and peel off Teflex sheet after 7-8 hours.

Note: When you place whole flax seeds in the food processor with the other ingredients, the flax seeds will stay whole. This is suggested just to grind the other ingredients and to blend the flax seeds into the mixture.

BANANA CRACKERS

Kids love these! Try topping them with raw almond butter and honey for an amazing dessert like treat!

2 cups whole golden flax seeds (soaked in 2 cups water for 4 hours or overnight)

3 bananas

1 1/2 oranges, juiced

1. Place bananas and orange juice in a food processor and blend until smooth.
2. Add in flax seeds and blend well.
3. Remove from processor and place on a Teflex sheet on top of a mesh dehydrator screen.
4. Spread batter into a thin sheet about 1/8 inch thick.
5. Dehydrate at 105 degrees for 10-16 hours, depending on degree of crispness desired. Flip crackers and peel off Teflex sheet after 7-8 hours.

Note: These crackers will be flexible and pliable like fruit leather but will harden a bit as they cool.

CORN CHIPS

Serve these with guacamole and salsa for a Mexican treat... *muy bien!*

For spicy corn chips, add in some cayenne.

6 ears of corn

CORN - Good for fighting eczema.

1/4 cup onion

1/8 teaspoon sea salt

1-2 shredded carrots (optional)

---

1. Scrape the kernels off of the corn.
2. Place all ingredients in a food processor and blend until well combined (except the carrots if you are using them).
3. Remove from processor, mixing in the carrot by hand, if desired.
4. Place on a Teflex sheet on top of a mesh dehydrator screen. Spread batter into a thin sheet about 1/8 inch thick.
5. Dehydrate at 105 degrees for 10-16 hours, depending on degree of crispness desired. Flip crackers and peel off Teflex sheet after 7-8 hours.

Note: These crackers may appear soft and flexible but will harden once they cool off.

LIME PEPPER CRACKERS

The tart taste of lime mixed with the peppers give these crackers their unique flavor.

2 cups whole flax seeds (soaked in 2 cups water for 4 hours or overnight)

6 cups spinach

3 whole large limes, peeled

2 cups tomatoes

1 1/2 cups red bell pepper

1 1/2 cups green bell pepper

1 1/2 cups yellow bell pepper

1. Place all ingredients in a food processor and blend until well combined.

2. Remove from processor and place on a Teflex sheet on top of a mesh dehydrator screen. Spread batter into a thin sheet about 1/8 inch thick.

3. Dehydrate at 105 degrees for 10-16 hours, depending on degree of crispness desired. Flip crackers and peel off Teflex sheet after 7-8 hours.

ROLLED NORI CRACKERS

A taste of Japan! A unique tubular looking cracker.

10 or more sheets raw nori

2 cups whole flax seeds (soaked in 2 cups water for 4 hours or overnight)

3 cups celery

1 cup tomatoes

———————

1. Place flax seeds, tomatoes, and celery in a food processor. Blend well.

2. Remove from processor and place in a bowl.

3. Remove nori sheets from package and cut each piece of nori in half.

4. Using a spoon or your hands, place a thick strip of the flax seed mixture on top of each nori sheet. (Use about 2 tablespoons of flax seed mixture per sheet) Roll up like you would a sushi roll but thinner and tighter. (I usually make these very thin, about 1/2 inch round; otherwise they take a long time to dehydrate.) Continue this process with all of the nori sheets.

5. Place the rolls on a mesh dehydrator screen and dehydrate at 105 degrees until the rolls are solid throughout. The time of dehydrating will depend on the thickness of the rolls, but these usually take a long time.

WHOLE WHEAT CRACKERS

A hearty, old time cracker. Make sure all herbs used are fresh!

2 cups sprouted wheat berries

1 cup soaked flax seeds

1 cup orange juice

4 cloves garlic

1/2 cup chopped onion

1/4 cup basil

1/4 cup cilantro

1/4 parsley

1/2 teaspoon sea salt

Dash cayenne

1. Measure out one cup of wheat sprouts and set aside.
2. Place the remaining ingredients in a food processor and blend well.
3. Add in the 1 cup sprouted wheat and pulse chop for a couple seconds to blend but keep mostly whole.
4. Remove from processor and place on a Teflex sheet on top of a mesh dehydrator screen. Spread batter into a thin sheet about 1/8 - 1/4 inch thick.
5. Dehydrate at 105 degrees for 10-16 hours, depending on degree of crispness desired.

SEA WAFERS

Exotic and delicious. The seaweed dulse is very high in minerals.

1 cup sunflower seeds

1/2 cup soaked flax seeds

1/4 cup sundried tomatoes, soaked

1/8 teaspoon fresh ginger

1/2 teaspoon sea salt

1/2 cup dulse flakes

Herbamare seasoning salt

1. In a food processor, grind sunflower seeds into a fine powder.
2. Add the flax seeds, ginger, sundried tomatoes and sea salt. Blend well.
3. Remove from food processor and place on a Teflex sheet on top of a mesh dehydrator screen. Spread batter into a thin sheet about 1/8 inch thick.
4. Sprinkle a heavy layer of Herbamare and dulse on top of the crackers.
5. Dehydrate at 105 degrees for 10-16 hours, depending on degree of crispness desired. Flip crackers and peel off Teflex sheet after 7-8 hours.

MEXICAN CRACKERS

These crackers are wonderfully thick and a bit chewy. They have a floury, grainy consistency as compared to the flax crackers. They also tend to be crumbly so make them thick to cut down on the crumbling.

1 orange, peeled

1 carrot

1 cup tomato

1/4 cup onion

1 stalk celery

1 clove garlic

1/2 cup parsley

1/2 cup cilantro

1 Tablespoon chili powder

1 Tablespoon lime juice

1/2 teaspoon jalapeno pepper

1 1/2 teaspoons sea salt

1/2 teaspoon cumin

1/2 cup whole corn

1 cup sunflower seeds (soaked 8 hours)

1 cup pumpkin seeds (soaked 8 hours)

---

1. Blend first 13 ingredients in a food processor until ground.
2. Add in the seeds and blend well until smooth.
3. Remove from processor and add in whole corn. Stir.
4. Place on a Teflex sheet on top of a mesh dehydrator screen. Spread batters into a sheet about 1/4 inch thick.
5. Dehydrate at 105 degrees for 10-16 hours, depending on degree of crispness desired. Flip crackers and peel off Teflex sheet after 7-8 hours.

PIZZA BREAD (THE ULTIMATE RAW FOOD WRAP!)

You will be able to make all kinds of sandwich rolls and wraps with this. If bread is something that has been hard for you to give up since going raw, wait until you try this! You will never miss pita, sprouted breads or flat breads ever again!

2 cups ground flax

1 cup soaked almonds, ground fine

2 cups carrot pulp (from whole carrot in food processor)

1 cup, diced red pepper

1/2 Tablespoon minced garlic

1/4 cup parsley

1/2 cup cilantro

1 1/2 teaspoon salt

1/2 teaspoon oregano

2 teaspoons Italian seasoning

1 Tablespoon fresh onion

1 teaspoon lemon juice

1/2 cup water

1 cup sundried tomatoes, measure before soaking.

---

1. Combine ground flax, almonds and carrots in a large bowl.

2. In a food processor blend until smooth the sundried tomatoes, garlic, parsley, cilantro and salt. Add this to the bowl with the flax, almonds and carrots.

3. Add in the remaining ingredients and mix together. Transfer this whole mixture back into the food processor and blend until smooth. (You may have to do this in batches).

4. On a Teflex sheet on top of a mesh dehydrator screen, spread this batter out into 4-6 inch crust, about 1/4 -1/2 inch thick. Dehydrate for 19 hours until crusts are solid but not hard.

Serving suggestions: roll this crust around your favorite fillings such as avocados, onions, tomatoes, etc... or top with your favorite pizza toppings.

SOUPS

ALTHOUGH THEY WON'T BE PIPING HOT, THESE SOUPS MAKE
FOR A SMOOTH, CREAMY, SOUL-SATISFYING MEAL.
THE BLENDING PROCESS MAY WARM UP THE SOUP A BIT, OR
YOU CAN HEAT UP THE BOWL BEFORE FILLING IT WITH YOUR
SOUP. MOST OF THE SOUPS ARE BEST CONSUMED SOON
AFTER PREPARING. WHILE NOT ESSENTIAL, A VITA-MIX WILL
MAKE THEM EVEN CREAMIER AND SMOOTHER!

BROCCOLI SOUP

So creamy and satisfying... one of my favorite soups! The cumin and sea salt are very important in this recipe, so make sure you have added enough of both of these to bring out the flavor of this soup.

3 cups water

1 cup almonds

1 teaspoon honey

2 cups broccoli

1 avocado

1/2 to 1 clove garlic

1 Tablespoon olive oil

1 teaspoon onion

1- 1 1/2 teaspoons sea salt

1/2 teaspoon cumin

1/8 teaspoon black pepper

1. In a blender or Vita-Mix blend water, almonds and honey until smooth.
2. Add in the rest of the ingredients and blend until creamy.

Note: Add more sea salt if this tastes bland.

BROCCOLI - Powerful anti-cancer food!

WATERMELON SOUP

I've fasted on this soup during the summer. Actually, I could probably live on this... it's that good!

5 cups watermelon, seeded and cubed

2 cups mango, peeled and diced

1/4 cup lime juice

3 Tablespoons fresh mint, chopped

1 Tablespoon fresh ginger, minced

1 Tablespoon honey

1/8 teaspoon ground cardamom

1. Place 3 1/2 cups watermelon and 1 cup mango in a food processor and blend until smooth.
2. Dice up the remaining 1 1/2 cups watermelon and 1 cup mango into tiny pieces and add to the puree.
3. In a small, separate bowl, combine the lime juice, mint, ginger, honey and cardamom. Add this to the previous mixture and stir well.
4. Chill and serve.

CORN CHOWDER

Fresh corn and creamy avocado make this another one of my favorite soups · smooth, creamy, and thick!

2 1/2 cups almond milk

5 ears corn on the cob, shaved

1 small avocado

1 teaspoon sea salt

---

1. In a blender or Vita-Mix, blend all but 1/2 ear of corn until smooth and creamy.
2. Stir in the remaining 1/2 ear of corn.

CREAMY PEA SOUP

If you can use fresh peas, make this soup and savor the flavor. Smooth, creamy and thick, just like the corn chowder!

2 1/2 cups almond milk

2 cups peas

1 small avocado

Sea salt to taste

Blend in blender or Vita-Mix.

CARROT SOUP

This is a very Indian tasting soup because of the earthy bold taste of cilantro and ginger. It's very creamy, but also light, airy, and frothy.

2 cups carrot juice

1 avocado

1 Tablespoon cilantro

1 Tablespoon ginger

1 teaspoon Bragg Liquid Aminos

Blend all in blender or Vita-Mix.

BERRY SOUP

This delicate soup tastes like an orange creamsicle in a bowl!

1/2 cup almonds

2 1/2 cups orange juice

1 1/2 cups water

2 Tablespoons lemon juice

1 Tablespoon honey

Dash cinnamon

Dash nutmeg

3 cups blueberries, raspberries, strawberries or blackberries (or a combination of all four)

---

1. Blend first 7 ingredients in a blender or Vita-Mix.
2. Pour blended soup over berries and chill before serving.

SWEETNESS

From Shazzie's *Detox Delights*. Read Shazzie's story in the "Testimonials" section of this book. You'll be amazed at her "before" and "after" pictures!

This is so simple. Very smooth and creamy.

1/4 of a cucumber

2 oranges

2 dessert spoons of tahini

Pinch of mustard powder

1 tomato

1 dessert spoon of onion

1/2 teaspoon of fresh ginger

1. In a food processor, blend all ingredients except the last three. This is the soup.

2. Finely chop the onion and ginger, and mix them together.

3. Finely slice the tomato.

4. Pour the soup into bowls.

5. Top it with 4 slices of tomato.

6. Place the onion and ginger mixture in the center.

EASY CUCUMBER SOUP

A simple, refreshing summer soup.

1 avocado

1 cucumber

4 Tablespoons dill weed

2 teaspoons lemon juice

1/2 teaspoon sea salt

Blend all ingredients in a blender or Vita-Mix until smooth and creamy.

SQUASH SOUP

This is a very sweet, dessert like soup.

4 cups butternut squash, peeled and seeded

5 cups orange juice

4 dates, pitted and soaked

1 large banana

1 teaspoon curry

————————

Blend all in blender or Vita-Mix.

CURRIED YAM BISQUE

A hearty, winter soup, this is mellow and smooth. Add more or less curry depending on your taste.

1 cup yam

1 1/2 cups cashew milk (cashews and water with honey or date to sweeten)

1/2 cup green apple

1 teaspoon mint

1 teaspoon curry (or less)

————————

Blend all in blender or Vita-Mix.

ZIPPY TOMATO SOUP

A very simple, quick tomato soup with lots of flavor

4 large Roma tomatoes

1/4 cup onion

1 clove garlic

1 teaspoon olive oil

3 basil leaves

1/4 teaspoon dried thyme

1/4 teaspoon paprika

Blend all ingredients in blender or Vita-Mix until smooth.

MUSHROOM SOUP

This soup has a creamed, almost smoky flavor. Consume this soon after making.

3 cups button mushrooms

3 cups almond milk

1/4 cup red bell pepper

1/2 teaspoon sea salt

Blend all ingredients in blender or Vita-Mix until smooth.

MISO SOUP

Smooth and soothing. The light taste of miso in an authentic, Japanese style soup.

1 1/2 cups water

1 Tablespoon fresh ginger root

MISO - Great for digestion.

Soothes upset stomachs.

2 teaspoons miso

1/4 teaspoon sea salt

2 Tablespoons scallion, chopped

1 Tablespoon carrot, shredded

1. Blend water, ginger, miso, and sea salt in a blender or Vita-Mix until smooth.

2. Place in a bowl, adding in the scallion and carrot in the center of bowl on top of the miso soup.

SPICY GREEN LIME CILANTRO SOUP

Cynthia Beavers is a raw food chef in Dallas, Texas, and offered this recipe, along with two others for this book. She makes this soup daily as it is one of her favorite and a great way to get in lots of greens!

Cynthia owns a Dallas-based food delivery service, in which she creates and delivers delicious, gourmet raw food dishes weekly. She has just opened a raw food restaurant called Pure.

2 -3 large handfuls of spinach

1 large handful of cilantro

Juice of 1-2 young coconuts

Meat of 1 young coconut

Juice of 1 1/2 limes

1/4-1/2 cup Living Olive Oil

1/4 cup or less of Nama Shoyu

1/2 teaspoon of mellow white miso

1 Poblano Pepper seeds

1/2 avocado

1/2 jalapeno or habanero depending on how hot you like it!

1 medium to large size dried Ancho Chile with seeds (stem removed)

2 cloves of garlic

Blend in Vita-Mix or Blender until smooth. Taste and adjust to meet your needs. The key ingredients are lime and ancho chiles: if it doesn't taste right add more of those ingredients.

THAI COCONUT SOUP

Lightly exotic and oh, so simple!

4 young baby white coconuts

1/2 cup pineapple

1 teaspoon cumin

---

1. Remove the milk from 4 coconuts and place in a blender or Vita-Mix.
2. Take the meat from 1 of the coconuts and place in blender along with the coconut milk.
3. Add the pineapple and cumin and blend well until smooth and creamy.

RED PEPPER SOUP

This soup is only slightly sweet, yet bursting with flavor!

4 1/2 cups red bell pepper

COCONUTS - Coconut milk contains the highest source of electrolytes found in nature. An excellent food for athletes.

1/2 teaspoon miso

1/2 cup chopped apple

1 cup cilantro

---

1. Blend all except 1/2 cup red bell pepper in blender or Vita-Mix until creamy.

2. Pour into a bowl.

3. Dice the remaining 1/2 cup red bell pepper and mix into bowl with the soup.

SAUCES AND CONDIMENTS

WONDERFUL CONCOCTIONS THAT WILL ADD LOTS OF SPICE AND VARIETY TO YOUR OTHER DISHES. MIX AND MATCH THEM WITH DIFFERENT MEALS!

MARINARA SAUCE

My all-time favorite...I use it for nearly everything requiring a tomato sauce. It's thick, rich, and sweet. *Viva Italiano!*

2 1/2 cups tomatoes

12 sundried tomatoes, soaked

1/4 cup olive oil

4 cloves garlic

3 dates, pitted and soaked

2 Tablespoons parsley

1/8 teaspoon cayenne

1 teaspoon sea salt

Place all ingredients in a food processor and blend until smooth.

TOMATO - Along with its many vitamins and minerals, the tomato contains lycopene which may help prevent prostate cancer and heart disease. Raw tomatoes reduce liver inflammation.

SUMMER TOMATO SAUCE

A light and tasty sauce, no matter what season you're in.

4 tomatoes

2 Tablespoons pine nuts

1 1/2 cups basil

1 1/2 clove garlic

6 Tablespoons olive oil

Herbamare or sea salt to taste

Place all ingredients in a food processor and blend until smooth.

TARRAGON PEPPER SAUCE

Pleasantly pungent, lively and aromatic, this sauce can be served as an alternative to my Marinara Sauce in most recipes.

4 red bell peppers

2 large tomatoes

6 Tablespoons olive oil

2 Tablespoons apple cider vinegar

2 Tablespoons tarragon

Sea salt and black pepper to taste

Place all ingredients in a food processor and blend until smooth.

Note: For added texture, set aside one bell pepper. After blending everything smooth in the processor, pulse chop the single pepper into chunky bits.

SPICY GINGER MARINARA

This is Chad Sarno's delicious marinara that he uses over his Thai Cannelloni recipe that he so graciously shared for this book! Executive Chef of *Vital Creations*, Chef Services, Chad also caters, teaches and conducts seminars.

2 cups red bell pepper, chopped

1 cup tomato, chopped

1/2 cup sundried tomato, soaked for 2-3 hours in filtered water

1/2 cup apple, chopped

2 cloves garlic

2 Tablespoons ginger, chopped

4 kefir lime leaves (optional)

2 Tablespoons olive oil

1 teaspoon Celtic sea salt

1/2 teaspoon black pepper, cracked

1 teaspoon cayenne (optional)

3 Tablespoons basil, fresh and chopped

2 Tablespoons chives, fresh and chopped

In a blender, blend the red pepper, tomato, sundried tomato, apple, garlic, ginger, lime leaves, olive oil, sea salt, pepper and cayenne until smooth consistency. Pulse in the fresh basil and chives, making sure not to blend fully leaving small pieces of herbs in sauce.

Serve over Thai Cannelloni

Notes: You may need to adjust quantity of sea salt to your liking, depending on the quality of tomatoes. Try a variation with tomatoes, omitting 2 cups of the bell peppers. With excess leftovers, simply add a bit of olive oil and apple cider vinegar for a salad dressing.

BARBECUE SAUCE

Adds an authentic Western touch to your menu. This recipe makes a great pizza sauce and is scrumptious when served with the "Noasted Turkey" or meatloaf.

1 small or 1/2 large onion

1 cup dates, pitted and soaked

1 cup sundried tomatoes, soaked

1/2 tomato

Blend all ingredients thoroughly in a food processor. If you prefer a chunkier sauce, dice the onions and tomato and fold into the other well-blended ingredients.

MUSHROOM GRAVY

Just like Mom used to make... almost! This gravy greatly enhances the mashed potatoes and meatloaf.

2 cups crimini mushrooms

2 Tablespoons Bragg Liquid Aminos

1 Tablespoon water

1 small clove garlic

1/2 teaspoon fresh sage

Sea salt and pepper to taste

Blend all ingredients thoroughly in a food processor.

Note: Portobella mushrooms can substitute for the crimini mushrooms.

STACIE'S MINT CHUTNEY

This aromatic condiment is beautifully authentic. This is just one of Stacie's delicious recipes she has offered for this book.

Owner of "Ripe and Raw Catering," Stacie Cohen is an amazing raw food chef! She also teaches raw and living food classes in the Portland, Oregon area.

2 cups fresh mint

1 1/2 limes, juiced

1 date, pitted and soaked

1/4 cup cilantro

1/2 teaspoon fenugreek seeds, ground

Pinch cayenne

Mix all ingredients in a food processor. Add water as needed to blend.

Note: Add shredded coconut for a nice taste treat.

CUCUMBER SAUCE

Light, refreshing, and delicious. Serve with the falafels.

1/2 large cucumber (about 1 1/2 cups)

1/4 cup tahini

1/4 cup fresh dill weed

1/2 lemon, juiced

1 Tablespoon honey

1/4 teaspoon sea salt

Blend all ingredients thoroughly in a food processor or blender.

CHINESE DIPPING SAUCE

With both a tangy and sweet taste, this is fabulous served with cabbage rolls and lettuce wraps.

1/4 cup honey

1/4 cup lemon juice

3 Tablespoons orange juice

2 Tablespoons olive oil

2 Tablespoons Bragg Liquid Aminos

1 Tablespoon fresh ginger

1 teaspoon apple cider vinegar

1/2 teaspoon dry mustard

Blend all ingredients thoroughly in a food processor or blender.

HONEY MUSTARD PASTE

Simple, yet versatile, this topping is wonderful in wraps, on breads and crackers, or as a dip. Serve this with the BBQ chicken fingers.

1/2 cup honey

2 Tablespoons yellow mustard powder

1 teaspoon lemon juice

Mix together by hand.

CURRY SAUCE

This delicious sauce is the perfect compliment to burgers or loaves! It is perfectly divine served over the Pecan-Carrot Burgers.

1 whole orange, peeled

1/3 cup raisins, soaked

1 large clove garlic

1/2 Tablespoon curry

1/2 teaspoon cumin

1/2 teaspoon fresh ginger

Blend all ingredients in a blender or food processor until smooth.

CHILI SAUCE

Wonderful over loaves and as a dressing in wraps!

2 tomatoes

1 lime, juiced

1 clove garlic

1 Tablespoon Bragg Liquid Aminos

1/2 Tablespoon cumin

1 teaspoon jalapeno

1 teaspoon chili powder

1 teaspoon oregano

1/8 teaspoon sea salt

Blend all ingredients in a blender or food processor until smooth.

APRICOT JAM

A wonderful jam to use on muffins and breads.

2 cups dried apricots, soaked
1 cup strawberries

_____

In a Vita-Mix or food processor, blend apricots and strawberries until smooth and creamy.

APPLE-CILANTRO CHUTNEY

Fragrant and delectable, this is a great topping for many dishes.

1/4 cup almonds
1/4 cup raisins, soaked
1 diced apple
1/2 cup water
2 Tablespoons cilantro
1/2 teaspoon lemon juice
1/2 Tablespoon honey
1/2 Tablespoon sea salt
1/2 teaspoon cumin
1/4 teaspoon sesame seed
1/4 teaspoon black pepper

1/4 teaspoon ginger

Pinch yellow mustard

Dash cayenne pepper

1. In a food processor or Vita-Mix, blend almonds into a fine powder.
2. Add remaining ingredients and blend until smooth.

STRAWBERRY SAUCE

Delicious over Crêpes, Banana Ice Cream, and other desserts.

1 cup strawberries

1 Tablespoon honey

Blend all ingredients thoroughly in a food processor or blender.

BLUEBERRY SAUCE

Like you would with its strawberry cousin, pour this sauce over your favorite desserts!

1 cup blueberries

1 Tablespoon honey

Blend all ingredients thoroughly in a food processor or blender.

PLUM SAUCE

Enhance your fresh fruits and ice creams!

4 plums, pitted

1 teaspoon honey

_____

1. Pit the plums and cut into fourths. (No need to peel the plums)
2. Place plums and honey in a food processor and blend until smooth.

IN THE "RAW FOOD WORLD" THE TEXTURE OF THE DISH OFTEN
CHANGES ITS FLAVOR. IN ANY GIVEN RECIPE DICING INSTEAD
OF SLICING, OR CHOPPING INSTEAD OF SHREDDING CAN
CHANGE THE ENTIRE FLAVOR OR APPEAL OF THAT DISH.
SO, WHILE I CERTAINLY ENCOURAGE YOU TO EXPERIMENT,
YOU MAY WANT TO START OUT BY PREPARING THE RECIPES
THROUGHOUT THIS BOOK USING THE INGREDIENTS AND
INSTRUCTIONS PROVIDED.

ENTRÉES

THEN, BY ALL MEANS, EXPERIMENT WITH YOUR OWN INNOVA-
TIONS! CREATE DIFFERENT TEXTURES AND TASTES BY BLEND-
ING OR CHOPPING IN NEW WAYS. USE ALTERNATIVE VEGETA-
BLES, NUTS, SEEDS, GRAINS, AND/OR SEASONINGS.

SOON, YOU WILL BE CREATING YOUR OWN RAW AND LIVING
FOOD MASTERPIECES!

CRÊPES

My absolute favorite, hands down. You won't believe how delicious they are, how easy they are to prepare, and how beautiful they look served on a white plate surrounded by whole strawberries!

CRÊPE SHELLS:

5-6 RIPE bananas

FILLING:

1 cup macadamia nuts

1 cup cashews

1 large lemon, juiced

4 teaspoons honey

2 teaspoons Bragg Liquid Aminos

1 teaspoon vanilla

2 teaspoons water

STRAWBERRY SAUCE:

1 1/2 cups strawberries

1-2 Tablespoons honey

FOR CRÊPE SHELLS:

1. Place bananas in a food processor and blend until smooth.

2. Remove from processor and spread about 1/8 inch thick onto a Teflex sheet on top of a dehydrator screen.

3. Dehydrate for 14 hours or fewer. (Begin checking the bananas a few hours before to make sure they are formed, pliable, and solid in texture, but not getting crispy)

4. Remove from dehydrator and slice into strips (about 4"x 2").

FOR FILLING:

1. Place filling ingredients in a food processor and blend until smooth.

FOR STRAWBERRY SAUCE

1. Combine strawberries and honey in a food processor and blend until smooth.

TO ASSEMBLE:

1. Pour strawberry sauce onto plate in a thin layer so as to cover bottom of plate.
2. Place scoops of filling onto banana fruit leather strips and roll up. Place on plate with enough room in between so each crepe is not touching.
3. Pour strawberry sauce over the rolled up crepes.

Note: It's important to let the crepes sit for at least a couple of hours with the strawberry sauce on top. The sauce will soften the fruit leather and make it "crepe like" instead of hard and chewy. These are also great the next day!

MOCK SALMON PÂTÉ

A delicious pink pâté with a hint of salmon flavor! I eat this all the time on top of a large salad with a vinaigrette dressing. It's such an easy pâté to prepare and oh so delicious!

2 cups walnuts

2 stalks celery

1 large red bell pepper

1 large scallion

1/2 -1 teaspoon sea salt

Combine all ingredients in a food processor and blend until smooth.

Serving suggestions: This can be served on a plate as is, over a salad, rolled up in a green leaf, or spread on crackers.

FETTUCCINI ALFREDO

It tastes so much like genuine Fettuccini Alfredo that my cooked food friends adore it! You'll love the ease in creating it, along with its creamy Alfredo taste and texture.

For added color and more variety you can add thin slices of red bell pepper, mushrooms or any other vegetables.

FETTUCCINI:

2 zucchini

2 summer squash

ALFREDO:

1 cup cashews

1 cup macadamia nuts

1 cup pine nuts

3 Tablespoons lemon juice

2 cloves garlic

2 teaspoons Bragg Liquid Aminos

2 Tablespoons water

FOR FETTUCCINI NOODLES:

1. With a vegetable peeler, peel zucchini and summer squash into long thick strips. These will be your "fettuccini noodles." Set aside in a large bowl.

RED BELL PEPPERS - Help prevent heart disease, stroke, and cataracts. Since they have had more time to mature and sweeten than green peppers, they provide even more vitamins A and C and are full with cancer fighting carotenoids.

FOR ALFREDO SAUCE:

1. Place the Alfredo ingredients in a food processor and blend until smooth and creamy.

2. Remove from food processor and place in bowl with "noodles".

TO ASSEMBLE:

1. With your hands, blend the Alfredo sauce through the noodles. This will take a few minutes as the sauce will be thick. The water from the vegetables will help thin it out while you knead it together with your hands.

BEAN-LESS FALAFEL!

I'm not all that crazy about eating a lot of beans, they just don't digest well for me. But, I love falafel, which is usually made with chickpeas. The solution: almonds! These are out of this world! Dehydrate them for only a few hours and they come out fluffy and soft.

ALMONDS - The most alkaline of all nuts, almonds are helpful in the treatment of heartburn and peptic ulcers. They are higher in protein than most nuts.

2 cups almonds

1/2 cup cilantro

1/4 cup parsley

4 Tablespoons lemon juice

2 Tablespoons tahini

1 Tablespoon olive oil

1 1/2 teaspoons ground cumin

1 teaspoon sea salt

3/4 cup water

1. In a food processor, blend the almonds until fine.

2. Add the remaining ingredients, and blend well.

3. Roll mixture into small balls and place on a mesh dehydrator screen.

4. Dehydrate at 105 degrees for 4-5 hours, longer if you desire a crispy falafel.

ALMOST TUNA

Adapted from an early Ann Wigmore recipe, I like this dish because it uses lots of sprouts, and isn't "nut-heavy," like many of the other entrées. If desired, substitute an extra 1/4 cup mung bean sprouts instead of the sprouted lentils.

3 cups alfalfa sprouts

1/3 cup sunflower seeds

1/4 cup sprouted lentils (or 1/2 cup just mung beans, no lentils)

1/4 cup mung bean sprouts

3 Tablespoons almond butter

1 Tablespoon kelp

1 teaspoon Bragg Liquid Aminos

1/2 cup onion

2 stalks celery

1 teaspoon sea salt (more to taste)

ALFALFA SPROUTS - Contain every essential amino acid. They also provide a good source of vitamins, minerals, trace elements, carotenes, chlorophyll, folic acid, and phytoestrogens. Alfalfa alkalizes and detoxifies the body, especially the liver.

1. Place 2-3 cups alfalfa in a bowl and put aside.

2. In a food processor, combine sunflower seeds, almond butter, Bragg Liquid Aminos, kelp, mung beans and lentils and blend until smooth.

3. Add in the onion and celery and pulse chop until onion and celery are blended but still chunky.

4. Remove from food processor and pour over alfalfa sprouts. Mix well.

5. If there is too much sauce, add more alfalfa sprouts. Add sea salt to taste.

Note: If this seems bland, add more sea salt. You will need a good amount of salt to bring out the flavors in this dish.

SUNNY PÂTÉ

Courtesy of *The Raw Gourmet* by Nomi Shannon. When Nomi told me to use this recipe instead of another one I wanted to use, I was hesitant. It seemed to be too simple to be as good as she claimed. Well, I tried it and Nomi was absolutely right! Since then, I've made this pâté many times, for many people.

SUNFLOWER SEEDS -

Outstanding source of Vitamin

E and essential linoleic acid,

as well as other vitamins

and nutrients.

3 cups sunflower seeds, soaked 8-12 hours, and sprouted 2-4 hours

1 cup lemon juice

1/2 cup chopped scallions

1/4 -1/2 cup tahini

1/4 cup Bragg Liquid Aminos

2-4 slices red onion, cut in chunks

4-6 Tablespoons coarsely chopped parsley

2-3 medium cloves garlic coarsely chopped

1/2 teaspoon cayenne pepper, or more to taste

1-2 Tablespoons ginger juice (optional)

1 teaspoon ground cumin (optional)

In a food processor, blend all ingredients until smooth.

Note: Nomi says this will last at least 10-14 days in the fridge.

CARROT PECAN BURGERS

These are to LIVE for! A moist and utterly delectable patty. Top with curry sauce for an exotic taste explosion!

CARROTS - Rich in sugar, potassium and carotene.

4 medium carrots

1 cup pecans

1 cup button mushrooms

1 cup onion

3 Tablespoons cilantro

2 Tablespoons olive oil

1/2 teaspoon dried fennel

1/2 teaspoon coriander

1/2 teaspoon curry

1/2 teaspoon sea salt

Pinch black pepper

1. In a food processor, blend carrots until diced.
2. Add the remaining ingredients and blend until smooth.
3. Remove from processor and form into burgers.
4. Place burgers on a mesh dehydrator screen and dehydrate at 105 degrees for 7-8 hours.

GNOCCHI

Like the heavy, dense, Italian dumplings, these are scrumptious! A very quick and easy dish that has a similar consistency as the well known potato filled pasta.

PASTA:

    4-6 avocados

FILLING:

    4 cups macadamia nuts

    2 1/2 – 3 cups water

MARINARA SAUCE:

    2 1/2 cups tomatoes

    12 sundried tomatoes, soaked

    3 dates, pitted and soaked

    1/4 cup olive oil

    4 cloves garlic

    2 Tablespoons parsley

    1/8 teaspoon cayenne

    1 teaspoon sea salt

FOR PASTA:

1. Slice and pit the avocados.
2. With a melon baller, make as many avocado balls as possible from the avocados.

FOR FILLING:

1. In a Vita-Mix or blender, blend nuts with enough water to turn over. Start with 1 1/2 cups of water, adding more as needed.
2. Place mixture in a bowl, cover with cheese cloth, and let sit at room temperature for at least 6-8 hours.

FOR SAUCE:

1. In a food processor, blend the Marinara Sauce ingredients until smooth.

TO ASSEMBLE:

1. Place the avocado balls on a large plate or platter.

2. Cut the balls in half and place a small dollop of Cream Cheese between each one. (So the Cream Cheese is sandwiched between the avocado like a cookie).

3. Continue until all of the balls are filled.

4. Pour Marinara Sauce over the entire plate of these avocado cream cheese balls.

Note: When using the melon baller, you will only be able to get a certain amount of round shaped balls. Don't worry if they are not perfectly round. Use as much of the avocado as possible.

ENCHILADA

Incredible! This is a warm, Spanish wonder, wrapped in a chewy corn tortilla. Make it early in the day and serve it for dinner that evening!

TORTILLA:

4 cups frozen corn

1/2 cup ground flax seeds (not soaked)

1/2 cup orange juice

1 clove garlic

1/8 teaspoon sea salt

FILLING:

4 cups mixed veggies, diced finely — red pepper, spinach, mushrooms, zucchini (broccoli, optional)

1/4 cup olive oil

1/8 teaspoon sea salt

Dash cumin

Dash chili powder

FOR TORTILLA:

1. Place all ingredients in a food processor and blend until smooth.

2. Place mixture on a Teflex sheet on top of a mesh dehydrator screen about 1/8 inch thick and dehydrate at 105 degrees.

3. When tortillas are solid enough to turn (after about 3 hours) flip onto mesh screen and dehydrate until other side is solid (another 1-2 hours or so).

FOR FILLING:

1. In a bowl, combine the filling ingredients and let sit for at least 1/2 hour or until tortilla is done dehydrating.

TO ASSEMBLE:

1. Slice the sheet of tortilla in half so you have two large pieces.

2. Place the mixed vegetables down the center of the tortilla in a long thick strip.

3. Roll the tortilla up. You should have a long, thick, enchilada-looking roll. If you can, seal the "seam" with your fingers and a little water if necessary. (The ends will still be open, that's fine.)

4. Continue to do the same with the second piece of tortilla and then place these rolls back into the dehydrator for another 1-2 hours.

Note: When you flip the tortilla after the first 3 hours, it's ok if it's still mushy. It will solidify more after another hour or so. Remember, the key to this recipe is not to let the tortilla get too crispy before you roll it.

I use frozen corn for this recipe since fresh corn gives this recipe an undesirable flavor and texture.

STUFFED PORTOBELLA MUSHROOM CAPS

I have been making these for the past 12 years. I forget about them for months at a time, making other, more gourmet recipes, and then something prompts me to make these and I'm reminded of how simple and truly sensational they are.

1 large Portobella mushroom

1 whole avocado

1/4 cup onions, diced (optional)

1 tomato, diced (optional)

1/8 teaspoon sea salt

Bragg Liquid Aminos

1. Wash and de-stem the mushroom. Place mushroom stem side up on a plate.
2. Mash the avocado, onions, tomatoes and sea salt and place in the mushroom cap.
3. Pour Bragg Liquid Aminos lightly over the top of the mushroom cap and on the plate to make sure the mushroom cap is marinated.
4. Eat as is or top with diced tomato, black olives and sprouts.

CALZONE

Of all the recipes in this book, I admit to being proudest of this one. Not only does this look like the real Italian thing... it tastes like it, too! After making this for friends, I was dubbed "The Raw Queen!"

This is a combination of three recipes: Burger Buns (doubled and altered a bit), Spinach Dip, and Mozzarella Cheese. But I've listed them here, so you don't have to flip through the pages.

DOUGH:

4 cups sprouted buckwheat

1 1/2 cups soaked flax seeds

3/4 - 1 cup olive oil

1 1/2 cups carrots

2 cloves garlic

1 teaspoon curry

1 teaspoon rosemary

1 teaspoon thyme

2 teaspoons sea salt

MOZZARELLA CHEESE:

1 cup macadamia nuts

1 cup cashews

2 Tablespoons Bragg Liquid Aminos

1 1/2 Tablespoons lemon juice

1/2 cup water

SPINACH DIP:

4 cups spinach

1 large avocado or 1 1/2 small avocados

1/2 Tablespoon lemon juice

1/2 teaspoon Herbamare seasoning salt

MARINATED VEGGIES:

1 cup broccoli, diced

1 cup mushrooms, diced

1/4 cup olive oil

Dash of sea salt

FOR THE DOUGH:

1. Grind the 1 1/2 cups of carrots in a food processor.
2. Add in the other ingredients and blend well until this forms a dough-like consistency.
3. On a Teflex sheet on top of a mesh dehydrator screen, form half of the dough into a half circle about a 1/4 -1/2 inch thick.
4. On a separate Teflex sheet form the remaining dough into a half circle about a 1/4 -1/2 inch thick.
5. Dehydrate at 105 degrees for 3 to 4 hours; then turn over and dehydrate for another 1 to 2 hours.

FOR MOZZARELLA CHEESE:

1. In a food processor, blend all of the mozzarella cheese ingredients together until smooth.

FOR SPINACH DIP:

1. In a food processor, blend all of the ingredients for the spinach dip together until smooth.

FOR MARINATED VEGGIES:

1. Marinate the broccoli and mushrooms in the olive oil and sea salt for 20 minutes or until dough is done in a few hours.

TO ASSEMBLE:

1. Remove one sheet of crust (the dehydrated dough) from dehydrator and spread the entire mixture of Mozzarella Cheese on top of the crust.
2. Place the spinach dip on top of the mozzarella cheese that is now on top of the crust. (These layers will be thick!)
3. Drain the marinated veggies and place these on top of the spinach dip.
4. Remove the other "half" of the crust from the dehydrator. With a very large spatula and with your hands flip the crust onto the top of the "loaded" crust.
5. You will have to push this down a bit and may have fillings seeping out. That's okay.
6. With your fingers, go around the sides of the calzone and pinch together the crust. You may have to wipe away any filling that is leaking out as you pinch. Just be sure to close the sides well.
7. Dehydrate your assembled calzone at 105 degrees for 14-18 hours.

This will stay in the refrigerator for a day or two but is really great warm, straight out of the dehydrator!

Notes: If you see the crust breaking or splitting, try to repair that before it goes back into the dehydrator by using your fingers and a bit of water to smooth it out. You will have to remove a few sheets to fit the assembled calzone into the dehydrator. You can re-warm your calzone by putting it back into the dehydrator for an hour or two before serving.

Serving suggestions: Slice into many pieces and serve with marinara sauce.

MOCK TURKEY LOAF

Adopted from the book *The New Raw Energy*, this is a favorite of mine, especially at holiday times. It has a wonderful flavor and looks beautiful on the table.

1 cup cashews

1 cup pumpkin seeds

1/2 cup Brazil nuts

5 stalks celery

1 scallion

1 teaspoon sage

1 cup cranberries

Honey

1. In a food processor, grind the cashews, pumpkin seeds, and Brazil nuts until fine.
2. Add the celery, scallion, and sage and blend until smooth.
3. Remove from food processor and place on a large plate. Form into a loaf.
4. Blend the cranberries in blender. Add honey to taste. Blend until smooth.
5. Spread cranberry sauce over the loaf.

Serving suggestion: Decorate the plate with whole cranberries and parsley.

NOASTED TURKEY

From the *Sprout Café* in Atlanta, this tastes just like traditional turkey stuffing to me. Although the Mock Turkey Loaf is prettier, this one is so good I thought I'd give you both... after all, Thanksgiving can be the toughest holiday to get through when you first go raw. I top this with Marinara Sauce to give it a bit more moisture.

2 cloves garlic, chopped fine

2 Tablespoons fresh sage

2 Tablespoons rosemary

2 Tablespoons fresh thyme

2 cups walnuts, soaked 12 hours and drained

2 cups almonds, soaked 12 hours and drained

1 Tablespoon organic unpasteurized white miso

1 large onion, chopped very fine

6 stalks celery, chopped fine

1 cup parsley sprigs (as garnish)

1 cup cranberries (as garnish)

---

1. Place garlic in a food processor and process well.

2. Add sage, rosemary, and thyme, processing well.

3. Add walnuts, almonds, and miso, one at a time and process well.

4. Remove to a bowl and stir in onion and celery.

5. Place on a sheet of Teflex and form into an oval loaf shape. Dehydrate at 105 degrees for 6 hours.

6. Remove and turn loaf over, removing the Teflex sheet from the bottom. Dehydrate for 4 to 6 hours more.

7. Garnish with parsley and cranberries.

ANGEL HAIR PASTA AND MARINARA SAUCE

I highly recommend using the Saladacco for the most beautiful, delicate and delectable Angel Hair. This is a fast and easy recipe. People are always surprised at how good this mock 'pasta' is!

ZUCCHINI – Good source of calcium, vitamin C, thiamine, riboflavin, and niacin.

ANGEL HAIR PASTA:

3-4 zucchini

MARINARA SAUCE

2 1/2 cups tomatoes

12 sundried tomatoes, soaked

3 dates, pitted and soaked

1/4 cup olive oil

4 cloves garlic

2 Tablespoons parsley

1 teaspoon sea salt

1/8 teaspoon cayenne

FOR ANGEL HAIR PASTA:

1. Spiralize the zucchini in the Saladacco.
2. Pour angel hair zucchini pasta into a large bowl.

FOR MARINARA SAUCE:

1. Place all of the Marinara ingredients into a food processor and blend until smooth.
2. Pour sauce over angel hair zucchini pasta and serve.

Serving Suggestions: Try topping with capers and yellow tomatoes for a beautiful presentation.

PAD THAI WITH SAUCE

I highly recommend using a Saladacco for this pasta. However, if you don't own one, a vegetable peeler will also work... just peel the squash into "pasta-like" strips. The sauce is so delicious! You can also use it as a dip, or pour it over other vegetables for a great tasting dish!

PAD THAI NOODLES:

1 large yellow squash

4 cups mung bean sprouts

PAD THAI SAUCE:

1 cup almond butter

1/2 cup orange juice

2 Tablespoons Bragg Liquid Aminos

2 Tablespoons honey

1-2 Tablespoons fresh ginger

FOR NOODLES:

1. In a Saladacco, spiralize the yellow squash into angel hair type "noodles" and place on a large, flat plate.

2. Place mung beans on top of the yellow squash.

FOR SAUCE:

1. In a blender, blend the sauce ingredients until smooth and creamy. (If you want a thicker sauce, add more almond butter. If you want a thinner sauce, add more orange juice)

2. Pour sauce over the mung beans and let it drip into the dish.

SPANISH RICE

A lovely Mexican medley that resembles Spanish rice in looks and taste.

4 cups sprouted barley

2 medium tomatoes, finely chopped

1/2 red onion, finely chopped

2 Tablespoons cilantro, diced

2 Tablespoons olive oil

1 teaspoon sea salt

2 teaspoons cumin

2 teaspoons chili powder

Cayenne to taste (optional)

Mix all ingredients together and serve.

Note: Let this sit for a few hours so the flavors have a chance to mingle.

RAW RAVIOLI

This is one of my favorite recipes. I often make these at seminars and events and people go wild over them! There is always at least one person who continues to ask me throughout the whole event: "What kind of pasta is this made from?" No matter how many times I tell people that the "pasta" is actually turnip, it's hard for anybody to believe!

TURNIPS - Good liver and

bile cleansers.

PASTA WRAPPER:

4 turnips

CHEESE FILLING:

1 cup pine nuts

1 cup macadamia nuts (you can substitute cashews for the macadamia nuts)

1 cup walnuts

1 cup parsley

8 teaspoons lemon juice

6 teaspoons Bragg Liquid Aminos

2 cloves garlic

MARINARA SAUCE:

2 1/2 cups tomatoes

12 sundried tomatoes, soaked

3 dates, pitted and soaked

1/4 cup olive oil

4 cloves garlic

2 Tablespoons parsley

1 teaspoon sea salt

1/8 teaspoon cayenne

FOR THE PASTA WRAPPER:

1. Slice the turnips into very thin slices by using a spiral slicer, mandolin or other vegetable slicer to make thin round disks. These will be used as the wrapper which would normally be the pasta dough.

FOR THE CHEESE FILLING:

1. Blend the pine nuts, macadamia nuts and walnuts in a food

processor until ground.

2. Add the rest of the ingredients and blend well, until creamy.

FOR THE MARINARA SAUCE:

1. Add all ingredients in a food processor and blend well.

ASSEMBLING THE RAVIOLI:

1. Remove a single turnip slice from the batch.

2. Place a teaspoon full of cheese filling in the turnip slice and fold the turnip over until all the sides meet. Squeeze the edges together. Some of the filling will ooze out, but this is what will hold the edges together. Just put the excess back into the bowl to reuse. If you don't have enough filling in them they will not stick together.

3. Continue to fill each turnip slice until all the filling is gone.

4. Place these half moon shapes in a single layer on a large plate and drizzle the tomato sauce on top.

5. Allow to sit for a few hours. The turnip will become soft from the tomato sauce. Use a spatula to scoop the ravioli up and serve.

Note: Buy small turnips as they are easier to slice. Make sure to slice these VERY thin or they will not become soft enough, and may taste bitter.

WALNUT MUSHROOM LOAF

I had a recipe very similar to this one, but when my friend Nancy served this for lunch one day, I knew mine needed adapting. This is delicious on a salad, served with fresh veggies and crackers, or stuffed into tomato caps. My favorite way of serving this though, is wrapped in arugula leaves.

3 cups portobella mushrooms

PORTOBELLA MUSHROOMS -

A Portobella mushroom has

more potassium than a glass of

orange juice or a banana.

2 cups walnuts

2 Tablespoons olive oil

1 clove garlic

1/4 teaspoon marjoram

1/4 teaspoon rosemary (optional)

1/4 -1/2 Tablespoon sea salt

In a food processor, blend all ingredients until smooth.

CHILI

As you can tell by looking at the ingredients, this makes a large amount, but I promise it won't go to waste, it's good enough to keep all for yourself! So whip up a batch and enjoy this excel·lent chili for a few days! Adjust the amount of cayenne to suit your taste. Top a serving of this with the Onion Dip and it tastes like old fashioned chili and sour cream!

CAYENNE· Warms the body up and improves circulation.

4 cups sprouted barley

1/2 teaspoon curry

2 Tablespoons Bragg Liquid Aminos

1 medium green bell pepper, diced

1/4 cup small red onion, diced

1 ear of corn, shaved from cobb

1/2 cup chili powder

1 Tablespoon Italian seasoning

1/2 teaspoon cayenne

4 cloves garlic, crushed

1/4 cup honey

1 cup water

1/2 cup olive oil

2 oranges, juiced

10 medium to large tomatoes, diced small

1 small onion

1 cup dates, pitted and soaked

1 cup sundried tomatoes, soaked

---

1. In a very large bowl mix together the barley, curry, Bragg Liquid Aminos, green bell pepper, red onion, and corn.

2. To the above mixture add in, chili powder, Italian seasoning, cayenne, garlic, honey, water, olive oil, oranges, and tomatoes.

3. In a food processor, blend the dates, onion, and sundried tomatoes into a thick paste.

4. Remove from food processor. Add this paste to the bowl with the other ingredients and stir until well mixed.

BUTTERNUT SQUASH PATTIES

With their delicious, unique flavor, these are even more amazing served with apple sauce!

2 cups sunflower seeds

1 cup walnuts

2 cups butternut squash

1 whole avocado

1 tomato

1/2 cup sundried tomatoes, soaked

1/2 cup onion

1/2 lemon, juiced

1 stalk celery

4 Tablespoons Bragg Liquid Aminos

2 Tablespoons flax seed oil

1 teaspoon jalapeno, minced

1 teaspoon garlic powder

---

1. In a food processor, blend walnuts and sunflower seeds until fine.

2. Add in butternut squash and blend.

3. Add the remaining ingredients and blend until smooth.

4. Remove mixture from processor, and form into flat round patties about 1/2 inch thick.

5. Place on a mesh dehydrator screen and dehydrate 8-12 hours at 105 degrees or until desired firmness is reached.

Note: These have a very different flavor after you dehydrate them. So don't be surprised if you don't love them before dehydrating!

EGGPLANT PARMESAN

While each ingredient is important to its success, the secret to the "breaded and cooked" flavor is the pine nut 'breading' and the oil.

Make sure you slice the eggplant thin enough and dehydrate this dish long enough so the eggplant is soft like butter. To transform this dish into "Chicken Parmesan," just substitute the "Chick-un Patties" for the eggplant!

BASE:

One very large or 2 medium eggplants

BREADING:

2 cups pine nuts

1 teaspoon sea salt

CHEESE:

2 cups macadamia nuts

2 cups cashews

4 Tablespoons Bragg Liquid Aminos

3 Tablespoons lemon juice

1/2 - 1 cup water

MARINARA SAUCE:

2 1/2 cups tomatoes

12 sundried tomatoes, soaked

3 dates, pitted and soaked

1/4 cup olive oil

4 cloves garlic

2 Tablespoons parsley

1/8 teaspoon cayenne

1 teaspoon sea salt

FOR BASE:

1. Peel and slice the eggplant into 1/4 inch round slices.
2. Soak the eggplant slices in salted water for 1-2 hours.

FOR BREADING:

1. In a food processor, combine the breading ingredients and blend until almost smooth. This should still be a bit "grainy" in texture.

FOR CHEESE:

1. In a food processor combine the cheese ingredients and blend until smooth.

FOR MARINARA SAUCE:

1. In a food processor, combine the sauce ingredients and blend until smooth.

TO ASSEMBLE:

1. Cover the bottom of a large lasagna pan, with a thin layer of olive oil.

2. Drain the eggplant slices and place them in the lasagna pan on top of the oil in a single layer, heavily overlapping each other.

3. Place the breading mixture on top of eggplant layer. It may be hard to spread; just be sure all the pieces are covered with some of the mixture.

4. Spread the cheese layer on top of the breading layer.

5. Pour the sauce over the cheese layer.

6. Place the lasagna pan in the dehydrator and dehydrate at 105 degrees for 14-18 hours

NORI ROLLS

SEA VEGGIES - High sources of minerals which help boost the metabolism and thyroid function.

The "rice" in these rolls is actually made of cauliflower... it looks and tastes like real sticky rice for an authentic Japanese flare!

4 Nori sheets

1/2 head cauliflower

1 avocado, thinly sliced

Any of the following veggies: shredded carrot, cucumber sticks, mung beans, etc.

1. In a food processor, grind the cauliflower until grainy.

2. Remove cauliflower mixture from food processor and place a thin layer of it on a nori sheet. Do not put cauliflower on the top few inches of the sheet.

3. Place slices of avocado and other veggies in the center of the sheet.

4. Roll the nori sheet, pulling tight as you roll up, and seal with a few drops of water along the seam.

5. With a sharp knife, cut nori roll into inch-thick slices and turn face up on a plate side by side.

6. Continue this process with the remaining sheets.

Serving suggestions: Place Bragg Liquid Aminos or Nama Shoyu in a small bowl to use as a dipping sauce.

SWEET APPLE NORI ROLLS

While not your typical nori roll, I love the apple, avocado, and honey combination. Don't roll these as tight as a typical nori roll... rather, eat them like a rolled-up sandwich.

4 nori sheets

1 avocado, sliced

1 apple, sliced

Honey to taste

Lettuce

1. Place slices of avocado and apple in the center of the nori sheet.

2. Pour a spoonful of honey over the avocado and apple.

3. Place a small amount of lettuce on top of the avocado, apple, and honey.

4. Loosely roll up the nori around the mixture and hold together while eating

5. Continue this process with the remaining sheets.

PIZZA!

Trust me: any cravings you have for pizza will be taken care of with this recipe! Crust, cheese, sauce and toppings... just like the real thing, only better!

There are 3 different crusts to choose from. The first one has sprouted wild rice and barley, so you need to plan ahead for that. The second one has buckwheat, which can be done with a days notice. The third one is quick and easy and equally as delicious. Try them all!

GOURMET CRUST:

1/2 cup sprouted barley

1/2 cup sprouted wild rice

2 dates, pitted and soaked

1/8 cup sundried tomatoes, soaked

1/4 cup olive oil

1/4 cup basil

2 cloves garlic

1 teaspoon oregano

Dash sea salt

EASY CRUST:

2 cups sprouted buckwheat

1 cup soaked flax seeds

1 cup red bell pepper

1 carrot

1 celery stalk

1 clove garlic

1/8 teaspoon sea salt

EASIEST CRUST:

2 cups ground flax seeds (not soaked)

1/2 cup onion

2 celery stalks

1 carrot

1 large tomato

2 large cloves garlic

1 teaspoon sea salt

1/2 cup water

CREAMY CHEDDAR CHEESE:

1/2 cup pine nuts

1/2 cup macadamia nuts

1/2 cup sunflower seeds

1 1/2 cups red bell pepper

1/2 peeled lemon

2 cloves garlic

1 Tablespoon Bragg Liquid Aminos

MARINARA SAUCE:

2 1/2 cups tomatoes

12 sundried tomatoes, soaked

3 dates, pitted and soaked

1/4 cup olive oil

4 cloves garlic

2 Tablespoons parsley (optional)

1/8 teaspoon cayenne

1 teaspoon sea salt

TOPPINGS:

Any assorted vegetables of your choice. I like to use avocado, mushrooms, spinach, onions, etc...

———————————

FOR CRUST:

1. Combine all ingredients for whichever crust recipe you are using in a food processor until well blended and smooth.
2. Remove from processor and place on a Teflex sheet on top of a mesh dehydrator screen.
3. Smooth crust into 1/4 inch thick large circle.
4. Make the edge of the circle a bit thicker, like a pizza crust would be.
5. Dehydrate crust for 2 hours at 105 degrees, then flip off of Teflex sheet and onto mesh dehydrator screen and dehydrate for another couple of hours until firm but not hard or crispy.

FOR CHEESE:

1. In a food processor, blend the cheese ingredients until smooth and creamy.

FOR SAUCE:

1. In a food processor, blend the tomato sauce ingredients until smooth.

TO ASSEMBLE:

1. Remove crust from the dehydrator and flip the crust back to

its original side before topping so you have the thick outer crust that you molded facing upward.

2. Spread cheese sauce over the pizza crust. (Leave a 1/4 inch of space near the edges of the crust.)

3. Pour Marinara Sauce over the cheese on the crust.

4. Top with your favorite toppings.

5. Place pizza back into the dehydrator and dehydrate at 105 degrees for 6-10 hours depending on desired texture.

Notes: I usually put the cheese sauce underneath the tomato sauce because it looks prettier and is easier to spread. You can use any cheese sauce you prefer... You can also use a small amount of cheese and sauce to make the pizza extra thin if you don't like it too thick. Experiment with the toppings and dehydrating times to suit your taste.

EGGPLANT PIZZA

A quicker alternative to the "crust" pizzas, with a sweet and satisfying topping!

EGGPLANT CRUST:

2 medium size eggplants

TOPPING:

1 cup pine nuts

1 date, pitted and soaked

1 teaspoon sea salt

1 cup spinach, chopped

1 cup sundried tomatoes, soaked

1/2 cup mushrooms, chopped

FOR PIZZA CRUST:

1. Peel and slice the eggplant into 1/2 inch slices. Lay the slices on a mesh dehydrator screen.

FOR TOPPING:

1. In a food processor blend the pine nuts, date and sea salt until smooth.
2. Add in the spinach, sundried tomatoes, and mushrooms. Pulse chop in food processor just enough to blend all ingredients but still leaving the vegetables chunky.

TO ASSEMBLE:

1. Remove mixture from food processor and place a layer of topping on top of each slice of eggplant.
2. Place eggplant pizzas in dehydrator and dehydrate for 8-10 hours at 105 degrees.

BUTTERNUT NOODLES WITH GOLDEN CURRY SAUCE

Another delicious recipe from Shazzie.

This recipe serves 2 as a main dish, or 4 as a side dish.

1 small butternut squash, peeled

1 small handful of coriander/cilantro

1 Tablespoon of Madras curry powder (Or to taste. If unsure, add a small amount and taste, keep adding and blending until you have a flavor you like.)

1 large or 2 medium avocados, skinned and pitted

1 stalk of celery

2 dried apricots, soaked for at least 2 hours

1/4 cup sultanas, soaked for at least 2 hours

1/2 a papaya, skinned and seeded

1/2 a mango, skinned and pitted

4 baby carrots

10 sticks of baby sweet corn

1 yellow pepper, seeded and chopped

1 large tomato

Juice of half a lime

---

1. Set your Saladacco (spiral slicer) onto the "spaghetti" setting and process all of the squash. You will have to do it in pieces, and cut out the seeds.

2. Dice the celery, papaya, mango, corn, tomato, pepper and carrots.

3. Mix these ingredients and add half of the mixture to a blender.

4. Add the avocado, curry powder, sultanas, lime juice and apricots to the blender. (Keep 6 sultanas for decoration.)

5. Blend the curry sauce until fine.

6. Finely chop most of the coriander and add this to the sauce. Place the noodles on a big serving dish, pour the mixed vegetables on top, and pour the sauce on top of that.

7. Flatten a little place out and place the 6 sultanas there, to make a 5 petal flower with a center. Use the reserved coriander to make the stem.

Serve with delight!

SAUSAGE

With its sensational sausage flavor, these little links are the perfect compliment to a Sunday brunch or a perfect snack any time of day!

2 cups portobella mushrooms

1 cup cashews

1/2 cup sprouted wheat berries

2 Tablespoons olive oil

2 teaspoons fresh sage

1 teaspoon fresh marjoram

1 teaspoon fresh basil

1 small clove garlic

1 teaspoon Bragg Liquid Aminos

1/2 teaspoon sea salt

Pinch cayenne

_____

1. In a food processor, blend all ingredients until smooth.

2. Remove from processor and form into flat round patties or 1 inch round strips. Place on a Teflex sheet on top of a dehydrator screen.

3. Dehydrate for 6-7 hours at 105 degrees. Flip half way through dehydrating time onto mesh screens so the bottom of the sausage gets dried.

Note: You can eat these after only a few hours in the dehydrator, but they will be firmer if you let them dehydrate the full time.

CHICK-UN PATTIES

With their mild chicken flavor and their texture, these remind me of the imitation, cooked, soy chicken I used to eat when I first became a vegetarian.

   You will have to make the Mayonnaise to use in this recipe, but that only takes a few minutes extra to do.

1 cup cashews

1 cup carrots

1 cup celery

1 head cauliflower

2 cups sprouted lentils

1 cup corn

3/4 cup onion

1/2 cup green bell pepper

4 Tablespoons Mayonnaise (Page 323)

1 Tablespoon almond butter

1 Tablespoon Herbamare seasoning salt

2 teaspoons dulse seaweed

1 teaspoon nutritional yeast

1 Tablespoon olive oil

LENTILS · Sprouted lentils are extremely high in B Vitamins and protein.

1. In a food processor, grind the cashews until fine. Empty into a large bowl.

2. Grind carrots, celery, and cauliflower until diced. Add to the bowl with the cashews.

3. Blend the rest of the ingredients in a food processor. Mix this into the cashews, carrots, celery, and cauliflower mixture.

4. Transfer this mixture back into the food processor (you may

need to do this in 2 or 3 batches) and continue to process until all ingredients are blended well into a smooth consistency.

5. Form into medium-sized patties and place on Teflex sheets on top of a mesh dehydrator screen.

6. Dehydrate at 105 degrees for 8-10 hours. Flip patties after 2-3 hours onto mesh dehydrator screens.

Note: Make sure Chick-Un Patties are not mushy inside. They should be firm but not hard, like the consistency of a burger.

Serving suggestions: Serve with Honey Mustard Dressing, place in between Burger Buns, or use as Chicken Parmesan in place of the Eggplant Parmesan recipe.

BBQ CHICKEN FINGERS

These offer a much stronger, spicier flavor than the Chick-Un Patties.

They are delicious served with honey-mustard sauce!

2 cups carrots

2 cups sprouted lentils

3/4 cup orange juice

1/4 cup onion

4 Tablespoons olive oil

2 Tablespoons honey

1 1/2 Tablespoons curry

1 Tablespoon poultry seasoning

2 teaspoons sea salt

1. In a food processor, not a Vita-Mix, process the carrots until

diced.

2. Add in all other ingredients. Blend until well blended. (These should not be completely smooth, but more grainy looking).

3. Pour onto Teflex sheets on top of mesh dehydrator screens in an oblong 2x4 mound.

4. Dehydrate at 105 degrees for 10 hours. (Flip half way through if possible).

Notes: These will seem a little soupy before you dehydrate them, just pour them out and try to build them up as much as possible, you don't want them to be paper thin. It is very important to use the right amount of orange juice.

CRAB CAKES

The dill is the secret to achieving the "crab cake" flavor. This recipe is also great as a pâté on crackers or over salads without dehydrating.

1 cup almonds

1 cup cashews

2 stalks celery

2 scallions

1 cup carrots

1/2 cup parsley

1/4 cup lemon juice

1 Tablespoon dried dill

1 small garlic clove

2 teaspoons Bragg Liquid Aminos

1 teaspoon kelp

CELERY - A natural diuretic, celery can relieve migraines, and is great for healing stomach acidity and acid reflux. A natural nerve calmer, celery is high in natural sodium which is vital to our major organs.

1/2 teaspoon dulse flakes

_____

1. In a food processor, blend the almonds and cashews until fine.
2. Combine the remaining ingredients in the food processor and blend until smooth.
3. Remove mixture from the food processor, form into medium-sized patties, and place on Teflex sheets on top of a mesh dehydrator screen.
4. Dehydrate at 105 degrees for 6-10 hours. Flip patties after 2-3 hours onto mesh dehydrator screens.

BETTER THAN BEEF

Matt Samuelson, Master Chef and Instructor for Living Light Culinary Arts Institute, has offered this simple yet delicious recipe.

4 cups pulp from your juicer of carrot, parsnip and/or celery root

1 cup sundried tomatoes, soaked one hour or more and pureed in a blender

1/3 cup extra virgin olive oil or flaxseed oil

1/3-1/2 red onion, finely minced

3 teaspoons onion powder

2 teaspoons garlic powder

3 teaspoons chili powder

2 teaspoons cumin powder

1/4 teaspoon cayenne

1 teaspoon Celtic sea salt

1 Tablespoon unpasteurized dark miso paste

Using your hands, mix all ingredients together well in a large bowl. Let sit for an hour or more for flavors to meld. Best served just after warming in the dehydrator at 105 degrees.

PESTO PASTA

There are many variations for this dish. You can slice the zucchini and summer squash with a vegetable peeler instead of using the Saladacco. Also, try adding other vegetables to this dish such as red pepper slices, mushrooms, and spinach.

NOODLES:

2 zucchini

1-2 summer squash

PESTO:

1/2 cup pine nuts

4-5 cloves garlic

1/2 cup fresh cilantro

1/2 cup fresh basil

2 Tablespoons lemon juice

3 Tablespoons Bragg Liquid Aminos

2 cups tomato, chopped

FOR NOODLES:

1. Slice or spiralize the squash and zucchini and place in a large bowl. Set aside.

FOR PESTO:

1. Place all pesto ingredients, except for the tomato, in a food processor and blend until well ground.
2. Add tomatoes and pulse chop a few seconds until well blend-

ed but not soupy.

TO ASSEMBLE:

1. Pour pesto over zucchini and summer squash and mix well.

CHILI RELLENOS

You can use different kinds of peppers for this dish, but I prefer the Italian peppers. Top this with a sauce (such as the Chili Sauce) for extra flavor.

  Also, try filling the peppers with a different stuffing, such as the Walnut Mushroom Pâté, Carrot Pecan Burgers, or Crab Cakes.

10 sweet long green Italian peppers

NACHO CHEESE:

2 cups macadamia nuts

1 1/2 cups red pepper

1 cup orange pieces (about 1 orange)

1 lemon, juiced

4 cloves garlic

2 Tablespoons Bragg Liquid Aminos

FOR PEPPERS:

1. Slice the peppers lengthwise and de-seed them.
2. Place them open side up in dehydrator and dehydrate 3-4 hours at 105 degrees until soft.

FOR CHEESE:

1. In a food processor, blend the nacho cheese ingredients until smooth.

TO ASSEMBLE:

1. Remove peppers from the dehydrator and fill with nacho cheese.

2. Place peppers back into dehydrator and leave in for 12-18 hours at 105 degrees.

MEATLOAF

For a hearty meal with unbelievable taste, this is the one to make! Barley is very easy to sprout, so don't let that stop you. You'll find this dish to be well worth it!

I always serve this with the BBQ sauce or mushroom gravy spread on top of the loaf (Place the loaf back into the dehydrator for an hour to warm the sauce or gravy).

1 cup sprouted barley

1 cup walnuts

1 cup almonds

1 cup red bell pepper

1 cup portobella mushrooms

1 stalk celery

1/2 cup sundried tomatoes, soaked

1 Tablespoon onion

1/2 cup fresh parsley

1/4 cup oil

1 large clove garlic

1 teaspoon minced ginger root

1 teaspoon poultry seasoning

1/4 teaspoon coriander

1/4 teaspoon cumin

1/2 teaspoon sea salt

———————

1. In a food processor, combine the almonds and walnuts and blend until fine.

2. Add the remaining ingredients and blend until smooth.

3. Remove from processor and place on a mesh dehydrator screen. Form into a large loaf about 1 1/2 inches thick.

4. Dehydrate at 105 degrees for about 15 hours.

5. Place a layer of Mushroom Gravy, Marinara Sauce, BBQ Sauce or your favorite topping over the meatloaf and place back into the dehydrator for an hour or so to warm and solidify the topping.

LASAGNA

When I held a taste-testing party to see how people liked the recipes in this book, I made this along with 40 other dishes... and this one was the hit of the party! Don't let the list of ingredients intimidate you. The "mini-recipes" that make up the dish all whip up quickly in your food processor. Just pile them on top of each other and voilá! Luscious lasagna!

NOODLES:

6-8 zucchini, depending on the size

1/2 cup olive oil

1/4 cup apple cider vinegar

2 Tablespoons honey

2 Tablespoons Bragg Liquid Aminos

RICOTTA:

  1 cup macadamia nuts

  1 cup almonds

  1/2 lemon, juiced

  1/4 cup orange juice

  1/4 cup water

MARINARA SAUCE:

  2 1/2 cups tomatoes

  12 sundried tomatoes, soaked

  3 dates, pitted and soaked

  1/4 cup olive oil

  4 cloves garlic

  2 Tablespoons parsley

  1/8 teaspoon cayenne

  1 teaspoon sea salt

SUMMER TOMATO SAUCE:

  4 tomatoes

  1 1/2 cups basil

  1 1/2 cloves garlic

  2 Tablespoons pine nuts

  6 Tablespoons olive oil

  Herbamare seasoning salt

MOZZARELLA CHEESE:

  1 cup macadamia nuts

  1 cup cashews

  1 1/2 Tablespoons lemon juice

  2 Tablespoons Bragg Liquid Aminos

1/2 cup water

FOR NOODLES:

1. In a spiral slicer, mandolin, or food processor with slicing blade, slice the zucchini into thin round slices. Soak these slices in the oil, honey, vinegar and Bragg Liquid Aminos for at least 1 hour.

FOR RICOTTA CHEESE:

1. In a food processor add the ricotta cheese ingredients and blend well until smooth.

FOR MARINARA SAUCE:

1. In a food processor, add the marinara sauce ingredients and blend until smooth.

FOR MOZZARELLA CHEESE:

1. In a food processor blend the mozzarella cheese ingredients until smooth. (You can dehydrate this cheese first and use it in the lasagna for a different and delicious taste, but it's not necessary).

FOR SUMMER TOMATO SAUCE:

1. In a food processor, add the summer tomato sauce ingredients and blend until smooth.

TO ASSEMBLE:

1. Drain the zucchini. On the bottom of a lasagna pan, lay one third of the zucchini slices flat, just overlapping one another until the entire bottom of the pan is covered.
2. Pour the ricotta cheese over the zucchini and spread evenly over the entire length of the pan.
3. On top of the ricotta, place another layer of zucchini in the

same manner as the bottom layer.

4. Pour the marinara sauce over the previous layer of zucchini and spread evenly over the entire length of the pan.

5. Pour the mozzarella cheese over the Marinara Sauce and spread as best as possible.

7. On top of the mozzarella, place another layer of zucchini in the same manner as the bottom layer.

8. Pour the summer tomato sauce over the previous layer of zucchini and spread over the entire length of the pan.

9. Place lasagna pan in dehydrator for 18 – 24 hours or until desired texture is achieved.

Note: If you want to just use the marinara sauce and omit the summer tomato sauce, that's fine, just double the marinara sauce recipe.

PESTO LASAGNA

I've been making this dish for years. It's delicious, with a lighter taste than the cheese and sauce lasagna. Smooth and flavorful, this dish is also lovely to look at!

MARINADE:

4 cups water

1 cup olive oil

1 cup basil, torn

1/4 cup Bragg Liquid Aminos

1 lemon, juiced

2 cloves garlic, minced or pressed

1 Tablespoon ginger, grated

VEGETABLE LAYERS:

1 yellow bell pepper, sliced thin

1 red bell pepper, sliced thin

1 green bell pepper, sliced thin

3-4 portobella mushrooms, sliced thin

4 zucchini, sliced thin

4 yellow squash, sliced thin

PESTO:

1/2 cup pine nuts

4-5 cloves garlic

1/2 cup fresh cilantro

1/2 cup fresh basil

3 Tablespoons Bragg Liquid Aminos

2 Tablespoons lemon juice

2 cups tomato, chopped

DILL CREAM CHEESE DIP:

2 cups cashews soaked for 4 hours or longer

2 cups water

1 1/2 - 2 cups fresh dill

Herbamare seasoning salt

MARINADE:

1. In a large bowl, mix together all of the ingredients for the marinade.

VEGETABLE LAYERS:

1. Add all of the ingredients to the bowl of marinade. Add in enough water to cover (a few cups).

2. Marinate for a couple of hours or overnight.

3. Drain the vegetables.

DILL CREAM CHEESE DIP:

1. Place half of the water into a blender and slowly add the cashews. Add water as needed, until all of the cashews are gone. Keep this thick by adding 1 or 2 cashews at a time until the blender is no longer able to turn over.

2. Add dill and Herbamare to taste.

PESTO:

1. Place all ingredients, except for the tomato, in a food processor and blend well until blended, but still chunky.

2. Add tomatoes and pulse chop a few seconds until well blended but not soupy.

TO ASSEMBLE:

1. In a lasagna pan, layer the zucchini on the bottom of the pan just slightly overlapping each other.

2. On top of the zucchini, layer the yellow squash in the same manner.

3. Pour pesto on top of squash and spread evenly the length of the pan.

4. On top of the pesto place another layer of the squash, (just one layer of both the squashes mixed).

5. On top of the squash layer, place a layer of the mushrooms.

6. Pour dill cream cheese dip over the previous layers and spread evenly though out the length of the pan.

7. Add another layer of squash on top of the dill cream cheese dip.

8. Place a layer of all of the peppers on top of the squash.

Note: This lasagna is best when you let it stand for a few hours to allow the flavors to mingle.

STACIE'S SAMOSAS

These taste great a bit crispy from the dehydrator, but they are delicious not dehydrated as well. Let these sit after mixing, so that the flax seeds hold the mixture in place. Stacie uses tamarind paste which can be found in Indian or Asian markets and is very simple to use.

2 cups zucchini or mild root vegetable, such as Jerusalem artichoke (sun choke), or kohlrabi

1 1/3 cup mild sweet squash (acorn or butternut)

Dash cayenne (or to taste)

1 Tablespoon cilantro, minced

2 teaspoons cumin

2 teaspoons coriander

1 teaspoons ginger

1 teaspoon cinnamon

1 teaspoon lemon juice

2 Tablespoons tamarind paste*

1/2 cup flax seed, ground

Blend first 3 ingredients in a food processor or Champion Juicer. Place in bowl and add the remaining ingredients. Mix well. Let sit for about 20 minutes. Form into mini-patties or balls. Serve with mint chutney.

TO MAKE TAMARIND PASTE:

Open the tamarind pods by peeling off the outer shell. Throw away the shell.

Break the pods into pieces. Cover them with water (use just barely enough water to cover them) and let them soak for a day or two. Strain the water off through a strainer. Mash the paste off of the seeds to form a thick paste (do this through the strainer). Add more water as necessary, but keep the paste thick.

Make sure the inside of the pods are brown inside and not white, since these will not be ripe.

PAUL'S PÂTÉ

My friend Paul created this when he first went raw. It's easy, versatile, and tasty.

Serve as is over a salad, or rolled-up in lettuce leaves, collard leaves, or in nori rolls.

1 cup almonds

1/2 cup sunflower seeds

3 scallions

1 large carrot

1 1/2 celery sticks

2-3 Tablespoons olive oil

2 Tablespoons Bragg Liquid Aminos

Pinch of sea salt and pepper

1. In a food processor, blend the almonds and sunflower seeds until fine.
2. Add in the other ingredients and blend until smooth.

PURPLE PÂTÉ

The beautiful color of this pâté will jazz up any raw food table! Serve this over a salad for a wonderful color combination, or as a spread for crackers.

1 cup almonds

1 cup walnuts

1 cup sunflower seeds

1 cup beets

1/4 cup onion

1/4 cup green bell pepper

1/4 cup purple cabbage

1/4 cup Bragg Liquid Aminos

1 stalk celery

1 carrot

2 cloves garlic

1 teaspoon tahini

1/4 teaspoon jalapeno

1/4 teaspoon sea salt

1/4 cup water as needed

---

1. In a food processor, blend the almonds, walnuts and sunflower seeds until fine.

2. Add in the remaining ingredients and blend until smooth.

THAI CANNELLONI BITES WITH PIGNOLI HERB PÂTÉ

Just one of Chad Sarno's delicious dishes. This is an amazing example of "East-meets-West" cuisine.

3 zucchini, sliced thin lengthwise with a mandolin

2 cups almonds or cashews, soaked 10-12 hours

1 cup Pignoli nuts, (pine nuts), unsoaked

2 Tablespoon olive oil

2 Tablespoon lime or lemon juice

1/2 teaspoon Celtic sea salt

1 Tablespoon garlic

1 1/2 Tablespoon ginger, minced

1 Tablespoon lemongrass, minced (optional)

1/2 teaspoon black pepper

1 Tablespoon curry powder

1/2 teaspoon cayenne

3 Tablespoons water

1/2 cup sundried black olives, pitted and minced

2 Tablespoon cilantro, fresh and minced

2 Tablespoons basil, fresh and minced

In a food processor blend the cashews, pignoli nuts, olive oil, lemon juice, sea salt, pepper, garlic, ginger, lemongrass, curry powder, cayenne and water until it becomes a smooth, thick paste. Pulse in the olives, thyme and basil.

TO ASSEMBLE:

1. Place two zucchini strips side by side.
2. Place a small scoop of pâté near end of strips facing you.
3. Fold over zucchini and proceed to roll until the paste actually holds the round together.
4. Slice off excess zucchini.
5. Place on a dehydrator screen. Dehydrate at 105 degrees for 6 hours or until firm.

Serve with spicy Marinara, Curry Sauce or with toothpicks as appetizers.

SPICY REFRIED BEANS

A very close resemblance to the true refried beans that I
missed when going raw! Make sure you use enough sea salt
to bring out the flavor of this dish and adjust the cayenne to
your liking.

2 cups sprouted chickpeas

1 cup walnuts

2 avocados

2 limes, juiced

1 clove garlic

2 teaspoons olive oil

4 teaspoons cumin

1/4 to 1/2 teaspoon cayenne

1/2 teaspoon sea salt

Pepper to taste

Mix all ingredients together in a food processor and blend until
smooth.

RAW VEGGIE STIR FRY

Another wonderful recipe from Cynthia Beavers.

*1-1/2 cup shiitake mushrooms soaked in Nama Shoyu for at least
25 minutes*

1/2 cup raw cashews, chopped

1/2 cup fresh young coconut meat, chopped

1 cup broccoli, chopped

1 cup carrots, sliced super thin (round disc slices)

1/4-1/2 cup parsley, chopped

1/2 cup purple cabbage, chopped

1/2 cup onions: purple, white, yellow, or chives chopped

1/2-1 cup zucchini sliced lengthwise, super thin (like matchsticks)

1/2-1 cup daikon, sliced like the zucchini

1/4 cup celery, peeled and finely chopped

1/2-1 Tablespoons jalapeno, chopped

1/2 cup shallots, chopped

1/2 cup yellow bell pepper, chopped

1/2 cup red bell pepper, chopped

1/2 cup water chestnuts, peeled and chopped

1/2 cup yams, sliced thin and into matchsticks

1/2 cup red beets, sliced like the yams

1 cup bok choy, chopped

*1/4-1/2 cup sprouted quinoa, wild rice, or any sprouted grain
you like*

(Optional)

1 Tablespoon minced ginger

1/3 cup fresh lemon juice

1/3 cup fresh orange juice

Nama Shoyu to taste

1/2-3/4 cup raw olive oil

If you like you can add fresh herbs of your choice.

Since you are not actually cooking, the key to "Raw Stir Fry" is to chop ingredients very fine and small; use a mandolin on the vegetables to make them soft.

1. Put all chopped ingredients into large bowl.

2. Add remaining ingredients

3. Mix well.

4. Let sit about 5-10 minutes for ingredients to soften and flavors to mingle before serving.

Bon Appetit!

Note: This recipe is very good as is, but sometimes I make a peanut sauce to add to it for an Asian variation.

PAKORA

This tasty recipe is from Robert Reed, the owner of the *Organic Garden* Restaurant in Beverly, Massachusetts. These Pakoras make wonderful appetizers or finger foods for a party.

1/2 cup flax seed, finely ground

1/2 cup sesame seed, finely ground

1/2 cup sunflower seed, finely ground

1/2 Tablespoon sea salt

1 2/3 Tablespoon onion powder

1 2/3 Tablespoon coriander

1 Tablespoon cumin

1 Tablespoon paprika

1/2 Tablespoon garlic powder

1/3 Tablespoon lemon pepper

1/3 Tablespoon curry

1 1/2 cup fresh processed carrot (blend the whole carrot)

1/2 cup tamari OR 1 1/2 Tablespoon Herbamare seasoning salt

1/3 cup olive oil

3 yellow medium-sized onions, chopped into 1/4 to 1/2 inch pieces

3/4 cup carrots, chopped into 1/4 to 1/2 inch pieces

1/4 bunch celery, chopped into 1/4 to 1/2 inch pieces

1 red or green pepper, chopped into 1/4 to 1/2 inch pieces

1/2 bunch parsley chopped into 1/4 to 1/2 inch pieces

1 cup broccoli, chopped into 1/4 to 1/2 inch pieces

2 cups cauliflower, chopped into 1/4 to 1/2 inch pieces

---

1. Combine finely ground flax, sesame, and sunflower seed in a mixing bowl.
2. Add and mix in sea salt, onion powder, coriander, and cumin, paprika, garlic powder, lemon pepper, and curry.
3. Add and mix in the fresh processed carrot, tamari OR Herbamare seasoning salt, and olive oil.
4. Add and mix in the chopped vegetables.
5. Measure out this mixture into 2 ounce balls directly onto dehydrator screen. (Teflex sheet is not necessary.)
6. Squish each ball to form odd shapes with veggies sticking out here and there.
7. Dehydrate at 105 degrees for 6-12 hours.

SPINACH MUSHROOM QUICHE

This is another one of Elaina Love's scrumptious recipes. When I heard that Elaina had a quiche recipe, I knew I had to have it for this book. It is a very different dish that actually has the consistency of a quiche. Fabulous!

CRUST:

3 medium sized yellow zucchini, chopped (about 3 cups)

2 teaspoons sea salt

1/2 cup olive or coconut oil/butter

1 cup flax meal (about 3/4 cup whole seeds, ground)

1 cup soaked almonds (about 1/2 cup before soaking for 8 hours)

1. Blend the zucchini, sea salt and oil until zucchini is smooth.

2. Add the almonds and continue to blend until the entire mixture is smooth. You may need to use a spatula or celery stick to get the mixture to blend.

3. Pour the blended mixture into a bowl and add the flax meal.

4. Shape into 4 pizza shaped crusts on dehydrator screens covered with Teflex sheets. Dehydrate the crusts at 105 degrees for 4 hours.

5. Remove the Teflex sheets and continue to dehydrate until the crusts are hard. It may take 8 or more hours altogether.

FILLING:

2 zucchini, chopped

1/4 cup water

1 1/2 cup cashews

1/3 cup light miso

1 teaspoon Celtic sea salt

2 Tablespoons lemon juice

1 teaspoon onion powder

3 cloves garlic

1/2 teaspoon white pepper

1/4 teaspoon nutmeg

Pinch of cayenne

1 head of spinach, pulsed in a food processor with 1/4 teaspoon sea salt and 1 Tablespoon olive oil

10 crimini mushrooms, thinly sliced and marinated in 1/4 teaspoon Celtic sea salt and 1 teaspoon lemon juice

1/2 cup sundried tomatoes, soaked until soft, then chopped

10 sundried olives, pitted and chopped

2 Tablespoons psyllium husk powder (if you can't find powder, just buy husks and grind them in a coffee grinder)

---

1. Place the zucchini and water in a blender and blend until smooth.

2. Add the remainder of the ingredients except the spinach, mushrooms, olives and tomatoes.

3. Blend until creamy. You may need to use a spatula or celery stick to get the mixture to blend.

4. Pulse the spinach in a food processor until it is well minced.

5. Mix all the prepared ingredients together in a bowl.

6. Let the mixture sit for 5 minutes and see how thick it gets. Add more psyllium if necessary to make the mixture thick enough to slice through when it is in the crust.

7. Fill the crusts and warm the quiches in the dehydrator for 1 hour at 105 degrees, if desired.

Note: It's great cold too. This dish will keep three or more days in the refrigerator. You can also dehydrate slices if you have leftovers.

SANDWICHES

REUBEN

Make this when you have some rye bread or bagels left over.
You can adjust these ingredients to your liking.

2 Slices Rye Bread or Bagels

SWISS CHEESE:

1 cup cashews

2 Tablespoons nutritional yeast

1 Tablespoon lemon juice

1/4 cup water

SANDWICH FILLINGS:

1/2 avocado

2 Tablespoons sauerkraut

1 Tablespoon mustard sauce or regular mustard

FOR SWISS CHEESE:

1. In a food processor, blend all ingredients for Swiss cheese until smooth. I normally dehydrate this cheese, but if you want to eat your sandwich right away, you don't have to.

2. If you are going to dehydrate it, remove from processor and place on a Teflex sheet on top of a mesh dehydrator screen.

3. Spread batter into a thin sheet about 1/8 inch thick.

4. Dehydrate at 105 degrees for 7-10 hours. Flip cheese and peel off Teflex sheet and onto a mesh screen after 5-6 hours

TO ASSEMBLE:

1. Start with 2 thick slices of rye bread or bagels.

2. Coat one piece of bread with mustard.

3. Place a few pieces (or spread the un-dehydrated cheese) on top of the mustard.

4. On the other slice of bread place a half of avocado and mash down with a fork.

5. Place a scoop of sauerkraut on top of the avocado.

6. Place the 2 slices together to form a sandwich and press together.

COLLARD ROLLS

These may sound unexciting, but they are superb! The marinated onion and portobella mushrooms give it a great flavor!

COLLARDS - High in calcium and chlorophyll.

2 very large collard leaves

1 small zucchini, shredded

1 carrot, shredded

1 avocado or guacamole

1 cup sliced onion ringlets

1 cup portobella mushrooms, cut into bite size pieces

1 cup Bragg Liquid Aminos

2 cups lettuce

1. Marinate the onions and portobella mushrooms in Bragg Liquid Aminos for 10 minutes (or longer)

2. Lay the collard leaves flat with the inside facing up.

3. Drain the onions and mushrooms well.

4. Place a scoop of avocado or guacamole, half the zucchini, half the carrot, half the mushroom and onion mixture and half the lettuce on one leaf.

5. Roll the leaf up and continue to do the same with the other leaf.

Note: If you are not using very large leaves you will have to put less filling in each one.

Serving suggestion: Place a beet in the Saladacco to make beet strings. Use a long beet string and wrap it around the Collard Rolls a few times to hold it together. This makes a very pretty presentation!

PURPLE POCKETS

Rolled in red cabbage leaves, these are as gorgeous as they are great tasting. Serve with Chinese Dipping Sauce.

2 -4 red cabbage leaves

1 cup mung bean sprouts

1 zucchini, shredded

1 carrot, shredded

Raw sauerkraut or Kim-Chi (optional)

Guacamole (optional)

Any nut or seed pâté (optional)

1. Place red cabbage leaves flat on a plate.

2. Place a scoop of each of the ingredients in each cabbage leaf and roll up.

MOCK PEANUT BUTTER AND JELLY SANDWICH

Any crackers will do, but something sweet like the Banana Orange, or the plain flax will taste best.

2 large crackers

1/4 cup raspberries

2-3 Tablespoons almond butter

1. Spread almond butter on one side of a cracker and top with berries.
2. Eat as an open face sandwich or top with another cracker.

TOMATO, ONION, AND AVOCADO SANDWICH

This was a staple for me when I first went raw. They're worth whipping up a big batch of crackers and keeping them on hand!

1/2 tomato

2 large slices onion

1/2 avocado, sliced

2 large crackers

Sea salt (optional)

1. Place slices of avocado on one of the crackers.
2. Top the avocado with tomato and onion.
3. Eat as an open face sandwich or top with another cracker.

AVOCADO SANDWICHES

Almost too simple to print, but sometimes you forget how simple and delicious things like this can be!

6 large lettuce leaves
2 avocados

OPTIONAL TOPPINGS:

Onions

Carrots

Tomatoes

Mushrooms

Sprouts

Sauerkraut

Kim-Chi

1. Wash, dry and lay out 6 large lettuce leaves from any type of lettuce.
2. Slice avocados and lay inside lettuce leaves.
3. Add toppings of your choice and roll up.

CREAMY CABBAGE ROLLS

They're simple, creamy and a nice change from a basic salad.

WRAPPER:

2 large or 4 small leaves of red or green cabbage.

CREAM SAUCE:

1/2 cup cashews

1/2 cup macadamia nuts

1 teaspoon Bragg Liquid Aminos

1 Tablespoon water

FILLING:

1 cup cauliflower, finely diced

1 zucchini, shredded

1 carrot, shredded

1 onion, sliced

1 red bell pepper, sliced

1/2 cup lettuce, diced

FOR CREAM SAUCE:

1. Blend all ingredients in a food processor until creamy.

TO ASSEMBLE:

1. Lay cabbage leaves out flat.
2. In each leaf, place a small amount of the cauliflower, carrot, zucchini, onion, red bell pepper, and lettuce.
3. Top with the cream sauce.
4. Roll up the leaves.

CABBAGE - In raw form, it cleanses the stomach and colon, while improving digestion.

BREAKFAST DISHES

PORRIDGE

Smooth, soft, creamy, with a familiar taste.

2 cups sprouted buckwheat

1 apple

6 dates, pitted and soaked

1/2 teaspoon vanilla

1/8 teaspoon cinnamon

1/4 cup raisins

1 banana, sliced

---

1. In a food processor, blend the buckwheat, apple, dates, vanilla, and cinnamon until smooth. (Add a little water if needed, but not too much since you want this to stay very thick.)
2. Stir in raisins and banana.

Note: You can also add any other type of fruit.

BUCKWHEAT CEREAL

A crunchy cold cereal type dish. Dehydrate a whole batch of buckwheat sprouts so you can have them handy when making this cereal. You can add coconut, different dried or fresh fruits and a variety of nuts and seeds to suit your liking.

1 cup dehydrated buckwheat sprouts

1-2 cups almond milk

1 cup banana, blueberries, strawberries or other fruit

1/2 cup raisins

Honey (to taste)

1. To make dehydrated buckwheat sprouts, sprout the buckwheat, then place on a Teflex sheet on top of a mesh dehydrator tray and dehydrator for 5-6 hours or until sprouts are crispy.
2. Remove from dehydrator and place in a bowl with all other ingredients.

BANANAS, BERRIES, AND CREAM

When I was little, my mother used to make me bananas and sour cream with sugar on top for breakfast. This recipe has taken its place!

FRUIT:

2 bananas, sliced

1 cup blueberries

PINEAPPLE NUT CREAM:

3/4 cup almonds

1 1/2 cups cashews

2 cups pineapple

FOR PINEAPPLE NUT CREAM:

1. In a food processor grind the almonds into a fine powder. Add in the other ingredients and blend until smooth.

TO ASSEMBLE:

1. Pour the pineapple nut cream over the fruit. Use as much or as little as desired.

GRANOLA

You can easily alter this recipe using ingredients you happen to have on hand: nuts, dried fruits, and seasonings such as vanilla and cinnamon. It makes a great snack! Or, break up the granola into a bowl and pour fresh almond milk on top!

2 cups sprouted buckwheat

1 cup soaked flax seeds

1 cup almonds, chopped fine

1/2 cup walnuts, chopped

1/2 cup sunflower seeds, chopped

1 cup dried apricots, soaked and diced

1 teaspoon vanilla

1 Tablespoon cinnamon

1 Tablespoon honey

1. Combine all ingredients in a bowl.
2. Spread thick (about 1/4 inch) on a Teflex sheet on top of a mesh dehydrator screen
3. Dehydrate at 105 degrees for 10 - 15 hours or until desired crispness is reached.

SALADS

GREENS ARE SO IMPORTANT FOR GOOD HEALTH! A LARGE
BOWL OF DIFFERENT KINDS OF GREENS, A FEW TOMATOES
AND AN AVOCADO IS ALWAYS MY FAVORITE AND SO EASY TO
MAKE! BUT WHEN YOU NEED SOMETHING DIFFERENT, HERE
ARE SOME INTERESTING SALAD COMBINATIONS. THESE
SHOULD ALWAYS BE FRESHLY PREPARED.

MANY OF THESE SALADS, LIKE THE WILD RICE SALAD,
CRUNCHY THAI SALAD, POTATO SALAD, AND JAPANESE DELIGHT
ARE MORE LIKE MAIN ENTREES. THEY'LL MAKE YOU RE-THINK
YOUR NOTION OF SALADS!

POTATO SALAD

No potato potato salad... the perfect dish for the family picnic!

2 pounds jicama, cubed small

1 red bell pepper, diced

2 ears corn, scraped off the cob

2 stalks celery, diced

1 medium onion, diced

1 avocado, diced

1/2 cup tahini

2 cloves garlic, minced

1/3 cup lemon juice

1 Tablespoon cilantro

1 teaspoon cumin

1/2 teaspoon chili powder

4 teaspoons fresh dill

2 teaspoons sea salt

1. Mix all ingredients together.
2. Chill for a few hours before serving.

CRUNCHY THAI SALAD

This crunchy salad has a lovely Thai taste. The marinated eggplant offers an additional, unique flavor.

SALAD:

   4 cups eggplant strips

   6 cups Napa cabbage, shredded

   4 cups mung bean sprouts

   2 cups spinach, torn

   2 cups snap peas, cut in half

   2 scallions, diced

   1 large or 2 small cucumbers, julienned

   1 cup carrots, julienned

   1 red bell pepper, julienned

   1 yellow bell pepper, julienned

   2 Tablespoons cilantro, diced

   1 Tablespoon basil, diced

   2 teaspoons mint, diced

   1/4 cup sesame seeds

   1/2 cup Bragg Liquid Aminos

THAI DRESSING:

   1/4 cup lime juice

   1 cup cilantro

   3 Tablespoons olive oil

   1 Tablespoon fresh ginger root

   1 small clove garlic

   1 teaspoon honey

   1 Tablespoon Bragg Liquid Aminos

   1/2 teaspoon jalapeño

1. Slice eggplant into bacon-like strips with a vegetable peeler.

2. Soak eggplant strips in Bragg Liquid Aminos for at least 15 minutes.

3. Combine all the other salad ingredients together in a large bowl.

4. Drain the eggplant strips and mix gently into the other salad ingredients.

5. Combine the Thai Dressing in a blender and pour over salad.

6. Toss gently and allow flavors to mingle for at least an hour before serving.

WALDORF SALAD

With the advantage of being able to make raw mayonnaise, this salad replaces the ever popular cooked food version.

SALAD:

4 apples, diced

2 stalks celery, diced

1 cup raisins

1/2 cup walnuts

DRESSING:

1/2 cup Mayonnaise (Page 323)

3/4 cup orange juice

1/2 lemon, juiced

2 Tablespoons honey

1/2 teaspoon orange rind

_____

1. Place salad ingredients in a large bowl.

2. Blend dressing ingredients in a blender.

3. Toss dressing gently with salad.

TOMATO, MUSHROOM, AND BASIL SALAD

Reminiscent of the tomato mozzarella salads served at Italian restaurants, I eat this regularly during the summer, using basil fresh picked from the garden!

4 Roma tomatoes

5-6 large button mushrooms

3/4 cup olive oil

1/2 cup basil, minced

2 large cloves garlic, minced

1/4 teaspoon sea salt

1. Slice mushrooms and tomatoes. Put into a bowl.
2. Place the basil, garlic, olive oil and sea salt in a small bowl. Mix until well blended.
3. Pour dressing over mushrooms and tomatoes and let marinate for at least 15 minutes.

WILD RICE SALAD

While running a raw food support group a few years back, Nancy and Ellen kept the group well supplied with this! It was the most popular dish there every week! This is a combination of both of their recipes. This is a very pretty dish because of the black rice, red peppers and other colorful vegetables. Feel free to add any vegetables you like in addition to the ones listed below.

SALAD:

 2 cups sprouted wild rice

 2 red bell peppers, diced

 2 carrots, diced

 2 zucchini, diced

 2 stalks celery, diced

DRESSING;

 1/4 cup honey

 1/4 cup miso

 1/4 Tablespoon apple cider vinegar

 2 Tablespoons olive oil

1. Combine all salad ingredients and place in a large bowl.
2. Combine dressing ingredients and pour over salad. Mix well and let sit for a few hours or overnight.

HIJIKI YAM MEDLEY

Another recipe from *The Raw Gourmet* by Nomi Shannon, this is one of my favorites. This salad has a very unique flavor from the seaweed, yam, and cinnamon.

 1 cup hijiki, soaked for 30 minutes

 2 cups grated yam or sweet potato

 4 Tablespoons dehydrated sunflower or pumpkin seeds,
  or soaked seeds (optional)

 1 Tablespoons sesame oil

 2 teaspoons grated ginger

 2 teaspoons tamari

Pinch cinnamon

In a small bowl, combine all ingredients and stir gently.

FENNEL SALAD

FENNEL - Digests fats, and relieves intestinal cramps and stomach pain.

I know, I know... not high on your "favorites" list. But try this and you'll become a Fennel Fan!

1 large fennel bulb

1 1/2 Tablespoons lemon juice

1 Tablespoon parsley

2 teaspoons olive oil

1 1/1 teaspoons chopped onion

1/2 clove garlic, minced

1/4 teaspoon sea salt

Pepper to taste

1. Remove stalks and leaves from fennel bulb and cut bulb into thin slices. (You should have about 2 cups).
2. Toss well with remaining ingredients and chill for at least 30 minutes.

WHEAT BERRY SALAD

This very pretty salad is perfect for festive occasions. If you're making it for more than 2 people, you can easily double or triple the recipe.

2 cups sprouted wheat berries

1/2 cup walnuts

1/2 cup raisins, soaked for 1-2 hours

1/2 cup dried apricots, soaked for 2 hours and diced

2 cups cucumbers, diced

2 Tablespoons scallions, diced

4 Tablespoons olive oil

4 Tablespoons lemon juice

4 Tablespoons dill, chopped

2 Tablespoons parsley, chopped

2 Tablespoons honey

Combine all ingredients in a bowl and mix gently.

PEAR, BEET, AND JICAMA SALAD

This is a gorgeous salad to serve your guests... and equally delicious.

Serve this with the honey mustard salad dressing.

3 medium beets, grated

1 cup jicama, peeled and cubed

1 Tablespoon lemon juice

2 medium pears, cubed

4 cups mixed greens

1/2 cup walnuts (optional)

BEETS - Helps eliminate kidney stones, are natural blood purifiers, and are intestinal, liver, and gallbladder cleansers.

---

1. Place jicama and pears in a bowl with the lemon juice for 30 minutes.

2. Add the beets to the bowl of jicama and pears and mix.

3. Place mixed greens in a large bowl. Place the pear, beet and jicama mixture on top and of the greens and mix well.

4. Top with walnuts if desired.

JAPANESE DELIGHT

This is very similar in taste to the seaweed salads served in the finest Japanese restaurants!

SALAD:

1 ounce dried wakame

2 1/2 cups button mushrooms, sliced

1 large carrot, shredded

1 zucchini, shredded

DRESSING:

1 1/2 limes, juiced

1/2 teaspoon flax oil

2 cloves garlic

1 Tablespoon olive oil

2 Tablespoons sesame seeds

2 teaspoons apple cider vinegar

1 teaspoon Bragg Liquid Aminos

1. Soak wakame for 20 minutes in water until soft.

2. Cut the wakame into pieces, about 1 inch in length.

3. Place in a large bowl.

4. Combine carrot, zucchini and mushrooms together with wakame.

5. In a separate bowl, whisk together the dressing ingredients.

6. Pour the dressing over the wakame mixture and stir together until all ingredients are well combined.

Let sit a few hours for the flavors to mingle.

FENNEL, QUINOA, ORANGE, AND BASIL SALAD

A very distinctive flavor is cast from the combination of these culminating ingredients. Lovely, light and original.

3 cups sprouted quinoa

1 cup chopped fennel bulb

2 Tablespoons minced shallots

2/3 cup orange juice

1/4 cup fresh basil

2 Tablespoons lemon juice

2 teaspoons olive oil

1 teaspoon grated lemon rind

1 teaspoon grated orange rind

1/4 teaspoon sea salt

1/4 teaspoon pepper

2 cups orange sections

1/4 cup walnuts, chopped

1. Combine quinoa, fennel and shallots in a large bowl.
2. Combine the next 8 ingredients in a small bowl and stir well.
3. Pour over quinoa mixture and toss.
4. Add in orange sections and mix gently.
5. Sprinkle 1 Tablespoon of walnuts over each serving.

CARROT RAISIN CRUNCH

A long time favorite of mine, this salad is sweet, crunchy, and vibrant!

SALAD:

6 cups shredded carrots

1 cup sunflower seeds

1/2 cup shredded coconut

1 1/2 cups raisins, soaked

DRESSING:

3 ounces orange juice

2 ounces lemon juice

4 teaspoons olive oil

1 teaspoons kelp

2 teaspoons honey

2 teaspoons cinnamon

––––––––––––

1. Combine salad ingredients and place in a large bowl.
2. Combine dressing ingredients and mix well.
3. Pour dressing over the salad and mix well.

KALE SALAD

While I was away, Chad Sarno was visiting in my area and pre-pared some of his dishes. Upon my return, everybody — clients and friends alike — were raving about this salad. One taste and I found out why! Even if you never liked kale, try this. It's simple to prepare and tastes so good!

1 head kale, (any variety is great) shredded

1 cup tomato, diced

1 cup avocado, chopped

2 1/2 Tablespoons olive oil

1 1/2 Tablespoons lemon juice

1 teaspoon Celtic sea salt

1/2 teaspoon cayenne

In a mixing bowl toss all ingredients together, squeezing as you mix to "wilt" the kale and creaming the avocado. Serve immediately.

KALE - Provides a rich supply of nutrients as well as lutein and zeaxanthin which may reduce the risk of age related muscular degeneration as well as cataracts. Kale also contains an indole phytochemical that may protect against cancer by making estrogen less potent.

PINEAPPLE PECAN SALAD ROLLED IN RADICCHIO LEAVES

When I make this salad, I cut the middle of the pineapple out, leaving the core, stem and base. Placing this pineapple 'tree' in the middle of this salad makes a wonderful presentation!

2 cups pineapple, diced

1 cup jicama diced

1 cup carrots, shredded

1/4 cup pecans, chopped

1/4 cup scallions, minced

1/3 cup fresh cilantro, minced

2 Tablespoons apple cider vinegar

12 large radicchio leaves

---

1. Mix together pineapple, jicama, carrots, pecans, scallions, cilantro, and vinegar.

2. Place a scoop of mixture on top of each radicchio leave and roll up or leave open.

EASY SLAW

Uncomplicated and delicious.

4 cups green cabbage, shredded

1 cup carrots, shredded

1/4 cup raisins

1/2 red onion, diced

1 Tablespoon apple cider vinegar

1 Tablespoon honey

1/2 Tablespoon caraway

1/8 teaspoon sea salt

————————

Combine all and toss.

WAKAME CUCUMBER SALAD

WAKAME - Abundant in vitamins, minerals and dietary fiber. It's the king of alkaline foods. Wakame expands to approximately 20 times its size when soaked.

Wakame is very versatile and mild in flavor. This marinated seaweed salad is a wonderful way to enhance the flavor of wakame.

1/3 package wakame

1 large or 2 small cucumbers, very thinly sliced

1/4 red onion, diced

2 Tablespoons lemon juice

2 Tablespoons Bragg Liquid Aminos

2 teaspoons sesame seeds

---

1. Soak wakame in water until soft and then rinse and drain.
2. Slice Wakame into pieces and combine with all other ingredients.

CURRIED CABBAGE AND ARAME

Arame has a mild, delicate taste. It has an almost sweet flavor and is not too fishy, making it a good introductory sea vegetable.

ARAME - A seaweed rich in iron as well as other vitamins and minerals

1/2 package arame (about 1 cup dry)

1/2 head small green cabbage, shredded

1/4 cup onion, diced

2 Tablespoons olive oil

1 Tablespoon Bragg Liquid Aminos

1 teaspoon curry powder

---

1. Soak arame in water until soft, and then rinse and drain.
2. Combine all other ingredients with the arame and toss.

CALIFORNIA SALAD

Inspired by my many California salads that combined raisins, veggies and nuts.

SALAD:

1 small crisp lettuce

LETTUCE - Contains lactucarium: a natural sedative which helps to calm the nerves and improve sleep.

8 ounces baby spinach leaves

2 carrots, coarsely grated

2 cups cherry tomatoes, halved

2 stalks celery, thinly sliced

1/2 cup raisins

1/2 cup sprouted almonds or raw cashews

2 Tablespoons sesame seeds

DRESSING:

1 small orange, juiced

3 Tablespoons olive oil

2 Tablespoons cider vinegar

2 teaspoons honey

Sea salt and pepper to taste

---

1. Mix together all ingredients for salad and place in a large bowl.
2. Mix together ingredients for dressing and pour over salad.

PRINCE CASPIAN SEA VEGGIE SALAD

Courtesy of the *Organic Garden* restaurant in Beverly, Massachusetts. I use olive oil in this instead of the toasted sesame oil and it comes out just as good! I also double the amount of seeweed if I'm going to use all of the sauce.

1/2 to 1 cup (2.1 ounce package) arame
and/or 1/2 to 1 cup (2.1 oz package) hijiki

SESAME GINGER SAUCE (MAKES 1 QUART):

1 cup olive oil

1/2 cup apple cider vinegar

1/3 cup ginger

1 cup hulled sesame seed

1/4 cup tamari

1/2 Tablespoon toasted sesame oil

1 cup purified water

1. Blend sauce ingredients until creamy in a blender.
2. Soak (re-hydrate) equal amounts of hijiki and arame sea veggies for 20 minutes in purified water.
3. Drain for 10 to 20 minutes in strainer/colander.
4. Mix in well with Sesame/Ginger Sauce.

Serving suggestion: Garnish with sesame sprinkles and diced red pepper.

Note: The sauce also makes a delicious salad dressing or dip for apples or veggies.

SPINACH SLAW

I call this 'slaw' because it contains cabbage, apples and raisins unlike a regular salad. With this combination of ingredients and the distinctive dressing that accompanies it, it is more like a spinach cole slaw.

SALAD:

1 large head spinach

1 cup cabbage

3 apples

1/2 cup raisins

1 orange, juiced

1 lemon, juiced

DRESSING:

3 dates, pitted and soaked

3 Tablespoons olive oil

3 Tablespoons lemon juice

1 teaspoon ground yellow mustard seed

1 teaspoon caraway

1 teaspoon Bragg Liquid Aminos

TO ASSEMBLE:

1. Soak the raisins in the lemon and orange juice for half an hour.

2. While the raisins are soaking, shred the spinach leaves and cabbage and grate the apples. Put all of this into a big bowl.

3. Add the raisins along with the orange and lemon juice that they have been soaking in. Toss well.

4. Blend all ingredients for dressing in a blender or food processor. Pour over spinach slaw and mix well.

SPINACH SALAD

A very simple, yet elegant salad.

1 bunch of spinach, finely shredded

3 Vadalia onions, thinly sliced

1 1/2 cups button mushrooms, finely sliced

3 red radishes, sliced

1/4 cup sunflower seeds

1/2 cup basil

1 stalk celery

1 clove garlic

---

1. Break the garlic clove and rub a large bowl with it.
2. Toss together all the other ingredients in the garlic · rubbed bowl.
3. Serve this salad with the French or Goddess In the Raw Dressing.

RADISHES · Clears mucus from the respiratory tract, and reduces sinus ailments and hay fever. Radishes also cleanse the liver and bile, and are an excellent source of sulfur which possesses anti-inflammatory properties.

LENTIL CUPS

An attractive and tasty sprout salad. You can top this with any dressing you prefer. I like this drizzled with Mrs. Ackerly's Dressing.

2 cups sprouted lentils

1 cup tomato, chopped

1/2 cup cucumber, chopped

1/2 cup yellow pepper, chopped

1 carrot, shredded

1/4 cup cilantro, chopped

1/2 lemon, juiced

Dash cayenne

Sea salt and pepper to taste

6-12 Romaine or radicchio leaves

1. In a large bowl toss together all ingredients except the romaine or radicchio leaves

2. Place a scoop of this salad into each leave of romaine or radicchio and place on a platter.

3. Drizzle with Mrs. Ackerly's Dressing (page 473)

GRATED TURNIP AND APPLE SALAD

Green apples and turnips give this salad its refreshing mellow taste.

PARSLEY - A great body cleanser. It helps maintain healthy blood vessels, reduces gallstones and kidney stones.

1 cup raw turnip (or rutabaga), peeled and grated

1 cup tart green apples, peeled and grated

1/2 cup parsley, chopped

1 large lemon, juiced

1 Tablespoon olive oil

1 Tablespoon honey

Sea salt and pepper to taste

———————

Combine everything, toss, and chill.

PINEAPPLE BOATS

A gorgeous fruit salad that is served in a pineapple shell!

1 pineapple

3 oranges

1 grapefruit

2 cups strawberries

1 cup grapes

GRAPES - They've been reported to help cure cancer.

---

1. Cut the pineapple in half from top to bottom.
2. Remove inner pineapple pieces from shell, but keep the shells intact.
3. Dice up the other ingredients and mix well, including the pineapple pieces.
4. Place fruit mixture into the pineapple shells and serve.

CABBAGE PEAR SALAD

The unusual combination of ingredients is what makes this dish so special!

Make sure to use ripe pears for this salad and fresh raw pear and pineapple juice as well.

SALAD:

8 cups cabbage, finely shredded

4 pears, thinly sliced

6 scallions, sliced

2 carrots, grated

CABBAGE PEAR DRESSING:

1 cup pineapple juice

1/4 cup pear juice

1/3 cup olive oil

2 Tablespoons apple cider vinegar

1 clove garlic

1 teaspoon ground yellow mustard seeds

1/4 teaspoon sea salt

1/4 teaspoon pepper

---

1. Toss together salad ingredients and place in a large bowl.
2. Blend together salad dressing and pour over salad. Toss well.

EASY PAPAYA SALAD

Don't let the 2 item ingredient list fool you, this is sensational! Make sure the papaya is ripe, and that you shred it for the proper texture for this recipe.

1 whole papaya

1/2 lime

---

1. In a food processor, shred the papaya with the shredding attachment.
2. Remove from processor and place in a bowl, squeeze lime over the papaya and mix.

DAIKON AND CELERY ROOT SALAD WITH MINT

I've included this salad because it contains two vegetables that you are probably not used to eating very often. It has a light refreshing taste and is a wonderful side salad to serve with a heavier meal.

SALAD:

2 cups celery root, peeled and julienned (about 1 medium celery root)

1 cup daikon radish, julienned (about 1 small daikon radish)

1/2 cup mint leaves, chopped

1/8 teaspoon sea salt

Pinch of pepper

DRESSING:

1/2 cup orange juice

1/4 cup olive oil

1 teaspoon lemon juice

1 clove garlic, minced

1/4 teaspoon sea salt

Dash pepper

1. Combine all salad ingredients in a bowl and toss.

2. Combine dressing ingredients and pour over salad. Toss well.

PINEAPPLE APPLE SALAD

A deliciously simple, fruity salad.

4 apples, peeled and diced

2 cups pineapple, chopped

1/4 cup raisins

2 Tablespoons lime juice

2 Tablespoons apple cider vinegar

1/4 cup honey

Combine all ingredients in a bowl and toss well.

SWEET 'N SOUR COLE SLAW

Cole slaw is so good for you that I've included quite a few to choose from in this book. This one is sweeter then the other versions.

1 medium cabbage, shredded

2 large carrots, shredded

1/3 cup dried apricots, finely chopped

1/3 cup olive oil

1 Tablespoon honey

3 Tablespoons apple cider vinegar

1/2 teaspoon sea salt

Pinch of allspice

1/2 cup raisins

1. Place the cabbage, carrots and apricots in a large bowl.
2. In a small bowl mix the rest of the ingredients except raisins and pour over the cabbage, carrots and apricots. Let sit for 1 hour.
3. Mix in raisins.

DRESSINGS

WITH ALL OF THESE CHOICES, YOUR SALADS WILL NEVER BE
BORING! NOTHING BOTTLED ON THE SHELVES CAN HOLD A
CANDLE TO THESE FRESHLY MADE DELIGHTS!

ITALIAN DRESSING

Jumpin' with herbs! The longer you let this sit, the better it tastes.

1 cup olive oil

1 cup fresh basil

1 cup fresh parsley

1/2 cup dried Italian seasoning

2 scallions

2 teaspoons onion

1 lemon, juiced

2 cloves garlic

1 Tablespoon honey

1/2 teaspoon sea salt

Blend all ingredients in a blender. Chill for at least 1 hour.

MARIKA'S "GODDESS IN THE RAW" DRESSING

If you like garlic, you'll love this!

2-3 limes, juiced

3/4 cup apple cider vinegar

1 bunch scallions

1/2 bunch parsley

GARLIC - Garlic has been valued for thousands of years as a cure to treat everything from ear aches to cancer.

4 cloves garlic

1 Tablespoon olive oil

_____

Blend all ingredients thoroughly.

TAHINI DRESSING

Tahini is not one of my favorite foods, but I love this dressing! It's a nice change from the oil that's in most of the dressings.

2 Tablespoons tahini

1/2 lemon, juiced

1/2 orange, juiced

1/2 cup parsley

1 teaspoon honey

_____

Blend all ingredients thoroughly.

DILL VINAIGRETTE

A zippy vinaigrette infused with the fresh taste of dill.

3 Tablespoons olive oil

2 Tablespoons apple cider vinegar

3 Tablespoons dill

2 Tablespoons parsley

1 clove garlic

1/2 teaspoon sea salt

Pinch black pepper

Blend all ingredients in a blender.

CREAMY ORIENTAL SPICY SWEET 'N SOUR SAUCE AND DRESSING

A creamy combination of the best flavors of the East!

1 Tablespoon almond butter

1 Tablespoon ginger root

1 scallion

2 teaspoons onion

1 teaspoon tahini

1/2 lemon, juiced

4 teaspoons flax oil

1/8 teaspoon curry

1/8 teaspoon cumin

1 teaspoon honey

Blend all ingredients in a blender.

FRENCH DRESSING

Serve it to anyone, raw or not, who likes French dressing...
they'll never know the difference! I usually triple or quadruple
this recipe.

1/4 cup flax oil

2 teaspoons vinegar

1 clove garlic

1/4 teaspoon ground yellow mustard seed

1/4 teaspoon paprika

1/4 teaspoon pepper

1/2 teaspoon sea salt

_____

Blend all ingredients in a blender.

CREAMY ITALIAN HERB DRESSING

Plenty of flavor from the herbs and seasonings, but in a
creamier version then the plain Italian dressing.

2 cups olive oil

1 cup basil

1/4 cup parsley

1/4 cup apple cider vinegar

2 teaspoons onion

2 scallions

1/2 lemon, juiced

2 cloves garlic

1 Tablespoon honey

2 Tablespoons dried Italian seasoning

1/2 teaspoon sea salt

1/4 teaspoon black pepper

———————

Blend all ingredients in a blender.

ALISSA'S DRESSING

My basic tried and true recipe. So easy, so delicious!

1/2 cup apple cider vinegar

1/2 lemon, juiced

1/4 cup olive oil

3 Tablespoons honey

1/2 teaspoon sea salt

———————

Blend all ingredients in a blender.

CAESAR SALAD DRESSING

This is the BEST dressing I've ever tasted, raw or cooked! Seth, a raw fooder from Maine, brought this to a pot luck I hosted. Everybody kept telling me that I *had* to taste the Caesar dressing. I couldn't imagine why, since there were so many amazing dishes there that night. But once I tasted it I *knew* why! It's so creamy, and the pine nuts give it a real cheesy taste. I altered Seth's recipe just a bit, and halved it. But it still makes enough for a few very large salads.

1 cup pine nuts

1 Tablespoon flax oil

1 1/2 teaspoon sea salt

1/3 cup olive oil

1 date, pitted and soaked

1 large or 2 small cloves garlic

2 1/2 Tablespoons lemon juice

2 Tablespoons water

1/2 Tablespoon white miso

Sea salt as needed

---

1. In a food processor, blend the pine nuts, flax oil and sea salt until grainy.
2. Remove from processor and place in a small bowl.
3. In a food processor or blender, combine the olive oil, miso, date, garlic, lemon juice and water and blend until smooth.
4. Remove this mixture and place in the same bowl as the pine nut mixture.
5. Mix well by hand.

Note: It is important not to "cream" the pine nuts with the other liquids as you want them to retain a grainy texture. This is what will give it a cheesy taste. If the dressing needs more 'bite' add more lemon juice and sea salt.

CYNTHIA'S RAW CAESAR DRESSING

Cynthia Beavers' Caesar Dressing version is a bit lighter than Seth's because there are no pine nuts or oil. It's another of my favorites!

1 cup tahini

1-1 1/2 cup filtered water

1/4-1/2 cup fresh lemon juice

1/4 cup Nama Shoyu

1-2 Tablespoons spicy or brown mustard

1/4-1/2 cup fresh organic parsley

3 or more cloves of minced garlic

Dash of cumin

---

1. Put all ingredients, except the parsley, in a blender or food processor and mix well.

2. Taste and add more water or tahini until you get desired creaminess and flavor.

3. When it is the desired texture and flavor add parsley and blend once more.

4. Chill. It will thicken a little in the refrigerator.

Serving Suggestion: Toss dressing on Romaine lettuce for an incredible Caesar Salad!

MOCK BLUE CHEESE DRESSING

It tastes — and even resembles — real blue cheese!

1 cup Fettuccini Alfredo Sauce (See Page 381)

1/2 cup olive oil

1/4 cup parsley

3 Tablespoons scallions

2 Tablespoons lemon juice

2 Tablespoons water

1 teaspoon garlic

1/2 teaspoon sea salt

1/4 teaspoon pepper

Pinch cardamom

———————

Blend all ingredients in a blender.

RASPBERRY VINAIGRETTE

A very fruity, colorful dressing!

1 1/4 cups raspberries

1/4 cup orange juice

2 Tablespoons olive oil

1/2 Tablespoon lemon juice

Sea salt and pepper to taste

———————

Blend all ingredients in a blender until smooth.

SMOOTH AND CREAMY AVOCADO DRESSING

When I make a salad, I usually just throw on some oil and lemon juice, or whip up some of "Alissa's Dressing" that I love and is so easy to make. But when I want something richer, nothing beats this dressing! It's so smooth and creamy!

1 avocado

1/2 cucumber (about 1 1/2 cups)

1/2 cup olive oil

1/4 cup honey

3 teaspoons apple cider vinegar

1 teaspoon sea salt

Blend all ingredients in a blender.

Note: If this dressing doesn't have enough zing, add more vinegar. If it's too bland, you can add more sea salt to bring out the flavor.

HONEY MUSTARD DRESSING

Great on salads, as a marinade, and as a dip.

1/3 cup olive oil

1 lemon, juiced

1 clove garlic

2 Tablespoons apple cider vinegar

2 Tablespoons honey

1 Tablespoon ground yellow mustard seed

1 1/2 teaspoon sea salt

Blend all ingredients in a blender.

GINGER VINAIGRETTE

GINGER ROOT - Improves circulation, prevents nausea, and is great for relieving cold symptoms.

A tasty oriental dressing that's delicious over salads and as a marinade for veggies!

1/2 cup olive oil

1/4 cup Bragg Liquid Aminos

1 - 1 1/2 Tablespoon lemon juice

1 clove garlic

1 Tablespoon fresh ginger

_____

Blend all ingredients in a blender.

CILANTRO VINAIGRETTE

A lovely green vinaigrette with an herbal appeal.

2 cups cilantro

1 cup apple cider vinegar

1/2 cup olive oil

1 large clove garlic

1 1/2 Tablespoons honey

1/2 teaspoon sea salt

1/2 teaspoon black pepper

_____

Blend all ingredients in blender.

ORANGE DRESSING

Smooth and light. The orange gives this dressing a tasty zing
instead of the usual lemon or vinegar.

2 whole oranges, peeled

1 cup olive oil

1/4 cup honey

1/8 teaspoon sea salt

Blend all ingredients in a blender.

MRS. ACKERLY'S DRESSING

The red pepper gives this dressing a sweet taste. This is also
wonderful as a marinade.

1/2 cup olive oil

1/3 cup onion

1/4 cup red bell pepper

1 carrot

2 Tablespoons apple cider vinegar

1 Tablespoon honey

1/4 teaspoon sea salt

Dash pepper

Blend all ingredients in a blender.

THEY'RE CALLED "DESSERTS," BUT OH, HOW DIFFERENT THEY
ARE FROM THOSE HEAVY, FAT-LADEN, SUGAR FILLED CONCOC-
TIONS THIS WORD USUALLY CONJURES UP! THESE ARE INFI-
NITELY SUPERIOR TO COOKED DESSERTS. AND THEY'RE
GUILT FREE!

FRUITS AND NUTS MAKE UP MOST OF THESE DELECTABLE
GOODIES.

DESSERTS

I'LL OFTEN EAT A DESSERT FOR LUNCH OR DINNER, INSTEAD
OF FILLING UP ON A MEAL AND THEN STUFFING MYSELF WITH
WHAT I REALLY WANTED IN THE FIRST PLACE. BECAUSE WE
HAVE BEEN CONDITIONED TO EAT OUR "DINNER" FIRST, AND
THEN HAVE DESSERT, THIS MAY SEEM UNUSUAL AT FIRST. BUT
REMEMBER: THESE DECEPTIVELY DELICIOUS DESSERTS MIGHT
TASTE SINFULLY SENSATIONAL, BUT THEY'RE RAW... AND
THEREFORE, HEALTHFUL!

APRICOT PUFFS

When fresh apricots are in season, regale your guests with these! Tasting like apricot puff pastry, they're also elegantly beautiful... a guaranteed hit!

10 large fresh apricots

1 cup dried apricots, soaked for at least 2 hours and diced

1 cup macadamia nuts

1/2 cup water

1 Tablespoon honey

APRICOTS - Potent antioxidants, great source of beta carolene, and they reduce anemia.

1. In a food processor or Vita-Mix blend the macadamia nuts, water and honey until smooth.
2. Remove from processor and place in a bowl.
3. Stir in the dried apricots and mix well.
4. Slice the fresh apricots in half and remove the pit.
5. Fill the fresh apricot halves with a generous serving of the macadamia mixture.

DATE NUT TORTE

Fudgey, creamy and sweet!

I bring this with me when I'm visiting someone I'd like to introduce to raw food. People can't believe it's raw! And it's one of the quickest and easiest desserts to make.

BASE OF TORT:

2 cups raisins

2 cups walnuts

FROSTING:

1 cup dates, pitted and soaked

1/2 lemon, juiced

FOR BASE:

1. In a food processor, combine raisins and walnuts and blend until well blended and moist. (This will take a few minutes and you may see it forming a ball. Just make sure the raisins come out looking like a fudgey mixture and are not still grainy).

2. Remove from processor and mold onto a plate in a round circle about 1 1/2 inches thick.

FOR FROSTING:

1. In a food processor, combine dates and lemon juice until smooth and creamy.

2. Spread the frosting on top of the torte

Note: I like this served at room temperature as the frosting and torte are still sticky, but if you want a firmer texture that will be easier to slice, refrigerate it for a few hours.

BLUEBERRY PIE

This pie has a jelled blueberry filling and mounds of whole blueberries just like the traditional blueberry pie.

CRUST:

2 cups almonds

1/2 cups dates, pitted and soaked

FILLING:

5 cups blueberries

2 bananas

1 1/2 Tablespoons honey

FOR CRUST:

1. In a food processor, grind the almonds until fine.

2. Add the dates and blend until smooth.

3. Remove from processor and pat down into a pie plate.

FOR FILLING:

1. In a food processor, combine 4 cups of blueberries, 2 bananas, and 1 1/2 Tablespoon of honey. Blend until smooth.

2. Remove from food processor and add in 1 cup of whole blueberries.

3. Pour into crust.

4. Refrigerate for at least 3 hours.

Note: This pie will solidify after a few hours in the fridge.

BLUEBERRIES - Good for your eyesight! Blueberries contain potent antioxidants.

BANANA PAPAYA PUDDING

You will be astonished that 2 simple fruits combined can make a dessert this good!

1 banana

1 papaya

PAPAYA - Contains the enzyme Papain which breaks down protein. Great for indigestion and gas.

1. Halve the papaya. Remove the black seeds, and discard.
2. Scrape out the inside meat.
3. Place the papaya meat and banana in a blender and blend until smooth.

CHOCOLATE TURTLES

These decadent little sweets are the perfect raw food "candy".

RAW HONEY - Aids stomach and digestion. Is good for allergies, healing ulcers, burns, and has anti-cancer properties. Honey is an antiseptic, antibiotic, antifungal, and antibacterial.

1/2 cup carob powder

1 cup honey

1/8 teaspoon vanilla

2 cups walnut pieces

_____

1. Mix the carob, honey and vanilla together in a medium-sized bowl.
2. Stir in the walnuts until well coated with the carob-honey mixture.
3. Place spoonfuls of the combination onto Teflex sheets on top of a mesh dehydrator screen.
4. Dehydrate for 24 hours at 105 degrees.

Notes: The walnuts will tend to stick out of the mixture and the mixture may spread. Try to keep it as "together" as possible in small circles. At the end of the dehydrating time, your turtles might not seem done, they'll be very sticky. Give them time to cool off, and they will harden.

EASY APPLE PIE

An all-American favorite, raw style! And it's a lot easier to make than the "traditional" version!

CRUST:

2 cups sunflower seeds

1 cup raisins, soaked

1/2 apple

FILLING:

7 apples

8 dates, pitted and soaked

1/2 cup currants (or raisins)

1/2 lemon, juiced

1 teaspoon cinnamon

FOR CRUST:

1. Blend crust ingredients in a food processor and form into a pie pan.

FOR FILLING:

1. In a food processor, blend 2 apples with the dates until smooth.

2. Pour into a bowl and set aside.

3. In food processor, pulse chop 4 apples into tiny pieces. Remove from food processor and place in bowl with the dates.

4. To the date mixture, add the cinnamon, lemon, and currants and mix well.

5. Pour filling into pie crust and let stand for at least an hour.

BLACK FOREST CAKE

I created this layered dessert while staying with a friend, and surprised her with it when she came home from work. We sat down and ate the entire cake that night. (I wouldn't recommend doing that... but it's *that* good!)

CHERRIES - Good for your joints, cherries fight gout, and help heal rheumatism and high blood pressure.

FIRST LAYER:

2 cups walnuts

2 cups raisins

1/2 cup carob powder

1 cup pitted cherries

SECOND LAYER:

1/2 avocado

2/3 cup dates, pitted and soaked

1/2 cup carob powder

1/2 cup almond milk

1/4 cup almond butter

1 cup pitted cherries

THIRD LAYER:

2 cups pitted cherries

FOURTH LAYER:

2 cups cashews, soaked

4 dates, pitted and soaked

1-2 cups water

FIRST LAYER

1. Combine the raisins and walnuts in a food processor until smooth.

2. Add in carob powder and cherries and blend until smooth. Remove from processor and mold into a pie plate.

SECOND LAYER

1. Combine all ingredients, except cherries, in a food processor until smooth.

2. Add in cherries and pulse chop until chunky but not smooth.

3. Spread this mixture on top of the first layer.

THIRD LAYER

1. Pulse chop the cherries in a food processor until chunky.

2. Spread cherries on top of the second layer.

FORTH LAYER

1. Place half of the water into a blender and slowly add the cashews. Add water as needed, until all of the cashews are gone. Keep this thick by adding a few cashews at a time and only enough water so cashews will blend.

2. Add dates and blend until smooth.

3. Spread this mixture on top of the third layer.

Chill and serve.

BERRY BARS

Although these bars are dehydrated, they are soft, moist and bursting with flavor!

2 cups blueberries

1 cup walnuts

1 cup dates, pitted and soaked

1 cup Brazil nuts (ground into a fine texture)

1 banana (chopped into bite-sized pieces)

1 cup strawberries (chopped into bite-size pieces)

---

1. Blend 1 cup blueberries in a food processor until smooth. Place in a bowl.
2. To the processed blueberries, add in 1 cup whole blueberries and refrigerate mixture for 1 hour.
3. In a food processor, grind walnuts until fine.
4. Add in dates and blend until smooth.
5. Remove from food processor and mix together in a bowl, the Brazil nuts, date mixture, refrigerated blueberry mixture, strawberries and banana.
6. Form into squares or bars on a mesh dehydrator screen and dehydrate for about 12 hours at 105 degrees.

CARROT CAKE

Smooth and satisfying, with a deliciously creamy frosting. Decorate this cake by sprinkling cinnamon over the frosting.

CAKE:

7 carrots

1 cup walnuts

1 cup dates, pitted and soaked

3/4 cup raisins, soaked for at least 1 hour

1/2 teaspoon ginger

1/2 teaspoon cinnamon

1/4 teaspoon cardamom

1/4 teaspoon nutmeg

FROSTING:

3 Tablespoons honey

3 Tablespoons orange juice

1 cup cashews, soaked

––––––––––––

FOR CAKE:

1. Blend carrots in a food processor until well ground. Set aside in a large bowl.

2. Blend walnuts until fine, remove from food processor and place in bowl with carrots.

3. Place dates in food processor and blend until smooth.

4. Add the cardamom, nutmeg, cinnamon, and ginger and blend well.

5. To the mixture of dates and spices in the food processor, add the carrot and walnut mixture.

6. Blend the entire mixture until smooth.

7. Remove from processor and stir in the raisins.

8. Place in a pie or cake pan.

FOR FROSTING

1. In a blender or Vita-Mix add the frosting ingredients and blend until smooth.

2. Spread the frosting over the cake.

FUDGE BALLS

I carried these around with me for the entire first year I was raw. If I had a craving, I'd just "pop" a fudge ball. These are amazingly fudgey. Rich enough to satisfy the most passionate chocoholic!

2 cups dates, pitted and soaked

2 cups almond butter

1/2 cup carob power

---

1. In a food processor, blend the dates to a smooth paste.

2. Add the remaining ingredients and process until smooth.

3. Remove from processor and form into round balls.

Note: These will keep for a long time in the refrigerator.

CANNOLI

When raw food taste this good, why eat anything else! You can make these larger to look like the real thing, but I like them in bite-sized pieces because of how sweet and rich they are. For chocolate cannoli add: 3 dates, 1 Tablespoon carob, and 1 Tablespoon almond butter to the filling mixture. Make the original ones first though. You'll be amazed!

WRAPPERS:

4 cups sprouted wheat berries

2 cup dates, pitted and soaked

3/4 -1 cup water, as needed

FILLING:

1 cup macadamia nuts

1 cup cashews

1 large lemon, juiced

4 teaspoons honey

2 teaspoons Bragg Liquid Aminos

1 teaspoon vanilla

2 teaspoons water

FOR WRAPPERS:

1. Blend dates in a food processor until smooth.

2. Add in wheat berries and enough water to turn over. Blend until creamy.

3. Remove from processor and spread onto a Teflex sheet, on top of a mesh dehydrator screen, about 1/8 inch thick.

4. Dehydrate at 105 degrees until formed and solid but not hard or crispy — about 6-8 hours — flipping after the first 5-6 hours.

5. Remove from processor and cut into 2" x 4" pieces.

FOR FILLING:

In a food processor, blend the filling ingredients until smooth and creamy.

TO ASSEMBLE:

1. Place a spoonful of filling on a 2x4 piece of wrapper and roll up.

2. Continue placing the filling onto each wrapper until all of the filling and wrappers are used.

APPLE CRUMB CAKE

Dehydrate this for a few hours, and you'll enjoy the kind of apple crisp you'd never thought possible with raw foods!

CRUST:

2 cups dried calimyrna figs, soaked at least 2 hour

2 cups dried apricots, soaked at least 2 hours

1 teaspoon cinnamon

1/2 teaspoon nutmeg

FILLING:

4 apples, diced

TOPPING:

1 cup almonds

1/4 cup honey

FOR CRUST:

1. In a food processor, blend the figs, apricots, cinnamon and nutmeg until smooth.
2. Remove from processor and pat down into a pie plate.

FOR FILLING:

1. Add the diced apples on top of the crust.

FOR TOPPING:

1. In a food processor, blend almonds to a fine powder.
2. Add the honey to the powdered almonds and blend well.
3. Dribble the almonds and honey on top of the filling.
4. Place pie plate in dehydrator and dehydrate at 105 degrees for at least a few hours.

SWEET POTATO PIE

The perfect holiday pie! Letting this pie sit overnight or at least a few hours allows the succulent flavors of the sweet potatoes and the frosting to meld into a glorious infusion for a truly magnificent taste sensation.

CRUST:

2 cups almonds

1/2 cups dates, pitted and soaked

FILLING:

5 cups sweet potatoes (or yams)

8 Medjool dates, pitted and soaked

1/4 cup apple juice

1 teaspoon cinnamon

1 teaspoon vanilla

FROSTING:

2 oranges, juiced

6 dates, pitted and soaked

2 Tablespoons lemon juice

2 Tablespoons almond butter

1 Tablespoon orange rind

1 Tablespoon lemon rind

FOR CRUST:

1. In a food processor, grind the almonds until fine.

2. Add the dates and blend until smooth.

3. Remove from processor and pat down into a pie plate.

FOR FILLING:

1. Peel and cut the potatoes into large chunks.

2. Place them in a food processor and blend until well blended.

3. Add the remaining filling ingredients and blend until smooth.

4. Remove from processor and pour the filling into the crust.

SWEET POTATO - Eases diarrhea and hemorrhoids.

FOR FROSTING:

1. Place all ingredients for the frosting into a blender and blend until smooth.

2. Spread over the filling.

3. Chill and serve.

Note: Make sure you use raw apple juice, by juicing the apple yourself or buying it from a raw juice bar.

MANGO PIE

Bananas and mangoes: my two favorite fruits! This pie is as easy as · well, pie! And the taste is incredible! You can also freeze this for a frozen mango pie.

CRUST:

2 cups almonds

1/2 cups dates, pitted and soaked

FILLING:

4 mangoes

6 bananas

———————

FOR CRUST:

1. In a food processor, grind the almonds until fine.

2. Add the dates and blend until smooth.

3. Remove from processor and pat down into a pie plate.

FOR FILLING:

1. Peel the meat off of 4 mangoes and place in a food processor with 4 of the bananas. Blend well until smooth.

2. Slice the remaining 2 bananas and place in a bowl.

3. Add the mango · banana mixture and stir well.

4. Pour filling into crust and refrigerate for a few hours until mixture solidifies.

PINEAPPLE CAKE

I love this cake because it's a nice change of pace from the sweet desserts. It reminds me of a bundt cake.

2 cups sprouted buckwheat

1 cup walnuts

2 cups pineapple

1/2 cup dried apricots, soaked

1/8 teaspoon vanilla

---

1. Place all but one cup of pineapple in a food processor and blend until smooth.

2. Remove from processor. Take half of the mixture and place on a Teflex sheet on top of a mesh dehydrator screen, making a 2 inch high round base.

3. Cut up the remaining 1 cup of pineapple and place on top of the base.

4. Add the remaining mixture on top of this cut up pineapple and, while keeping it thick on top, seal the edges between the bottom mixture and the top mixture so the middle pineapple pieces are not showing.

5. Dehydrate at 105 degrees for 15 · 20 hours or until solid and not mushy inside.

PINEAPPLE · Contains the natural enzyme bromelain which contains compounds that reduce pain and swelling.

PUMPKIN PIE

This recipe is taken from Jamey Dina and Kim Sproul's book, *Uncooking* with Jamey and Kim. It is one of the best pumpkin pies I've ever had and easy too!

CRUST:

2 cups almonds

1/3 – 1/2 cup dates, pitted and soaked

FILLING:

2 cups shredded pumpkin or butternut squash

1 cup dates

1/2 cup almonds (soaked) or sunflower seeds

2 teaspoons cinnamon

1 teaspoon ginger

1/2 teaspoon ground cloves

1/2 teaspoon nutmeg

1/4 cup water

FOR CRUST:

1. Add all ingredients and blend until smooth

2. Pat down into a pie plate.

FOR FILLING:

1. Mix shredded pumpkin or squash in a food processor for several minutes. Add other ingredients and blend until smooth.

2. Place filling on top of pie crust.

Best served chilled.

Alissa's note: I use squash instead of pumpkin and the almonds instead of the sunflower seeds.

RASPBERRY BANANA CREAM PUDDING PIE

Two delectable layers and a delicious topping! You can use fresh or frozen raspberries for this pie.

CRUST:

2 cups almonds

1 1/2 cups dates, pitted and soaked

LAYER ONE:

2 cups raspberries

3 Tablespoons honey

LAYER TWO:

4 bananas

1 cup pine nuts

8 dates, pitted and soaked

Pinch cinnamon

Dash vanilla

TOPPING:

2 cups raspberries

FOR CRUST:

1. In a food processor, grind the almonds until fine.

2. Add the dates and blend until smooth.

3. Remove from processor and pat down into a pie plate.

LAYER ONE:

1. Blend raspberries and honey in a food processor until smooth.

2. Pour into crust.

LAYER TWO:

1. Place layer two ingredients in food processor and blend until smooth.

2. Remove mixture from food processor and pour onto first layer.

TOPPING:

1. Place whole raspberries on top of pie.

Allow pie to sit for a few hours or chill before serving

CREAMY NO-CRUST FRUIT PIE

KIWI - May help prevent tumor growth, and block detrimental changes in cells that can lead to cancer.

There are times I just don't want the heaviness of a crust, and this pie is the solution! It's rich, creamy, and a snap to make.

4 cups mixed fruit, cut up (papaya, bananas, peaches, mangoes, kiwis, and pineapple)

2 cups mango

2-3 bananas

———————

1. Place the cut up fruit into a bowl.
2. Blend mangoes and bananas in a blender or food processor until smooth and creamy and pour over the cut up fruit.
3. Mix well and pour into a pie plate.

WALNUT FUDGE

This fudge tastes like a blonde brownie, with a flavor reminiscent of butterscotch!

2 cups walnuts

1/4 cup dates, pitted and soaked

2 Tablespoons honey

1 teaspoon cinnamon

1. Grind walnuts in a food processor until fine.
2. Add the rest of the ingredients and blend until creamy.
3. Form into balls or a big block and keep in the refrigerator.

PECAN PIE

You'll be winning your guest over with this luscious pie!
Looking at the ingredients, it's easy to see why this is a very
sweet and rich dessert, so I save this one for special occasions.

CRUST:

2 cups pecans

1/2 cup dates, pitted and soaked

1/4 teaspoon cinnamon

1/8 teaspoon vanilla

FILLING:

1 1/2 cups dates, pitted and soaked

1/2 cup pecans

1/3 cup honey

1/4 teaspoon cinnamon

1/2 cup macadamia nuts

1/2 cup water

TOPPING:

1 cup pecans

FOR CRUST:

1. Blend pecans in a food processor until fine.

2. Add remaining ingredients and blend until smooth.

3. Remove from processor and pat down into a pie plate.

FOR FILLING:

1. Place pecans in food processor and blend until smooth.

2. Add in the remaining ingredients and blend until creamy.

3. Pour filling into pie crust.

TOPPING:

1. Place pecans decoratively on top of filling.

PEACH PIE

Simple and delicious. Wonderful in the summertime when fresh peaches abound!

CRUST:

2 cups almonds

1/2 cup dates, pitted and soaked

FILLING:

8-10 peaches, diced

1/2 teaspoon cinnamon

1 teaspoon vanilla

PEACHES - Assist in the removal of intestinal worms.

FOR CRUST:

1. In a food processor, grind the almonds until fine.

2. Add the dates and blend until smooth.

3. Remove from processor and pat down into a pie plate.

FOR FILLING:

1. Place all of the filling ingredients into a food processor and blend until smooth.

2. Pour filling on top of the crust.

CHAROSES

This is so simple and it reminds me of the Jewish New Year!

6 apples

2 cups almonds

1 cup honey

2 Tablespoons cinnamon

------

1. Cut apples into large chunks. Place apples in a food processor and pulse chop into finely diced pieces.

2. Remove apples from food processor and set aside in a large bowl.

3. Grind almonds in food processor until fine.

4. Add the rest of the ingredients to the food processor and blend well.

5. Remove from processor and place in bowl with the apples. Mix well.

HONEY CINNAMON TOASTER TARTS

These taste like brown sugar Pop-Tarts!

WRAPPERS:

2 cups sprouted wheat berries

1 cup dates, pitted and soaked

3/4 cup water

FILLING:

2 cups macadamia nuts

2 cups honey

2 teaspoons cinnamon

FOR WRAPPER:

1. In a food processor, blend the "wrapper" ingredients until smooth.

2. Remove "wrapper" mixture and place on a Teflex sheet on top of a mesh dehydrator screen. Smooth mixture out into an 1/8 inch thick square.

3. Dehydrate for a few hours at 105 degrees until strong enough to flip over. Dehydrate again for another few hours until solid but not hard.

4. Remove sheet from food processor and immediately slice into large squares before the wrapper cools.

FOR FILLING:

(Make this filling while the wrapper is in the dehydrator so it is ready to spread.)

1. In a food processor, blend macadamia nuts until fine.

2. Add in the other filling ingredients and blend until creamy.

TO ASSEMBLE:

1. Place a thin layer of filling on top of the wrapper squares.

2. Fold wrapper in half. Seal the edges by squeezing them together.

3. If necessary, dehydrate assembled tarts at 105 degrees for a few hours until they're solid.

STRAWBERRY TOASTER TARTS

I admit, you need to plan ahead to sprout the wheat. But, like the honey-cinnamon ones these are so simple and so worth it!

WRAPPERS:

2 cups sprouted wheat berries

1 cup dates, pitted and soaked

3/4 cup water

FILLING:

3 cups strawberries

3 bananas

FOR WRAPPER:

1. In a food processor, blend wrapper ingredients until smooth.

2. Remove mixture and place on a Teflex sheet on top of a mesh dehydrator screen. Smooth mixture out into an 1/8 inch thick square.

3. Dehydrate at 105 degrees for a few hours until strong enough to flip over. Dehydrate again for another few hours until wrapper is solid but not hard.

4. Remove sheet from food processor and immediately slice into large squares before the wrapper cools.

FOR FILLING:

(Make this filling while the wrapper is in the dehydrator so it is ready to spread.)

1. In a food processor, blend the strawberries and bananas until creamy. Freeze for a half an hour.

TO ASSEMBLE:

1. Place a thin layer of strawberry filling on top of the wrapper squares.

2. Dehydrate at 105 degrees for another 10-12 hours while wrapper is still flat.

3. Remove dehydrated squares while still flexible. Fold wrappers in half. Seal the edges by squeezing the wrapper edges together.

4. If necessary, dehydrate assembled tarts at 105 degrees for a few hours until they're solid.

Note: The wrapper will still be flexible even after dehydrating for 10-12 hours because of the wet topping on it.

HAMENTASCHEN

Traditionally filled with a prune or poppy seed filling, this is like a Jewish Pop-Tart!

WRAPPERS:

2 cups sprouted wheat berries

1 cup dates, pitted and soaked

3/4 cup water

FILLING:

2 cups prunes, pitted and soaked for at least 2 hours

1 – 2 Tablespoons poppy seeds

FOR THE WRAPPER:

1. In a food processor, blend wheat berries, dates, and water until smooth.

2. Remove mixture and place on a Teflex sheet on top of a mesh dehydrator screen. Smooth the mixture out into an 1/8 inch thick square.

3. Dehydrate at 105 degrees for a couple of hours until strong enough to flip over. Dehydrate again for another few hours until "wrapper" is solid, but not hard.

4. Remove sheet from food processor and immediately slice into large squares before the wrapper cools.

FOR FILLING:

1. In a food processor, blend prunes until creamy. Add in poppy seeds and blend until mixed thoroughly.

TO ASSEMBLE:

1. Place a thin layer of prune mixture on top of the "wrapper" squares.

2. Fold wrapper corner to corner to make a triangle, sealing the edges by squeezing them together.

3. Dehydrate finished hamentaschen triangles at 105 degrees for another few hours, until solid.

FIG SQUARES

If you like Fig Newtons, you'll love these!

WRAPPER:

2 cups sprouted wheat berries

1 cup dates, pitted and soaked

3/4 cup water

FILLING:

2 cups dried figs, soaked for at least 2 hours

FOR WRAPPER:

1. In a food processor blend wheat berries, dates, and water until smooth.

2. Remove mixture and place on a Teflex sheet on top of a mesh dehydrator screen. Smooth mixture out into an 1/8 inch thick square.

3. Dehydrate at 105 degrees for a couple of hours until strong enough to flip over. Dehydrate again for another few hours until "wrapper" is solid but not hard.

4. Remove sheet from food processor and immediately slice into large squares before the wrapper cools.

FOR FILLING:

1. In food processor, blend figs until creamy.

TO ASSEMBLE:

1. Place a thin layer of fig mixture on top of the "wrapper" squares.

2. Fold wrappers in half, sealing the edges by squeezing the wrapper edges together.

3. Dehydrate assembled "cookies" at 105 degrees for a few
   hours until solid.

BLUEBERRY CHEESECAKE

Very sweet, very rich, and no-guilt! You can top this pie with
additional sliced fruit — blueberries, kiwi, strawberries, mangoes. Substitute, if you like, another fruit — strawberries, for
instance, work very well — for the blueberries. Also, I often
make this pie without the crust. Simply pour the filling into a
bowl, top with sliced fruit, chill and serve!

CRUST:

2 cups almonds

1 cup raisins

FILLING:

4 cups cashews

1 large lemon, juiced

8 Tablespoons honey

2 teaspoons vanilla

2 cups blueberries

1 cup water

FOR CRUST:

1. Place the almonds in a food processor and blend until fine.

2. Add raisins and blend until well blended.

3. Pat crust down into a pie plate.

FOR FILLING:

1. Place the cashews, honey, vanilla, lemon and water in a

blender or food processor and process until smooth and creamy.

2. Remove this mixture from blender and stir in the blueberries.
3. Pour filling into pie crust. Chill.

Note: The filling can be made in the food processor but will be creamier if you use a Vita-Mix or a strong blender. Soaking the cashews for a few hours will help to make this creamier if you're using a food processor.

ALMOND BUTTER BALLS

I whipped this together almost every night when I first went raw, since the ingredients are common ones I usually had on hand and it's so simple to prepare.

1/2 cup almond butter

1/2 cup sunflower seeds

1/2 cup raisins

1/2 cup honey

Grind sunflower seeds until fine. Place in bowl with other ingredients. Mix well and form into balls

NUT BRITTLE

This is a vast improvement over traditional "peanut brittle." Rather than that "jaw-breaking" hardness of ordinary peanut brittle, it poses no threat to the teeth! This treat is softer, more flexible, and boasts a wonderful honey flavor.

3 cups almonds, sprouted

3 cups sunflower seeds, sprouted

3 cups sesame seeds

2 cups honey

---

1. Place almonds and sunflower seeds in a food processor and pulse chop for only a few seconds until the almonds are broken up into large pieces.
2. Place almond and sunflower seed mixture into a large bowl.
3. Add in sesame seeds and honey and mix thoroughly.
4. Place on a Teflex sheet on top of a mesh dehydrator screen and spread about 1/8 inch thick.
5. Dehydrate for 24 hours at 105 degrees.

Note: This will be flexible when you take it out of the dehydrator but will firm up a bit as it cools off.

CHOCOLATE CAKE

I love this cake because, although it's satisfyingly dense, it's not super sweet. For a more decadent cake, you can add 1 cup of mixed berries into the frosting. You can then top the entire cake with whip cream, crushed nuts and shredded coconut. But, this basic cake is still delicious!

CAKE:

2 cups figs, soaked for at least 2 hours

2 cups walnuts

SESAME SEEDS -

Very high in calcium.

1/2 cup carob powder

FROSTING:

1 1/2 cup cashews

1/2 avocado

1/4 cup carob powder

1 1/2 Tablespoons honey

FIGS - One of the highest plant

sources of calcium.

3/4 cup water

FOR CAKE:

1. Place figs in a food processor and blend well.

2. Add in walnuts and blend until smooth.

3. Add in carob powder and blend until creamy and mixture forms a large "ball" in the food processor. (Continue to break up the "balled" mixture and process a few times to make sure mixture is well blended.)

4. Remove from food processor and shape into a round loaf on a plate.

FOR FROSTING:

1. In a food processor or blender, blend the frosting ingredients until creamy.

2. Thickly frost the cake on top and on all sides.

Notes: Be sure to blend the "cake" ingredients well. The little seeds of figs left whole will not be as pleasant as when blended until creamy and smooth. It's the frosting that really "makes this cake".

ANN WIGMORE'S BANANA CREAM PIE

Courtesy of the book, *Recipes for a Longer Life*, by Ann Wigmore. I've been making this pie for 12 years and it's still one of my favorites!

CRUST:

1/2 cup pecans

2 cups dates, pitted and soaked

1 1/2 cups dried coconut

1 teaspoon vanilla

FILLING:

4-5 bananas

1 cup shredded coconut

1/2 cup apple juice

2 teaspoons tahini

2 teaspoons honey

1 teaspoon pure vanilla

FOR CRUST:

1. Grind the pecans in a food processor until fine.
2. Add the dates and blend until creamy.
3. Add the remaining ingredients and blend well.
4. Remove from food processor and form into a pie plate.

FOR FILLING:

1. Mash 2 bananas and place in a blender with the apple juice, 1/2 cup of coconut, tahini, honey, and vanilla. Blend until smooth.
2. Remove from food processor and place in a bowl.

3. Slice the remaining bananas and mix into the filling.

4. Pour into pie crust and sprinkle with the remaining coconut.

Note: Make sure you use raw apple juice by juicing the apple yourself or buying it from a raw juice bar.

ELAINA'S CINNAMON ROLLS (WITH FROSTING)

This dessert from Elaina Love is so amazing. I usually need to double the filling though. They are doughy and sweet, just like the real thing!

DOUGH:

2 1/2 cups almond meal (leftover from making almond milk)

2 1/2 cup flax meal (grind 1 1/3 cups whole flax seeds in your blender or spice grinder)

1 cup soft pitted dates firmly packed

1/8 cup pure water

1/4 teaspoon Celtic sea salt

Dash cayenne

1/4 cup olive oil or coconut butter (flax oil is too heat sensitive)

1. Blend the dates and water together in a food processor or blender until it becomes a paste.

2. Mix everything together in a large bowl and work with your hands until the dough is well mixed.

3. Place the dough on a Teflex sheet or piece of wax paper and form into a 1/4 inch thick square using your hands to shape it.

4. Cover with another Teflex sheet or wax paper and roll with a rolling pin until the dough is a uniform thickness.

5. Prepare the filling.

FILLING:

1/2 cup soft pitted dates firmly packed

1/2 cup raisins

1 Tablespoon cinnamon

1/8 cup water

Extra raisins

1/2 cup soaked and dehydrated walnuts, coarsely chopped

1. Puree the first 4 ingredients in a food processor until it becomes smooth.

2. Spread the mixture onto the dough.

3. Sprinkle with extra raisins and walnuts.

4. Using the Teflex sheet on the bottom to push, roll the dough tightly.

5. Wrap the roll in the Teflex or wax paper and refrigerate until chilled.

6. Slice into desired thicknesses and dehydrate at 105 degrees until warm.

FROSTING (IT'S OPTIONAL, BUT IT SURE TASTES GOOD!):

1 cup sunflower seeds soaked 4 or more hours (1 1/2 cups after soaking)

3/4 cup water

6 Tablespoons honey or dates

Juice of 1 small tangerine and the entire peel.

1 teaspoon vanilla

Blend all ingredients until smooth and creamy. Add a little extra water if you want it thinner. Drizzle on top of dehydrated cinnamon rolls.

Tip: Keep rolls in your freezer. Remove and dehydrate as needed.

BANANA ICE CREAM

I've made frozen banana ice cream with my juicer for years. But if you don't have a juicer that homogenizes, just use your food processor. It will take a few extra minutes, but it'll work!

2-3 frozen bananas (Freeze without peel!)
Feed frozen bananas through juicer with homogenizing attachment in place, OR place in food processor and blend until super smooth!

Note: As you blend this in a food processor, you will notice the banana looks gritty. Continue to blend and it will 'cream' up like a soft serve ice cream.

Serving suggestions: Place on top of fudge and then top with Carob Fudge Sauce, Strawberry Sauce, and Whipped Cream for an ice cream sundae.

Note: You can also add carob powder, coconut, or any other flavoring that catches your fancy!

BANANA BUTTER BERRY PIE

Almond butter, bananas, and berries unite to produce this creamy, out of this world pie!

CRUST:

2 cups almonds

1/2 cup dates, pitted and soaked

LAYER ONE:

7 frozen bananas

1/3 cup carob powder

LAYER TWO:

1 cup macadamia nuts

2 Tablespoons almond butter

1 teaspoon honey

TOPPING:

3 cups mixed berries (strawberries, blueberries, etc...)

1/2 teaspoon cinnamon

FOR CRUST:

1. In a food processor, blend almonds until fine.

2. Add dates and blend until smooth.

3. Remove from processor and pat down into a pie plate.

FOR LAYER ONE:

1. Blend bananas in a food processor until smooth and creamy.

2. Add in carob powder and blend well.

3. Place in pie crust.

FOR LAYER TWO:

1. Place nuts in food processor and blend until well ground.
2. Add almond butter and honey and blend until smooth.
3. Place this mixture on top of Layer One.

FOR TOPPING:

1. Place berries and cinnamon in food processor and blend until smooth.
2. Remove from processor and place on top of Layer Two.

Refrigerate or freeze pie until solid and ready to serve.

LEMON PUDDING

LEMONS - High in Vitamin C, fiber, and phytochemicals, lemons are excellent cleansers for the liver, bowel, and blood.

Close your eyes when you eat this. The green color will throw you off when you taste the velvety, yellow, lemony flavor. Just keep thinking: "yellow, yellow, yellow..."

1 cup dates, pitted and soaked
1 avocado
2 whole lemons, peeled

Place all ingredients in a blender. Blend until smooth and creamy.

LEMON MERINGUE PIE

A light, very lemon, chiffon-tasting pie!
For an easier version without the fresh coconut, use dried

coconut for the crust and the Lemon Pudding as your filling (double the Lemon Pudding recipe). This will produce a heavier, thicker pie.

CRUST:

1 cup fresh coconut

1 cup raisins

1/2 cup cashews

1/2 cup pecans

FILLING:

3 cups fresh coconut

2 whole lemons

2 teaspoons honey

TOPPING:

1 cup cashews

1/2 cup water

1/2 teaspoon honey

_____

FOR CRUST:

1. In a food processor blend the cashews and pecans until fine.

2. Add the remaining ingredients and blend until well ground.

3. Remove from processor and pat down into a pie plate.

FOR FILLING:

1. Blend filling ingredients until smooth and creamy.

2. Pour into pie crust.

FOR TOPPING:

1. Blend topping ingredients until smooth.

2. Place topping on top of the filling.

BANANA CRUNCH

Stick a Popsicle stick into one end and these look like something you get from the ice cream truck!

5-10 Bananas

1 cup almonds, crushed

1 cup walnuts, crushed

1 cup carob powder

1 cup dried coconut

1. Place all of the above ingredients on separate plates.
2. Roll one banana at a time into the almonds, then the walnuts, then the carob, then the coconut.
3. Place the 'loaded' banana on top of a piece of wax paper and freeze.
4. Continue rolling each banana until they are all covered with a bit of each ingredient. Keep the entire batch frozen until you are ready to eat them.

PINEAPPLE SUNDAE

This is an adaptation of an old Ann Wigmore recipe. It's a wonderful combination of pineapple, apples and cream sauce that I've made many times!

PINEAPPLE SUNDAE:

3 cups diced fresh pineapple

3 cups grated apple

6 chopped pecans (optional)

6 fresh strawberries (optional)

APPLE NUT CREAM:

3 apples

3/4 cup cashews

3/4 cup water

1 Tablespoon tahini

FOR SUNDAE:

1. Dice the pineapple and grate the apple by hand, or in a food processor. Set aside in a large bowl.

FOR APPLE NUT CREAM:

1. Blend all ingredients in a food processor or blender until smooth.

2. Place in a separate bowl.

TO ASSEMBLE:

The original recipe calls for placing alternating layers of the fruit and apple nut cream into 12 ounce glasses and then sprinkling the glasses with pecans and a strawberry. When I make this, however, I just combine the fruit and the Apple Nut Cream in a large bowl and omit the pecans and strawberries.

KEY LIME PIE

A truly tart and creamy lime pudding placed on top of a deca-dent crust.

CRUST:

1 1/2 cups macadamia nuts

1 cup soft dates, pitted and soaked

1 ripe banana

BANANAS - High in potassium. One medium-sized banana provides 400 mg of potassium. Potassium is a mineral that is lost during physical exercise. It is required to regulate your heartbeat, blood pressure, and may help reduce the risk of stroke in older people. Bananas are also rich in Vitamin B6 and they are a good source of fiber, Vitamin C, and magnesium. Keep bananas in a paper or plastic bag to help them ripen.

FILLING:

3 whole large limes

2 cups dates, pitted and soaked

2 avocados

———————

FOR CRUST:

1. In a food processor, blend the macadamia nuts until well ground.
2. Add in the banana and blend until smooth.
2. Add dates, blending until smooth.
3. Pat down mixture into a pie plate.

FOR FILLING:

1. In food processor, blend all filling ingredients until smooth and creamy.
2. Pour filling on top of pie crust.

STRAWBERRY PIE

Loaded with beautiful strawberries, this pie is hearty and delicious! Make sure the bananas are really ripe.

CRUST:

2 cups almonds

1 1/2 cup dates, pitted and soaked

1 cup strawberries, diced

FILLING:

3 1/2 cups strawberries

3 very ripe bananas

FOR CRUST:

1. In a food processor, blend almonds until fine.

2. Add dates and blend until smooth.

3. Place in a bowl, and stir in the diced strawberries.

4. Mold into a pie plate.

FOR FILLING:

1. Dice 1/2 cup of the strawberries. Set aside.

2. In a food processor, blend the remaining 2 cups of strawberries and the bananas until smooth.

3. Place in a bowl, and stir in the diced strawberries.

4. Pour into crust.

STRAWBERRIES - Contain ellagic acid which can reduce and often neutralize the damaging effects of the carcinogen PAH found in cigarette smoke.

STACIE'S SOUL FRUIT COBBLER

One of Stacie's amazing desserts!

1 cup shredded coconut

1 1/2 cup dried peaches or nectarines, soaked for 1 hour in water

1 cup dates, pitted and soaked for 1 hour in water

5-6 medium bananas

1/2 cup fresh young coconut or shredded coconut

10 fresh peaches, pitted, sliced or diced

2 cups blackberries or strawberries

1 Tablespoon grated lemon peel

NECTARINES - Can reduce cystitis

1. Cover the bottom of a 9" x 12" pan with 1 cup shredded coconut.

2. Puree soaked peaches (or nectarines) in a food processor,

adding soak water as necessary. Place pureed fruit into a bowl.

3. Mash bananas into pureed fruit with fork (do not machine blend).

4. Course or finely chop young Coconut in a food processor (do not puree).

5. Blend young coconut with banana mixture by hand.

6. Spread mixture over coconut layer in the pan.

7. Spread sliced (or diced) peaches over banana mixture.

8. Blend 1 1/2 cups berries with dates and lemon peel and spread on top.

9. Sprinkle cobbler with remaining berries.

Note: Try other fruit combinations such as figs, apples, pears.

FRUIT LEATHERS

Fruit Leathers are *so* easy to make! Below are instructions for banana, pear, and apple/prune leathers, but try experimenting with different kinds of fruit and fruit combinations. Remember, make sure the fruit you use is *ripe*.

BANANA LEATHER

6 RIPE Bananas

1. Place bananas in a food processor. Blend until smooth.

2. Remove from processor and spread onto Teflex sheets on top of a mesh dehydrator screen.

3. Dehydrate at 105 degrees for 18-24 hours.

Note: For faster drying times, flip leather half way through onto mesh screen, peeling off Teflex sheet.

PEAR LEATHER

6 RIPE Pears

---

1. Place pears in a food processor. Blend until smooth.
2. Remove from processor and spread onto Teflex sheets on top of a mesh dehydrator screen.
3. Dehydrate at 105 degrees for 24 hours.

Note: For faster drying times, flip leather half way through onto mesh screen, peeling off Teflex sheet.

APPLE PRUNE LEATHERS

2 apples, diced
6 prunes, soaked

---

1. Place apples and prunes in a food processor. Blend until smooth.
2. Remove from processor and spread onto Teflex sheets on top of a mesh dehydrator screen.
3. Dehydrate at 105 degrees for 24 hours.

Note: For faster drying times, flip leather half way through onto mesh screen, peeling off Teflex sheet.

JUICE POPS

These are so much better then store bought popsicles.
Use any combination of fruit you like!

4 oranges

2 cup berries

_____

1. Blend berries and oranges until smooth, or leave chunky, depending on what texture you want your pops to be.
2. Pour berry and orange mixture into Popsicle holders or ice cube trays with Popsicle sticks and freeze.

MINT THUMBPRINT DELIGHTS

PRUNES - Natural laxatives, prunes are an excellent defense against anemia.

Your own thumbprint makes these cookies beautiful to behold. (And they taste as good as they look!)

BASE:

1/2 cup almonds

1/2 cup dates, pitted and soaked

2 cups shredded coconut

FILLING:

1 cup prunes, pitted and soaked

1 teaspoon mint leaves

_____

FOR BASE:

1. In a food processor grind almonds until fine.

2. Add in dates and blend until smooth.

3. Place in a bowl and mix in coconut.

4. Form this mixture into round balls.

5. Press your thumb or finger tip into each ball to make a dent. Refrigerate for an hour to harden a little.

FOR FILLING:

1. In a food processor, combine prunes and mint leaves until smooth.

2. Top the cookies with a dollop of this mixture.

CHOCOLATE MOUSSE

One of my all time favorite desserts, I never imagined I would be able to eat this again once I went raw. All the 'chocolate' taste, none of the guilt!

1 avocado

1 cup almond milk

2/3 cup dates, pitted and soaked

1/2 cup carob powder

1/4 cup almond butter

In a food processor or blender, combine all ingredients and blend until creamy.

SPICE BARS

This recipe was adapted from an old raw recipe book called

Light Eating for Survival by Marcia Acciardo. It's a lovely little book with a lot of earthy raw food dishes. This is one of my favorites from it.

2 cups apples, chopped

4 cups shredded coconut

1/2 cup honey

1 teaspoon almond butter

2 teaspoons ground cinnamon

1 teaspoon ground allspice

1. In a food processor, combine all ingredients and mix until well blended.

2. Remove from processor and form into bars.

3. Refrigerate until firm.

CAROB FUDGE SAUCE

Great over Banana Ice Cream!

4 dates, pitted and soaked

4 Tablespoons carob powder

1 banana

2 Tablespoons honey

2 teaspoons vanilla

Water as needed

Blend all ingredients, adding small amounts of water as needed, until you get a thick, "saucy," consistency.

COOKIES

CHOCOLATE CHIP COOKIES

Soft and warm like 'just out of the oven' cookies! They even look like the Toll House brand: chips and all!

DOUGH:

1 cup cashews

1 cup walnuts

1 cup dried apricots (soaked for 2 hours)

1/2 cup raisins (soaked for 2 hours)

1 Tablespoon honey

1/2 teaspoon vanilla

1/2 cup water

CHOCOLATE CHIPS:

1/2 cup dried apricots (soaked for 4 hours)

1/2 cup carob powder

1/4 cup water

1/2 Tablespoon honey

FOR DOUGH:

1. In a food processor blend the cashews and walnuts into a fine powder. Remove from food processor and set aside.

2. In food processor, blend the remaining 'dough' ingredients and blend well until smooth.

3. Add in cashew and walnut mixture and blend again until smooth.

4. Remove dough from processor and form into cookies on a Teflex sheet on top of a mesh dehydrator screen.

FOR CHIPS:

1. In a blender add the chocolate chip ingredients and blend well until creamy.
2. Place small bits of the chocolate chip batter onto the tops of the cookies and press into cookies.
3. Dehydrate the chocolate chip cookies at 105 degrees for 6-12 hours.

LEMON POPPY COOKIES

These quick and easy, lemony treats are bursting with flavor.

1 cup almonds

3/4 cup dates, pitted and soaked

1/2 cup freshly squeezed lemon juice

2 Tablespoons poppy seeds

1. Blend almonds in food processor until fine.
2. Add in the dates and lemon juice, and process until smooth.
3. Add in the poppy seeds and blend until poppy seeds are mixed in well.
4. Spoon out into small round balls or flat cookies onto mesh dehydrator screens.
5. Dehydrate for 3-4 hours at 105 degrees.

BANANA MACADAMIA NUT FUDGE COOKIES

Rich fudgy taste, and so easy to make!

1 cup raisins

1 cup walnuts

1 cup macadamia nuts, chopped into big pieces

1 cup bananas, peeled and chopped

1. In a food processor, blend raisins and walnuts until smooth.
2. Remove mixture from processor and place in a bowl.
3. Stir in macadamia nuts and bananas.
4. Form into cookie shapes and dehydrate for 8 to 10 hours at 105 degrees.

ALMOND BUTTER AND RAISIN COOKIES

These cookies have an unusual taste from the buckwheat, but I've been making them for years and I just love them. I like the fact that they are not too sweet.

2 cups sprouted buckwheat

2 Tablespoons almond butter

1 Tablespoon vanilla

2 teaspoons cinnamon

1 teaspoon honey

1 cup raisins, soaked 1 hour

1. Place all ingredients, except raisins, in a food processor and blend until smooth.
2. Remove mixture from processor and place in a bowl.
3. Drain the raisins, and mix them into the other ingredients by hand.
4. Form into cookie shapes on a mesh dehydrator screen.

5. Dehydrate at 105 degrees for 8 hours.

Note: The cookies should be firm but not hard.

APPLE COOKIES

These cookies are very sweet and chewy. You will have to sprout the buckwheat, but the rest takes only minutes to prepare!

1/2 cup walnuts

1 apple

1/2 cup sprouted buckwheat

1/2 cup raisins, soaked at least 1 hour

1/2 cup dates, pitted and soaked

1 teaspoon vanilla

1/2 teaspoon cinnamon

1. In a food processor, grind walnuts until fine.
2. Add in all other ingredients and blend well until smooth.
3. Form into cookie shapes and place on a mesh dehydrator screen.
4. Dehydrate at 105 degrees for 8-10 hours.

APRICOT COOKIES

Apricots and cinnamon... perfection on the palate!

1 cup almonds

1 cup Brazil nuts

20 dried apricots, soaked for at least 2 hours

6 dates, pitted and soaked

1 Tablespoon cinnamon

1 Tablespoon honey

---

1. In a food processor blend almonds and Brazil nuts until fine.

2. Add remaining ingredients except for 4 apricots, and blend until smooth.

3. Remove mixture from processor and place in a bowl.

4. Dice the remaining 4 apricots. Add to the mixture and mix well.

5. Form into cookie shapes on a mesh dehydrator screen.

6. Dehydrate at 105 degrees for 12 hours.

NECTARINE COOKIES

Nice and crunchy, and not too sweet.

1 cup almonds, ground until still a bit chunky

2 nectarines, pitted and sliced

2 dates, pitted and soaked (add more dates if you want them sweeter)

1/2 teaspoon vanilla

1/2 teaspoon cinnamon

---

1. In a food processor, combine nectarines, vanilla, cinnamon, and dates. Blend until smooth.

2. Remove from food processor and add in ground almonds.

3. Form into cookies and place on a mesh dehydrator screen. Dehydrate for 10 to 15 hours at 105 degrees.

DRINKS

THERE ARE VIRTUALLY ENDLESS COMBINATIONS THAT MAKE
EXCELLENT DRINKS! THERE ARE SO MANY VARIETIES OF CAR-
ROT DRINKS FOR INSTANCE: CARROT, BEET AND CELERY – CAR-
ROT, SPINACH, APPLE, ETC... WHAT I HAVE LISTED HERE ARE
JUST A FEW OF MY FAVORITES THAT YOU MAY NOT BE AWARE
OF; SOME OF THE MORE UNUSUAL ONES! YOU SHOULD
ALWAYS DRINK THESE IMMEDIATELY AFTER PREPARING THEM,
EXCEPT FOR THE NUT MILKS, WHICH WILL LAST A DAY OR TWO
IN THE REFRIGERATOR.

ALMOND MILK

Almond milk and other nut milks are so easy to make! Many people like to strain these through a cheesecloth, or a very fine strainer. If you have neither, don't let that stop you! And don't think that these take a lot of work to prepare...they don't! Just blend the nuts and water with a sweetener (such as honey or dates) and that's all there is to it! Unless I'm making a certain soup, or a dish I really don't want to have a gritty texture, I often don't even strain the milk.

1 cup almonds, sprouted

3 cups water

Sweetener such as 1 Tablespoon honey

1. In a blender or Vita-Mix, blend the almonds and water and sweetener until smooth.

2. Strain through a cheese cloth or fine strainer or use as is.

Note: You can use other nuts such as sunflower, sesame, etc.

ALMOND MILK -

A great body builder!

ALISSA'S GREEN DRINK

My basic green drink. I use very large handfuls (or half a head) of each of these greens. Sometimes I'll use different veggies, like bok choy, lettuce, or sprouts. I always sweeten it with 1/2 an apple or a pineapple, and I use a whole cucumber for beautiful skin! You will need a juicer for this drink.

Kale

Collard

WHEN CHOOSING GREENS,

look for ones that are darkest in

color to get the most nutrients.

Swiss chard

Spinach

1 whole Cucumber

2 stalks Celery

1/2 apple or pineapple

_____

Place all ingredients through a juicer and drink promptly.

LEMON GINGER CAYENNE SHOT

This'll cure what ails ya! Great for a cold, or for helping to detox!

1/4 cup water (optional)

1/4 cup fresh lemon juice

1 teaspoon fresh ginger, grated

Pinch cayenne (use as much as you can tolerate!)

_____

Place all ingredients in a small glass and blend well.

DENNIS'S MORNING SMOOTHIE

A very basic, simple, yet extraordinarily delicious smoothie!

2 oranges

1 banana

1/2 cup berries (mixed or one single kind)

Place all ingredients in a blender and blend until smooth.

Note: If you want a frozen smoothie, use a frozen banana or berries.

POWER UP

A great drink for bodybuilders. You'll get all the minerals and protein from the greens, electrolytes from the coconut, and potassium from the banana.

2 cups coconut water

1 scoop "Alissa's Green Food Powder Supplement" (see resource section)

1 banana

In a blender or Vita-Mix, blend until smooth.

DOCTOR DOUG'S SHAKE

I'd been making my buckwheat-banana shakes for many years. But one day, after an extremely strenuous workout with Doug Graham, he made me a HUGE shake using just water and a banana. Not only are they filling and satisfying, but they really hit the spot after a hard workout. If you like, add celery... it cuts down the sweetness and gives you natural sodium!

5-6 bananas (Ripe! Otherwise it will not be sweet enough.)

1 cup water

_____

In a blender or Vita-Mix, blend until smooth.

MUDSLIDE

A filling drink that really 'hits the spot' when you get a craving for sweets.

1/2 cup almonds

1 1/2 cups water

1 banana

3 dates

_____

In a blender or Vita-Mix, blend until smooth.

MANGO LASSIE

From Stacie, as her Indian theme continues!

2 cups almond milk

1 cup mango pulp

3 dates, soaked and drained

1/4 cup orange juice

1/8 teaspoon vanilla (optional)

_____

1. Blend mango, orange juice, and dates.
2. Place in a bowl and freeze for 20 minutes.

3. Return to the blender with almond milk (and vanilla, if desired) and blend until frothy.

Serve chilled.

LEMONADE

No need for a glass of sugary lemonade when this tastes even better!

4 apples
1/2 lemon

Juice all together through a juicer.

BANANA NUT DRINK

It was hard for me to resist putting drinks like this into the dessert section!

1 1/4 cups almond milk
1 banana
2 Tablespoons almond butter
1 Tablespoon carob powder
Pinch of cinnamon
Pinch of nutmeg
5 ice cubes

In a blender or Vita-Mix, blend until smooth.

PIÑA COLADA

The only thing that would make this more authentic would be one of those paper umbrellas decorating your glass!

6 ounces orange juice
1 cup pineapple
1/2 cup fresh coconut milk

In a blender or Vita-Mix, blend until smooth.

GREEN APPLE AND PARSLEY

I had this in a little café years ago and never forgot it. Make sure you use green apples to achieve this unique taste.

4 green apples
1/2 head parsley

Juice all ingredients through a juicer.

CHOCOLATE MOCHA MILKSHAKE

If you're craving a mocha frap, or a mocha chino, try this!

1/2 cup sesame seeds
2 cups coconut milk
1/2 cup coconut meat
1 Tablespoon honey

1 Tablespoon carob powder

1 banana

In a blender or Vita·Mix, blend until smooth.

CELEBRATION OF LIFE!

Fresh pineapple and red grapes combine to make this bountiful drink. Filled with antioxidants from the grapes, bromelain from the pineapple, and Vitamin C from the lemon, it's a natural cleanser and healer!

1 bunch grapes

1 cup pineapple

1/2 lemon

Juice all together through a juicer.

SMOOTH AS SILK

This is a very light drink, but I love the creamy smoothness of the coconut mixed with a hint of vanilla flavoring.

2 cups young baby coconut milk

1/2 cup young baby coconut meat

1 teaspoon vanilla

In a blender or Vita·Mix, blend until smooth.

NATURE'S DIURETIC

Fasting on watermelon juice is great during the summer months!

Watermelon

Juice watermelon in juicer, rind and all.

NO MORE CELLULITE!

Grapefruit helps to breakdown fat that can deposit in the body causing cellulite.

Grapefruit juice

Juice 2-3 grapefruits through a juicer or manual juice extractor.

PAIN RELIEF

Pineapple contains natural bromelain which is a natural pain reliever. But I just drink this for its delicious taste!

Pineapple

Peel and core the pineapple. Juice the meat though a juicer.

B - HAPPY

Cantaloupe contains the highest amount of B vitamins found in any fruit! This is also one of my favorite juice drinks, naturally sweet!

Cantaloupe

Remove skin from cantaloupe and discard. Juice cantaloupe through a juicer.

CRAMP RELIEVER

If you're suffering from cramps of any kind, juice these up!

1/2 med pineapple
1/4 large fennel bulb
2 1/2 oz spinach
1/2 piece ginger

Juice all together through a juicer.

SKIN REPAIR

Acne, rashes, tired, sagging skin? Juice up this gem!

2 cucumbers
1/2 red bell pepper
1 carrot
1/2 apple

Juice all ingredients through a juicer.

RESOURCES

APPLIANCES

Dehydrators
Dehydrators with temperature controls.
Distributor: Alissa Cohen
1-888-900-2529
www.alissacohen.com

Spiral slicer (saladacco)
This handy little gadget is great for making angel hair pasta and slicing vegetables very thin. It makes beautiful decorations for any main meal or salad.

Distributor: Alissa Cohen
1-888-900-2529
www.alissacohen.com

Vita–Mix, Juicers, and other appliances
Distributor: Alissa Cohen
1-888-900-2529
www.alissacohen.com

SUPPLEMENTS

Enzymes: premium and therapeutic
Green food supplement: potent blend of greens and sprouts
Distributor: Alissa Cohen
1-888-900-2529
www.alissacohen.com

HEALTH RETREAT CENTERS AND INSTRUCTION

Alissa Cohen, LLC.
1-888-900-2529
www.alissacohen.com

Ann Wigmore Institute
Box 429
Rincon, Puerto Rico 00677
787-868-6307
www.annwigmore.org

Creative Health Institute
918 Union City Road
Union City, MI 49094
517-278-6260
www.creativehealthinst.com

Hippocrates Heath Institute
1443 Palmdale Ct.
West Palm Beach, Fl 33411
561-471-8876
www.hippocratesinst.com

Tanglewood Wellness Center
6135 Mountaindale Road,
Thurmont, MD 21788
301-898-8901
www.tanglewoodwellnesscenter.com

Living Light Culinary Arts Institute
Director: Cherie Soria
704 N. Harrison
Fort Bragg, CA 95437
800-816-2319
www.rawfoodchef.com

Optimum Health Institute of San Diego
6970 Central Avenue
Lemon Grove, CA 91945
619-464-3346
www.optimumhealth.org

Optimum Health Institute of Austin
Rural Route 1
Box 339-j Cedar Lane
Cedar Creek, TX 98612
512-303-4817
www.optimumhealth.org

Tree of Life Rejuvenation Center
P.O Box 1080
Patagonia, AZ 85624
520-394-2520
www.treeoflife.nu

MAIL ORDER RAW AND LIVING FOOD SOURCES

Alissa Cohen
888-900-2529
www.alissacohen.com
Raw bar, Nama Shoyu, olive oil, coconut oil, agave nectar, and much more.

Diamond Organics
P.O Box 2159
Freedom, CA 95019
888-674-2642
www.diamondorganics.com
Fresh Organic produce, including wheatgrass and sprouts shipped anywhere in the U.S.A.

The Date People
P.O. Box 808
Niland CA 92257
760-359-3211
This is a small farm that grows over 50 varieties of rare and exotic dates. Jamie and Anjou are a husband and wife team who run the place themselves. Jamie has been raw since 1978. They have been serving the raw and living food community since 1985. They have great prices and the best dates! Try the peanut butter dates.

Wheat Grass Juice
16128 Ninth Line
Stouffville, ON
L4A 7X4
Canada
www.organicwheatgrassdirect.com
They ship organic frozen wheat grass juice next day to the United States and Canada.

Glaser Organic Farms
19100 SW 137th Avenue
Miami, FL 33177
305-238-7747
Glaser Farms ships foods by mail order and has over 50 products available, including all raw entrées, dressings, dips, spreads, desserts, cookies, crackers, breads, fresh fruit pies and a full line of organic produce. They also offer food preparation classes.

The Grain and Salt Society
www.celtic-seasalt.com
273 Fairway Drive
Ashville, NC 28805
1-800-867-7258
Celtic sea salt. Celtic sea salt cured olives! They also have many other products including sea vegetables, pickling crocks for homemade sauerkraut, miso, raw organic grains, beans, and seeds. Call or send for their catalog.

Jaffe Bros.
P.O Box 636
Valley Center, CA
92082-0636
760-749-1133
This is where I get my raw carob powder. Large selection of other products as well. Call or write for their catalog.

Lifeforce Growers
46 Howard Street
Waltham, MA 02451
781-894-3183
Certified organic growing facility specializing in sprouts and wheatgrass.

Living Tree Community Foods
P.O Box 10082
Berkeley, CA 94709
510-526-7106
800-260-5534
www.livingtreecommunity.com
Mail order catalog for organic dried fruits that have been low-heat dehydrated, nuts, nut butters, olive oil, and more. Call or send for their catalog.

Maine Seaweed
P.O Box 57
Steuben, ME 04680
207-546-2875
They dry their seaweeds below 100 degrees within 48 hours of harvest. The first day the seaweeds are dried outside in the

sun and wind. Larch is a raw fooder and a super nice guy who gave me a lot of information on the drying process of seaweed. Call or write for his catalog. If you're in the New England area during the months of July and August, call him for a seaweed boat tour!

Rejuvenative Foods/Deer Garden
P.O. Box 8464
Santa Cruz, CA 95061
800-805-7957
www.rejuvenative.com
Raw cultured vegetables and raw low-temp ground fresh-dated nut and seed butters. "We monitor temperature during grinding so that heat friction doesn't cook out nuts and seeds." Their almond, cashew, tahini and halva are the best nut butters I've found, and their Kim-Chi and Caraway Sauerkraut is delicious!

The Sprout House
www.sprouthouse.com
Call toll-free 1-800-SPROUTS (800-777-6887)
P.O. Box 754131
Forest Hills, NY 11375
Fax (718) 575-8570
Carrying over 30 different varieties of sprouting seeds, they ship internationally. Also available are many books on sprouting, raw food books, and wheat grass supplies and juicers. Rita, the owner, is very nice: call her for any information you need. She is more than willing to answer any questions you may have.

Sun Organic Farms
P.O Box 2429
Valley Center, CA 92082
888-269-9888
www.sunorganic.com
Mail order business with a large variety of foods that cater to the raw fooder. Low temperature dried fruits, raw nuts and seeds, sprouting seeds, grains, oils, herbs, spices and more. Call or send for their catalog.

RESTAURANTS AND RESOURCES BY STATE

ALASKA

Enzyme Express
1330 East Huffman Road
Anchorage, AK 99515
Phone: 907-345-1330

ARIZONA

The Tree of Life Cafe
771 Harshaw Road
Patagonia, AZ 85624
Phone: 520-3941589
The Tree of Life Rejuvenation Center has a raw food restaurant open to the public. Fresh raw food direct from their garden!

CALIFORNIA

Raw Energy Organic Juice Café
www.rawenergy.net
2050 Addison Street
Berkeley, CA 94704
510-665-9464
Organic juice bar with many raw food items, such as breakfast muesli, raw pizza, crackers, salads, and desserts.

Beverly Hills Juice Club
8382 Beverly Blvd, Los Angeles, CA 90048
323-655-8300
They have been here for 23 years. Organic juices and smoothies, raw ice cream made with almonds and bananas, raw hummus, raw sushi rolls, and more.

Roxanne's
www.roxraw.com
320 Magnolia Avenue
Larkspur, CA 94939
415-924-5004 (voice)
415-924-7294 (fax)
Check out this web-site! Roxanne's is an elegant, 62-seat fine dining restaurant offering gourmet organic living foods' cuisine.

The Stand
238 Thilia Street
Laguna Beach, CA
Full juice bar. They have many raw food entrées, large selection of salads, and great fresh fruit soft serve desserts.

Au lac
16563 Brookhurst Street
Fountain Valley, CA 92708
714-418-0658
Mai, the owner, is expanding the menu to include raw foods. This is a mostly vegan, Vietnamese and Chinese restaurant, but if you call a day ahead they will make you a 4 or 7-course raw food meal.

Living Lighthouse
1457 12th Street (N.E. corner at Broadway)
Santa Monica, CA 90401
310-395-6337
Not a restaurant, but they have weekly meals and potlucks.

Good Mood Food Café
5930 Warner Ave,
Huntington Beach, CA 92649
714-377-2028
www.goodmoodfood.com
All raw menu. Chef Ursula Horaitis, offers a great selection of raw entrees such as 'Spinach Quiche,' Butternut Squash 'Pasta,' Mushroom 'Stroganoff' and a vast array of delicious raw deserts.

The Living Temple
7561 Center Avenue, #24
Huntington Beach, CA 92647
714-891-5117 (voice)
714-531-8573 (fax)
Organic and hemp clothing, accessories, books, videos, natural cosmetics, vegan candles, and more. Bulletin board and free literature for local and national events. Regular seminars and workshops with raw food speakers, authors, and chefs. This is a great resource place for raw food! Robin Jones is a wonderful guy with a strong passion for animal rights, vegan raw foods and environmental issues.

IDAHO

Akasha Organics
Chapter One Bookstore
106 North Main
Ketchum, Idaho 83340
208-726-4777
An all-raw café inside Chapter One bookstore. Juices, smoothies, soups, salads, living entrées and dehydrated goodies.

ILLINOIS

Karyn's Fresh Corner
3351 North Lincoln Avenue
Chicago, Illinois, 60657
773-296-6990
Beautiful raw food restaurant and great food. Serving breakfast, brunch, lunch, and dinner. Karyn has monthly detox classes as well as other events.

MASSACHUSETTS

Organic Garden
www.organicgardencafe.com
294 Cabot Street
Beverly, MA 01915
978-922-0004
Large Raw, organic menu.

MINNESOTA

Ecopolitan
2409 Lyndale Avenue, South
Minneapolis, MN 55405
612-87-GREEN (47336)
All raw restaurant.
A completely organic, vegan and raw restaurant and an ecological shop selling natural, non-toxic home and body goods.

NEVADA

The Raw Truth
East Wind Center
2381 East Windmill Lane

Las Vegas, NV 89121
702-450-9007
Fax: 702-433-1142
Organic, all raw foods café. Large menu filled with delicious entrées such as pizza, meat loaf, lasagna and many salads and desserts.

NEW YORK

Caravan of Dreams
405 East 6th Street
Manhattan, NY
212-254-1613
Although not all raw, they are a totally vegan restaurant and they always have raw available.

Green Paradise
609 Vanderbilt Avenue
Brooklyn, NY
718-230-5177
Organic Vegan Raw Food restaurant and juice bar with a caribbean touch.

Quintessence
263 East 10th Street
New York, NY 10009
646-654-1823
All raw menu, all organic, all amazing! The food is incredible and the atmosphere is great!

Bonobo's Restaurant
18 East 23rd Street
New York, NY
800-525-7973
All raw restaurant which offers a very simple and fresh organic raw menu.

OREGON

Ripe and Raw
503-771-5605
Portland, OR
A roving restaurant and catering company.

PENNSYLVANIA

Arnold's Way

319 West Main Street (rear)
Lansdale, PA 19440
215-483-2266
www.arnoldsway.com
Health food store, juice bar, and raw food café serving juices, salads, desserts, and entrées. Great menu! They distribute a variety of their raw food nationally: fruit bars, cookies, crackers, breads, burgers, and a nut steak. They also have free classes on raw food preparation and healing, along with monthly guest speakers.

WASHINGTON

Sun Raw

www.sunraw.com
Seattle, WA
Opening soon. Check website for info.

RECOMMENDED READING

Conscious Eating by Gabriel Cousens

Diet For a New America by John Robbins

Enzyme Nutrition by Dr. Edward Howell

Grain Damage by Douglas Graham

How I Conquered Cancer Naturally by Eydie Mae

Intuitive Eating by Humbart Santillo

Living Foods for Optimal Health by Brian Clement

Mad Cowboy by Howard Lyman

Nutrition and Athletic Performance by Douglas Graham

Raw Family by Victoria, Igor, Sergei, and Valya Boutenko

Raw Knowledge I and *Raw Knowledge* II by Paul Nison

The Food Revolution by John Robbins

The Raw Life by Paul Nison

The Sunfood Diet Success System by David Wolfe

The New Raw Energy by Susannah and Leslie Kenton

There Are No Incurable Diseases by Dr. Richard Schulze

RAW RECIPE BOOKS

Recipes for a Longer Life by Ann Wigmore

Vibrant Living by Natalie Cederquist and James Levin, MD

The Raw Gourmet by Nomi Shannon

Hooked on Raw by Rhio

Sunfood Cuisine by Fred Patenaude

Raw by Juliano

Living in the Raw by Rose Lee Calabro

The Raw Truth: The Art of Loving Foods by Jeremy Saffron and Renee Underkoffler

Garden of Eden Raw Fruit and Vegetable Recipes by Phyllis Avery

Shazzie's Detox Delights by Shazzie

WEBSITES

These sites are filled with everything you need. Find raw restaurants, order raw food books, read articles on raw and living foods, recipes, products, and more. The following are just some of the top sites that are loaded with information. They all contain links to other sites, where you will surely find whatever it is that you need.

www.rawfoodtalk.com
My other site for asking questions, getting advice, staying motivated and meeting new raw friends. Post your daily journal and pictures. Read other people's success stories. All for free, to help you with your raw food journey!

www.alissacohen.com
My site. Information on seminars, retreats, consultations, and events. Before and after pictures, online journals, products and more.

www.living-rawfoods.com
Large site with lots of resources and information.

www.rawtimes.com
Great site with lots of information.

www.sunfood.net
Great site with lots of information.

www.rawfood.com
Lots of info and tons of products, books, videos, raw foods, etc.

www.livingnutrition.com
Promoting the "Living Nutrition" magazine.

www.rawfamily.com
The Boutenko family website.

www.rawgourmet.com
Nomi Shannon's website promoting her book *The Raw Gourmet.*

www.rawhealth.net
Lots of info and products.

www.doctorgraham.cc
Speaker, author, trainer to world-class athletes, and 20-year raw fooder.

www.gardenofhealth.com
Lots of information.

www.rawfoodinfo.com
Rio's website. Tons of info for the raw world!

www.thegardendiet.com
Retreats and info.

www.rawfoodliving.com
Loads of information and articles. You could spend days on this site!

www.fresh-network.com
U.K. based site. Loads of info and products.

www.harmonious-living.com
Good site with various information.

www.highvibe.com
Products, recipes and lots of other info on raw food.

www.rawfoodsnews.com
Lots of raw food news, pot luck and event info.

www.vegsource.com
Tons of information on vegetarian and vegan diets. Some raw info also.

www.notmilk.com
Tons of articles and information on the dangers of milk with many links.

www.madcowboy.com
Howard Lyman's website. Ex-cattle rancher turned vegetarian.

www.geocities.com/chlorophil.geo/rawresources.htm
Raw food resource list from oils, crackers, and seaweeds to hemp products and wheatgrass supplies.

www.rawfoodnetwork.com
Huge site connecting the raw food world. Tons of links and information.

www.rawlife.com
Speaker and author Paul Nison's website.

www.TheRawWorld.com
Great site with lots of books and products for the raw lifestyle.

www.rawchef.org
Chad Sarno's website.

www.purejoylivingfoods.com
Elaina Love's website.

www.shazzie.com
Shazzie's website.

www.rawheaven.com
Cynthia Beaver's website.

THE LIVING ON LIVE FOOD WITH ALISSA COHEN <u>DVD</u> IS ALSO AVAILABLE!

This DVD is an up close and private session with Alissa that is filmed on location at a client's house. Watch and listen as Alissa reveals how to go raw and how to stay raw through a lively and inspiring teaching session filled with questions and answers.

Throughout the filming, Alissa will clearly explain everything you need to know about how to prepare raw food while demonstrating in detail more than 20 of the recipes that are in this book!

For information on Alissa's Products, Seminars, Consultations, and Events Please visit:

www.AlissaCohen.com

or call 1-888-900-2529 / 978-985-7217

INDEX